Paracelsus *at the age of 47*

Woodcut by August Hirschvogel

Henry M. Pachter

Paracel

MAGIC INTO

being the true history of the troubled life, adventures, doctrines, miraculous cures, and prophecies of the most renowned, widely traveled, very learned and pious gentleman, scholar, and most highly experienced and illustrious physicus, the Honorable

Philippus Theophrastus Aureolus

Bombastus ab Hohenheim, Eremita,

called **Paracelsus**,

doctor of both medicines and professor of theology, also adept of the Holy Cabbala and expert of the alchemical art, friend of the common man and defender of liberty. He cured patients whom ordinary doctors had abandoned for doomed, and he knew wonderful elixirs that restore youth to the old.

sus

SCIENCE

Henry Schuman
New York

Contents

Illustrations

Preface

Each generation must rewrite its history books in the image of its own experience. Our fathers saw their own optimistic outlook mirrored in the brilliancy of the Renaissance leaders. With less confidence than they had in the "modern age," we have become critical of the great men who laid its foundations in the past. Our attention turns to the historical failures, to those who lived in the dark or were crushed between the millstones of reaction and revolution in their time. We study the controversial figures and the undercurrents of history; we re-evaluate the contributions which unsung martyrs made towards the formulation of our own problems; we recognize unaccomplished tasks where previously we had seen only vain fantasies.

Among the controversial characters of the Renaissance age, Paracelsus aroused my interest first as a partisan of a lost cause, one whom the struggle between the Pope and the Reformers left politically homeless. I came across his work again when I studied the intricate ways in which science developed out of magic conceptions of Nature. For a third time his fascinating character, so singularly astride between the past and the future, injected itself into a study of the philosophy of man. His significance, I found, had been apparent to the contemporaries who had identified him with the legendary Dr. Faustus, the symbol of modern man's striving for omnipotence. For me, the story of his life became a clue to the riddle of the Renaissance.

HENRY M. PACHTER

Paracelsus

MAGIC INTO SCIENCE

CHAPTER I

The Errant Knight of Science

PARACELSUS AND FAUSTUS

> *Eritis sicut Deus,*
> *scientes bonum et malum.*
>
> GENESIS, II, VERSE 3
>
> *"We shall be like Gods."*
>
> PARACELSUS

In the year of our Lord, one thousand five hundred and twenty-five—not long after Columbus had landed in the West Indies—a square-built man of odd appearance rode into the Emperor's good town of Ingolstadt on the Danube. His satchel was bursting with medicine pots, precious stones, astrological charts and surgical instruments. His hat and coat showed the lining of miniver fur doctors were privileged to wear, but from his belt hung an enormous sword, and his leather jacket was dusty and sooty. People noticed that the stranger wore his sword wherever he went, and the wiseacres whispered: "It's be-witched; in the pommel he keeps the Elixir of Life."

The celebrated and much-decried Dr. Theophrastus Bombas-tus ab Hohenheim—known to posterity by his Latin name, Para-celsus—was then thirty-two years old; the fame of his miraculous cures had preceded his arrival at Ingolstadt. At once, therefore, one of the aldermen called him to the sickbed of his young daughter. The girl, the chronicle says, had been paralyzed since birth, and the town's doctors had given her up. Paracelsus, how-ever, declared that "only ignoramuses allege that Nature has not provided a remedy against every disease," adding some un-polished words on the incompetence of the "learned fools who make their patients worse."

Promptly shown to the sickroom, the doctor examined the in-valid. He inquired about the sign and ascendent of her birth and held her water in a vessel against the window; for urine inspection was supposed to reveal the bad humors in the body. Having further satisfied himself that the paralysis had not been cast upon the girl by a sorcerer, Dr. Theophrastus decided that she was suffering from a deficiency of *spiritus vitæ*—a malady he was able to cure with his new and wonderful medicine, Azoth of the Red Lion. Suspicious of all pharmacists, he prepared the prescription himself in the host's kitchen, and gave the patient a grain of it dissolved in wine. Then he told her to sleep, and to work up a heavy sweat.

As was then the custom, the doctor stayed at the patient's house and had dinner with the family. What happened next is reported dramatically in an alchemist's almanac, published a hundred and fifty years after the event: "While everybody was seated at the dinner table, of a sudden the door opened and in walked the lame girl. She threw herself at Paracelsus' feet and with tears in her eyes thanked him for his wonderful cure." [1]

Not content that Paracelsus had healed the girl, the report would also have us believe that she had learned to walk during her sleep. The men of the time, credulous, suspicious, and superstitious all at once, wondered. Wagging their heads neighbors asked what magic powers might be at the disposal of this wonder-worker, and had he come by them in a Christian way?

Rumors spread through the town. Sedate burghers took note that the doctor avoided churches; and one had heard that in Basle he had burnt the books of "the most Christian doctor," Galen (see Chapter 4), as the wicked Luther had burnt the Papal Bull.

Nor could the host deny that in his kitchen the doctor was brewing mysterious and wonderful essences, some glittering like gold, others stinking like hellish sulfur; and the story went the rounds again that Paracelsus had received the secret of the Philosopher's Stone from an infidel in Byzantium.

Before anyone could tell where he had heard such rumors, everybody seemed to know that Theophrastus was not the doctor's real name. Rather, it would seem, he was the damnable Doctor Faustus who, as all knew, had bartered his soul for the command of secret powers. The populace, at last, became so threatening that the frightened alderman implored his benefactor to leave.

THE PARACELSUS LEGEND

In the eyes of his contemporaries, Paracelsus was a sorcerer and wonder healer. Even in his lifetime, tall tales of his miraculous cures had reached the borderlands of Europe; and shortly after his death, in 1541, legends began to circulate that he had been seen in several places at a time, that he had owned the Philosopher's Stone, that he had raised the dead and conversed with spirits.

The uneducated were not alone in entertaining such superstitious notions. Envious doctors, irked by Paracelsus' success or humiliated by his arrogant tongue, also fostered them. He often complained: "They begrudge the honor I won healing princes and noblemen, and they say my powers came from the Devil." [2] Even great scientists attributed these cures to unavowable arts. Scholarly Dr. Conrad Gesner informed a friend that Paracelsus

"certainly was an impious man and a sorcerer. He had intercourse with demons. . . . His disciples practice wicked astrology, divination, and other forbidden arts. I suspect they are survivors of the Celtic Druids who received instructions from their demons. . . . This school also is responsible for the so-called vagrant scholars, one of whom, famous Dr. Faustus, died only recently." [3]

And no less a man than our own John Donne, enlightened and philosophic poet, scholar and priest, accused Paracelsus of carrying out Lucifer's orders "by thy [the Devil's] minerals and fire."

Nor did Time snap the thread of legend. Scarcely a hundred years ago, during an epidemic of cholera in Austria, people made a pilgrimage to Paracelsus' grave at Salzburg, hoping to be healed by the special powers which, they supposed, were still at his command.

Even in our day, he remains the patron saint of faith healers, occultists, theosophists, and other sects which bemoan the age of reason. Some maintain that through his possession of ancient and oriental magic and of the cabbalistic teachings of the rabbis he had prevision of such modern inventions as radio, television, and nuclear physics. Had not Paracelsus prophesied that "natural magic" would make it possible to see beyond the mountains, to hear across the ocean, to divine the future, to cure all diseases, to make gold, to gain eternal life, and even to duplicate "God's greatest miracle—the creation of man?" He reports nursing into life in one of his alchemist's alembics the *homunculus* (little man), whom he had fathered without the cooperation of a woman. Asserting that "nothing is so secret that it cannot be made apparent," [4] he presumed to God-like knowledge of the occult, the hidden forces of nature; and he proffered blasphemous claims, unheard-of before his day: "God can do everything through His wisdom and art. Likewise, we shall be able to do everything. Nothing shall resist us, neither magic nor spells; for these things are from God, and they are His arts." [5]

Yet, this necromancer, who composed a veritable cyclopedia of occult sciences, praised "reasoning and experiment" as the true sources of knowledge.[6] This alchemist urged his fellow adepts to *"stop making gold; instead, find medicines."* [7]

His challenge opened the triumphant path for a new science, biochemistry, and revolutionized two older ones, medicine and alchemy. A vagrant quack whose faulty acquaintance with anatomy barred him from academic honors, he taught the learned doctors how to use man-made drugs; a mystic who pondered over the one-ness of man and Universe, he formulated the first modern theory of metabolism. However crude it was, it shook the foundations of the ancient four-humor doctrine (Chapter 4) to which most doctors still subscribed.

Many scholars have tried to understand this puzzle of Paracelsus' two faces: Was he a medieval "magus" (see Appendix A) or a modern scientist? A charlatan or a gifted healer? An impostor who grafted half-baked speculation on to careless and ill-conceived experiments, or a deep thinker whose genius grappled with problems beyond the grasp of his time? He has been praised beyond his merits by some, and underestimated by others, as the emphasis fell on one side or the other of his dual nature. Our endeavor will be to understand the man, Paracelsus, "with all his conflicts." The two aspects of his character, together, not this on the one hand and that on the other hand, were his personality. We shall show, moreover, that the very traits which to many today appear "medieval," inspired some of his most astonishingly "modern" concepts.

In a larger context, the same is true of all great Renaissance thinkers. Neither Copernicus nor Luther and Calvin were "modern men." The wells of their revolutionary thought sprang from medieval rock. Unwittingly, they destroyed the foundations of a society to whose ideals they were deeply devoted. The religious reformers shifted medieval piety toward a new experience which they called "modern devotion"; Paracelsus turned magic into science. The central interest of this biography will lie in *watching that transition at its turning point.*

Luther put the modern concept of conscience in the place where medieval ethics had set "virtues" and "works"; Paracelsus substituted a *functional conception of physiology—the living organism*—for the ancient anatomy of "humors" and "qualities." The one established the individual as an autonomous religious personality; the other recognized the body as a biological unit, a little universe whose growth and decay were governed by forces independent of the "signs of the zodiac" (see plate V).

"LUTHER OF MEDICINE"

Doctors, long resigned to accept the verdict of the stars as final, suddenly saw a new chance to fight disease. A wave of medical optimism swept over the schools. Ardent disciples eagerly followed the reports of unusual cures and even indulged the hope that eternal life no longer was a utopian dream. Ready to scrap all theories of classical "physicks," they hailed Paracelsus as the "Luther of Medicine"—the while his enemies used the same name to denounce him. There were other reasons for the analogy, however.

One midsummer night, Paracelsus solemnly committed to the flames the famous textbook of medieval medicine, the *Canon* of Avicenna. The defiant gesture, imitating Luther's burning of the Pope's Bull, became a symbol of rebellion against pedantry and unthinking acceptance of ancient doctrines. It condemned the rote-learning of medieval education, with its reliance on memorizing, its hair-splitting erudition and its disregard for experience. Medical students of that period, who hardly ever saw a patient before they graduated, were aroused by Paracelsus' battle cry: *"The patients are your textbook, the sickbed is your study."* [8]

Only ten years apart in age, Luther and Paracelsus appear like cuttings from the same stem—of German peasant stock, knotty and pugnacious, devout, but more attentive to their inner voice than to established authority. Just as Luther translated the Bible into the people's language, so Paracelsus used the vernacular—his native Swiss dialect—in scientific and philosophical essays, discarding the moribund Latin which made learning the preserve of the élite. Both were accomplished users of invective and obscenity. But whereas Luther's was clear and persuasive, Paracelsus' style betrays his searching, groping, often tense and emphatic, rather than logical, thinking. Here is his own account of his doubts and vacillations, and of his final call to reform medicine:

"I have put much work to find out the fundamentals of medicine, whether it is an art or not. For it is very uncertain, and little honor can be gained from its work. So many sick have been injured, killed, left paralyzed or abandoned as incurable. . . . In my time there was no doctor who could heal a toothache, not to speak of severe diseases.

"I also found many errors in the writings of the classics.

Even many princes and noble and rich men, who would have given all their wealth, nevertheless had been forsaken by the doctors who wear silken cloth and rings and are always full of boasts.

"Often I thought I ought to leave the art alone because it is inaccessible and I am not worthy of it; most doctors, on the other hand, only think of money.

"But I was not consistent in my resolve, and took medicine up again. I went to school for long years, in Germany, in Italy, in France, always seeking the foundation of medicine.

"Academic medicine, however, did not satisfy me. So I wandered on to Granada, Lisbon, England, Brandenburg, Prussia, through Lithuania, Poland, Hungary, Walachia, Transylvania, Croatia and other lands, more than I need mention. And everywhere I sought certain and experienced knowledge of the art. I did not seek it from the learned doctors alone; I also asked shearers, barbers, wise men and women, exorcizers, alchemists, monks, the noble and humble, the smart and the dumb.

"But none could tell me anything for certain. I pondered over this a great deal, how uncertain an art medicine is, and how difficult to apply. Unless one is favored by good luck, he may injure ten patients while curing one.

"And I thought demons were misleading men in this way, and again left the art alone, and engaged in other pursuits.

"However, I returned to it and I found that Christ was right when he said that the sick need the doctor. But I could do so only in a new spirit: That the art should be true, just and perfect, one which is most helpful when it is most needed.

"As I thought this over I found that the medicine which I had learned was faulty, and that those who had written about it neither knew nor understood it. They all tried to teach what they did not know. They are vainglorious babblers in all their wealth and pomp, and there is not more in them than in a worm-eaten coffin.

"So I had to look for a different approach." [9]

Few scholars before Paracelsus had written in this vein. More than any specific discovery of the Renaissance, this new self-reliance of the individual characterizes its wonderful spirit. At many points the gulf between the Middle Ages and modern times may be more bridgeable than a conventional view of history concedes. In the sciences, particularly, empiric progress may have smoothed the transition. Many a doctor, certainly, had laid aside the textbook, had experimented with unconventional remedies or even made autopsies. Yet it was unheard-of for the masters to be rejected wholesale. With rare exceptions, at the height of the enlightened thirteenth century, the great scientists of the Middle Ages still modestly attributed their inventions to the study of the Ancients. When corrections had to be made in textbooks, the errors were laid on the copyist rather than on the author. But creative writers and inquisitive researchers now took pride in their own achievements. No longer bound by authority, they relied on their own inspiration and called each other *"vates"* (poet-prophet): "Many doctors . . . have blindly adhered to the dicta of Hippocrates, Galen, Avicenna and others, as though these proceeded like oracles from the tripod of Apollo, and wherefrom they dared not diverge a finger's breadth." [10]

For the first time, Progress was acclaimed, and the *search for truth valued higher than its possession.* Paracelsus took more pride in the mistakes that were his own than in proven knowledge, learned from others. His pen-name, defiantly flung in the face of the academicians, means, "better than Celsus." (Aulus C. Celsus and Pliny, the two great encyclopedists of the first century A.D., ruled science when Theophrastus began

studying medicine, and Celsus' *De Re Medica* was the first work
of its kind to appear in print, in 1478.) A "Super-Celsus" demanded to be heard by the right of his own research.

THE "LIGHT OF NATURE"

Freedom from the tutelage of the Ancients was one aspect of the
new science. Another was even more important—the freedom
to push research into fields which hitherto had been barred as
improper. All of nature, with all the provinces formerly sur-
rendered to demons, was henceforth to be opened to scientific
exploration.

> "Christ said: 'Seek and ye shall find; knock and the door
> shall be opened.' And whatever research teaches us shall be
> preserved and shall remain with us undespised and shall not
> be suppressed as the theologians seek to do." [11]

New fields became legitimate subjects of research; the concept of Nature itself was expanded, the realm of the occult
reduced. Not more than a generation before Paracelsus,
scientists still distinguished between two kinds of magic, "one
which depends entirely on the work and authority of demons, a
thing to be abhorred, so help me God, and monstrous; the
other, when rightly used, is nothing but the utter perfection of
natural philosophy." [12]

The quotation is from the famous *Oration on the Dignity of
Man* by Pico della Mirandola (died 1494), which has been
called the manifesto of the Italian Renaissance. Paracelsus, who
followed Pico in many other respects, denied that demons have
any authority whatsoever. Nor did he concede any freaks of
nature. If witches rode to the Black Mass on broomsticks, they
were using the wind craftily.[13] On the other hand, incredible

experiments, such as the transmutation of lead into gold, were God's, not the Devil's work:

> "Some will say this is pagan or superstitious and witch-craft. As though conjuring could achieve anything! They ask how metals, in conjunction with characters and formulas, might have such power if not through the Devil?
>
> "To such skeptics I say: my friend, can't you believe that the Lord is powerful enough to give such virtues to roots, metals, stones and herbs? Dare you say that the Devil is more artful than God?" [14]

The Devil "cannot invent anything, not as much as a louse on your head," but the magus (i.e. the scientist) who studies nature can use her forces. That does not make him a servant of Hell. On the contrary, man constantly is appropriating the powers of the Devil. Science dethrones him, debunks his demons. *The scientist conquers Hell and his art is "divine because it comes from God and from no other source."* [15] *"Magic is neither white nor black, for Nature has no master."* [16]

One more step was necessary to make man omnipotent, and science autonomous. Once liberated from the arbitrary powers of the Devil, science also forced God to abide by the laws of nature: "He might have made man by fiat, from nothing. However, He did not do so, but created him out of nature and in nature." [17]

Whenever God wishes to cure a patient, He does not work a miracle but sends him a doctor.[18] If God is omniscient, His light also illuminates the human mind. "The Holy Spirit himself lit the Light of Nature." [19] Paracelsus, like other mystics before him, remodeled the old Catholic concept of "The Light of Nature," as opposed to "The Light of God," to suit the new ideas. The term had served to indicate the limitations of man's ability to find the truth without divine inspiration. Now it proclaimed the mind's boundless possibilities. The Light of Nature was the temporal reflection of the Eternal Light. God manifests Himself in the forces of nature and reflects His spirit in the minds of man. How then could man fail in his effort to know Nature? "Inasmuch as He is Nature, He acts through Nature. . . . His spirit in man is Nature, and so is man. His spirit is Nature in man." [20]

THE LEGEND OF DR. FAUSTUS

Such dangerous deductions frightened scholars of that time. Uncovering the "occult" not only was dangerous; it was impious. At the threshold of freedom humanity crossed itself in holy fear. The movements of the Renaissance were accompanied by religious qualms, witch hunts, and renegacies. Paracelsus himself, we shall find, broke down under the burden of the new knowledge.

Torquemada was a contemporary of Columbus, and St. Ignatius Loyola of Copernicus. In the imagery of legend the proud figure of Prometheus, a favorite of Renaissance writers, was confronted with the tragic figure of Dr. Faustus, who rued the heavenly fire which his Greek ancestor had brought down to earth. Frightened by the atomic "Hell Bomb," our generation can understand the shudders provoked by earlier ventures into the unknown. Yet, men will never relax in their strivings for omniscience and omnipotence. In pursuit of knowledge, scientists have spent their fortunes, ruined their health, and risked their lives. Many have endured defamation and torture in asserting the right to free thought, and some have sealed this profession of faith by dying at the stake.

The legend of Dr. Faustus tells of one who even risked more than life. He was ready to forego salvation and brave everlasting hellfire to gain power over the mysteries of nature. A knight-errant of science, he had traveled in all lands, listened to all the professors and studied all the books of philosophy, medicine, and theology—all without satisfaction. He felt that the learning of his age had failed to lift the veil which concealed the secret of creation from human eyes.

At the peril of eternal damnation, he turned to black magic and concluded the "pact with the Devil" which gave him power over space and matter. He traveled through the air, drew wine out of dry wood, rode on a barrel up the staircase of Auerbach's wine cellar in Leipzig (the scene, immortalized in Goethe's drama, is represented on a mural in that famous restaurant); he called Homer's heroes back from Hades. Finally, he created the *homunculus*.[21]

But Faustus paid the price. His servant-master, in the shape of a black poodle, was at his side wherever he went. When he died, the beast ran off with his soul. Thus goes the old saga, as narrated in the second half of the sixteenth century. It has fathered masterpieces exploring the gulf between man's limited powers and his limitless striving. In our day, Thomas Mann has returned to Faustus' damnation to symbolize man's doomed endeavor to reach out beyond himself into the realm of omnipotence. The price of freedom, the poets say, is happiness. Knowledge and power can be gained only at the risk of damnation. One of the first, and still one of the most powerful treatments of the theme was Christopher Marlowe's (1564–1593) *Tragical History of Doctor Faustus.* At the curtain rise, Faustus takes leave of philosophy, medicine, law, and theology, to become a magus:

Divinity, adieu!
These metaphysics of magicians
And necromantic books are heavenly:

Lines, circles, scenes, letters, and characters:
Ay, these are those that Faustus most desires.
O, what a world of profit and delight,
Of power, of honor, of omnipotence
Is promised to the studious artisan!
All things that move between the quiet poles
Shall be at my command: emperors and kings
Are but obeyed in their several provinces,
Nor can they raise the wind or rend the clouds;
But his dominion that exceeds in this
Stretcheth as far as doth the mind of man.
A sound magician is a mighty god:
Here, Faustus, try thy brains to gain a deity.[22]

The words are Marlowe's, but he might have gleaned them from a biography of Paracelsus. Here is the discontent with the science of his age; here are the cabbalistic books; and here is the echo of Paracelsus' promise that "we shall be like gods." [23] In *Ignatius*, John Donne represented Paracelsus as one of four pretenders to the "principal place right next to Lucifer's own throne," beside Copernicus and Machiavelli. When Goethe, two centuries later, took up the Faustus theme, Faustus and Paracelsus had become linked in tradition, and he found it necessary to become a Paracelsus scholar. Allusions to Paracelsus' life and opinions, alchemical symbolism, and Paracelsian cabbala abound in his version.[24]

Paracelsus was not the only model of Faustus. Fascinated researchers have sifted out several medicine peddlers who actually went by the name of Faustus. All lived in the first half of the sixteenth century—Paracelsus' lifetime. The oldest of them, one Georg Faust, born around 1480, was sometimes a schoolteacher and always a prankster and charlatan who brought little honor to his powerful protectors. Others who have used the famous name entertained crowds at the country fairs doing alchemical tricks or posing as initiates of secret wisdom. None of these mountebanks showed any of the true heroic Faustian features.[25]

THE CONQUEST OF HELL

Legend also wove into the Faustus character threads from the lives of other scholars and vagrant quacks (see Chapter 6). One contributed the conjuring up of the beautiful Helena, another the adventurous travels, a third the alchemical and cabbalistic symbolism. Whoever the real Faustus was, the obscure mountebank and necromancer was not the one who made bold to breed the *homunculus* and to explore good and evil. The one whose craving to be like God inspired the poets had written the words which Marlowe put in the mouth of Dr. Faustus. I believe that more of Paracelsus' image went into Faustus than is generally admitted, and this opinion is supported by no less an authority than Goethe.

Of all the poets whom the Faustus problem enticed, Goethe alone dared to absolve the hero; he would not believe that knowledge leads to damnation. In his version, the Devil, Shylock-like with his contract in hand, appears in due time to fetch the sinner to Hell. But the angels, too, are there to claim his soul. They say:

> Him who unwearied still strives on
> We have the power to save.

Thus the Devil is foiled. He gave man the instruments to save himself—mastery of nature. This precisely is the turn Paracelsus gave the concept of magic, and Goethe knew Paracelsus' works well enough. His interpretation of the Devil as a dupe is Paracelsian, and so are the "two souls" which dwell in Faustus' heart. But Goethe tried to reconcile the two worlds, the pagan and the Christian, whereas Paracelsus was rent apart by their conflict.

Legend goes strange ways. It first grafted Paracelsian traits upon the obscure necromancer Faustus; then, through the sensitive imagination of inspired poets, it rediscovered the sources of Paracelsian symbolism: Faust's yearning, in Goethe's version, "to know what holds the world in its joints" only echoes Paracelsus' claim: "Man may get hold of and enclose the entire world in his grasp, with all its foundations and in clear perception of its perfect wholeness." [26]

CHAPTER 2

The Mountain

ORIGINS AND BACKGROUND

> *Throughout his life, a man cannot cast off that which he has received in his youth. My share was harshness, as against the subtle, prudish, superfine. Those who were brought up in soft clothes and by womenfolk have little in common with us who grew up among the pine trees.*
>
> PARACELSUS

Paracelsus' real name was Philippus Theophrastus Bombastus von Hohenheim. The Bombasts, an old family of Swabian nobles now in decline, hailed from Hohenheim Castle near Stuttgart, in southern Germany. Theophrastus' grandfather, Georg, a commander of the Teutonic Knights, accompanied his duke on a warlike pilgrimage to the Holy Land and, at one time, was stationed at Cyprus with the Knights of St. John.

Back in Germany, however, the commander, whose temper

Paracelsus seems to have inherited, became involved in a political brawl, fell into disgrace, and lost his estate at auction. His son Wilhelm, whom he had "by Dame ——, his concubine for seven years," was brought up at an uncle's farm in the village of Rieth.[1] This was Paracelsus' father.

As a natural child, Wilhelm had no legal right to bear his father's noble name. By feudal law, the parent of lower birth then determined one's station. Nor did he have any money. The Students' Register of the University of Tübingen for 1481 listed him as "pauper" under the name of Wilhelm von Rieth.[2]

He became a licentiate of medicine, but lack of funds, wanderlust, or attraction to the alchemists interfered with his post-graduate studies. He never received the doctor's kiss, the title which would have raised him to the status of a patrician, eligible to marry into a wealthy family. Instead, he wandered through southern Germany and into Switzerland to the old canton of Schwyz.

Winding south from the shores of lovely Lake Zurich, the ancient pilgrims' road leads to the shrine of Our Black Lady of Einsiedeln. The Abbey looks down on the wild Siehl River, whose picturesque cascades were crossed by travelers at the Devil's Bridge. Beside this bridge stood an inn which the Ochsner family, retainers of the Abbot, held in fee. The host's daughter, Elsa, served as a nurse's aid in the nearby hospital conducted by the monks.

In this inn, Wilhelm von Hohenheim settled as a country doctor and treated the footsore pilgrims. In 1492 he married Elsa Ochsner, and on St. Philip's Day of the following year, a son was born to them.[3] Doctor von Hohenheim called him Theophrastus, dedicating him to the pursuit of knowledge. For Theophrastus (Tyrtamos of Eresos) had been a great scientist of antiquity, the successor of Aristotle as head of the Lyceum at Athens.

THE HERMITAGE

Theophrastus was an ailing child. The effects of rickets can still be seen in the etching August Hirschvogel made of the adult man. The typical rachitic deformation of the skull makes him resemble that other German thinker, Immanuel Kant, who had the same affliction.[4]

Legend also tells of another deformity of his body. Allegedly, Paracelsus was a eunuch. An encounter with a wild boar, so it has been said, deprived young Theophrastus of his manhood. According to another tale, drunken soldiers, carousing in the doctor's house, performed the lurid operation on the boy.

The sources of this information, however, are dubious. Most likely, the tradition originated in a simple error of translation. Einsiedeln, in German, means The Hermitage. Since it was customary for authors to add their birthplace to their name, early editors of Paracelsus' works mistakenly identify him as "Theophrastus Eremita," or "Theophrast the Hermit." The title stuck with him, and was used by his enemies to ridicule him and his theories.

Although Paracelsus was never a hermit, no woman ever figured in his life. His detractors, who attributed many vices to him, never added lechery. He advocated chastity, and once declared it better to be a castrate than an adulterer. Moreover, no authentic picture shows Paracelsus with a beard, the sign of manhood.[5] On the other hand, in his later years, Paracelsus was bald, and baldness almost never is found in eunuchs.

Speaking of hair—German scholars, determined to find Nordic racial features in their great men, have speculated that Paracelsus must have been fair. They interpret his alchemist name, Aureolus, as a tribute to his "golden mane." Paracelsus indeed used this name on occasion, and his disciples called him "the golden one"—an obvious allusion to his alchemical gold-making ventures, not his complexion. Aureolus, incidentally, was an ancient alchemist, whose writings were in old Doctor von Hohenheim's library.

The only portrait of Paracelsus on which any hair color is discernible is one falsely ascribed to Tintoretto. This portrait, not done from life, gives him a dark brown beard. On the so-called Scorel portrait in the Louvre, which is authentic, Paracelsus wears a wig. A zealous "Aryan," peeping through a magnifying glass beneath this head-gear, thinks he saw a fair strand of hair shining forth. Such was bound to happen to the memory of one who flouted and derided the sterility of scholarship while he was alive.

More important than his racial heritage was Hohenheim's low social status. Pilgrims and Alpine peasants were a poor source of income for a doctor, and poverty gripped the family in Einsiedeln. Paracelsus later complained: "I grew up in great misery, and never was in a position to do what I wanted." [6] When he compared his ways with those of his adversaries, the "beringed and berobed" academic doctors, he reminded them that in his rough country, among the pines and in view of the barren Alps, "people are brought up on cheese and simple farm food and don't learn polite manners and refined language." [6] But, he says, "my parents' house was quiet and peaceful."

Simple ways characterized Theophrastus throughout his life. Though sometimes the guest of kings, he kept faith with the commoners and "*villeins*" (serfs) who were his relatives. He was twice removed from nobility. His father was a bastard and his mother a bondwoman of the Benedictines. At his death, his cousin came to claim the inheritance, not for himself but on behalf of his overlord, the Abbot of Einsiedeln.

Resentment against his father's family rings in his pen name. Writers used to latinize and simultaneously ennoble their names. Thus, Paracelsus' adversary Schwarzert (Black Earth) became Melanchthon, his friend Heusgen (Heuschein, transformed into House Shine) became Oecolampadius. "Paracelsus" may simply be such a bombastic translation of Hohenheim, which means the Mountain Home. But Paracelsus loved to play with double meanings, and Para-Celsus may just as well be a snub: above, higher than the Hohenheims, to avenge their injustice to his father.[7]

Paracelsus' writings, although silent about his mother, render homage to his father. Even after he had left the traditional paths of medicine, he praised Wilhelm as his first teacher and the one who had opened his eyes to the true method of gaining knowledge and experience.[8] Father and son, going on Alpine hikes together, collected herbs and talked to peasants, midwives, and shepherds, who knew the medicinal virtues of plants. The Alpine flora became a rich source for Paracelsus' pharmacopoeia, and folk medicine one of the stores of wisdom which he opposed to the academic medicine of his time.[9]

Indirectly, the mother also left her mark in Paracelsus' medical theories. Tradition has it that she suffered from manic-depressive states. Her helpless suffering seems to have impressed itself deeply on the youth's mind. Later, in his essay on *Fools* and on the *Afflictions Depriving Man of His Reason*, he was to attack the ineptitude and heartlessness of medieval psychiatry, pleading for a more sympathetic understanding of the mentally diseased [10]—enough to entitle him to be called the first modern psychiatrist.

Elsa Ochsner died when the boy was nine years old. In one of her fits she threw herself from the Devil's Bridge into the Siehl River.

No sentimental ties now held Wilhelm von Hohenheim to the solitary valley, and he departed with his son.

THE YOUNG ALCHEMIST

In their wanderings the horizon of their world expanded from the Alpine canton to the width of the Hapsburg dominions. They settled in the second largest city in the Archbishopric of Carinthia. Dominating the highway from Italy to Vienna, Villach was an outpost of the German Empire. When the Turks invaded Western Europe, it was here that Maximilian halted them.

Not far from the town, in the neighborhood of Doberatsch, was the "Lead Mountain," owned by the mighty bankers of the Empire, the Fuggers of Augsburg. At Hutenberg (Foundry Mountain) they mined iron, alum, and vitriol ores, as well as some gold, tin, and mercury. The ore was processed and analyzed in smelters and laboratories, likewise Fugger enterprises. There a school of mining trained new adepts.

At this school Wilhelm von Hohenheim found rewarding employment for his expert knowledge of mineralogy. He was a collector of minerals, an adept of alchemy, and an ardent connoisseur of the mantic arts. He owned a library on these subjects and, as Paracelsus gratefully acknowledges, taught his son *adeptam philosophiam*—the mysterious relations which existed between the metals and the stars.

Young Theophrastus, working as his father's assistant, had ample opportunity to observe the wonderful transformations worked in the alchemist's crucible, or in the big vats. The miners, in whose welfare he was later to concern himself, told him how the metals grow in the bowels of the earth and how jealous gnomes protect them with poisonous vapors.[11] Staring into the glowing and bubbling mixtures and pondering over the mysteries of transmutation, he wondered whether one day he would decipher these signs. Common lead, he dreamed, if properly treated, would yield gold and make the inventor rich and famous. He who found the formula would find the *"Elixir."* Had he not seen his father take out of the crucible a metal that shone brighter than gold?[12]

At the Benedictine cloister of Lavanttal, near Villach, Theophrastus learned what little Latin and grammar he was able to master. Neither these nor rhetoric and logic were his forte. His writings are pervaded by his aversion to textbooks and to the formal education which was the pride of contemporary humanists. "I tell you it is much easier to learn the stars and herbs than those intricate Latin and Greek grammars. It would be much better to learn medicine first and Latin later."[13]

This apparently was the method of his teacher, Bishop Erhard of Lavanttal, whom Paracelsus thankfully remembers in his autobiography. To the neglect of his pupil's grammar the two spent their days over crucibles and in speculations on the Philosopher's Stone.

Although Theophrastus' Latin never came up to humanist standards, it is not true that he "knew no Latin" as some have asserted. Latin was the necessary common language on the university campuses of that time with their "all nations" student body, and without a working knowledge of it, no student could have followed a course or read a book.

The neglect of his formal education, however, was to have undesirable consequences. Paracelsus never learned the art of scholastic dissertation and never mastered the required elegant style in speech or letter. In debate he frequently was beaten by lesser men who knew how to polish up inanities. The vigorous dialect of his native land was not subtle enough to conduct the piercing current of his thought. "My stammering tongue cannot justify me, so I take to writing, and I make over to the paper that which my mouth cannot accomplish."[14]

CHAPTER 3

Town and Gown

CONTROVERSIES OF
THE SIXTEENTH CENTURY

*Reason is Unity. . . . All arts
lie in man, though not all are apparent. The awakening brings
them out. To be taught is nothing; everything is in man, waiting to be awakened.*

PARACELSUS

In 1507, at the age of fourteen, Theophrastus changed the sooty jacket of the metal worker for a velvet hat and yellow scarf, the attire of the traveling student. With other *scholares*, he wandered from school to school, but no university gave him the knowledge he craved. In Heidelberg he found the students more intent on pleasure than on knowledge. Freiburg was a "house of indecency." In Ingolstadt he felt frustrated by the dogmatic instruction of its orthodox *schoolmen*. At Cologne he fretted at the obscurantism which was soon to become the laughing-stock of humanist Europe. He compared academic education to a dog's being trained to leap through a ring.[1]

For two years he wandered in German lands, never taking root. In those days the vagrant *scholares* swarmed over the country, following a famous teacher or seeking instruction. Some traveled in crowds, drinking and jesting, often hardly distinguishable from marauders. Luther preached against their ignorance and debauchery. For their living they sang in inns, pulled teeth, told fortunes by the stars, sold drugs, and begged. They had their fun with the burghers, the despised "philistines," and sported with their daughters and maids.

Since the students were exempt from local law, their off-campus conduct was difficult to control. Peaceful citizens had no legal means to check the rowdyism which made the university a plague, not an honor, to a city. In Vienna, the guilds finally united against the students and beat them in a pitched battle, the famous "Latin War," which lasted several days and did considerable damage to property.

In Paris, the faculty had to remind the students that it was not proper to bring sweethearts into lecture rooms or *"actum Veneris exercere in publico."* It also was explicitly forbidden to throw stones or dung during lectures. This latter precaution may have been necessary because the polemics between rival theological factions and doctrines had degenerated into "mud slinging" among the professors themselves.

When "rhetoric" was one of the three prime arts a student had to master, debates were as popular on the campus as football is today. But to young Theophrastus they were shocking. He had come to the university as a faithful son of the Church, eager to learn The Truth from the lips of its appointed guardians. Instead, he heard professors denouncing each other as heretics. He had naïvely assumed that all Truth is one and that

Reason, God's most precious gift to man, if rightly used, could never be at odds with Faith. Now he learned that truth is twofold, and all the great doctors of the Church, for all their love and labor, had been unable to bridge the gulf separating Faith from Reason. At Wittenberg an Augustinian monk, Professor D. Martinus Luther, taught that "Reason is the Devil's harlot."

The proud and icy architecture of medieval philosophy had fallen into ruins during the fourteenth and fifteenth centuries. When humanists spoke of the "Dark Age" they had in mind the decline of learning in those generations of the Black Death, the Hundred Years War, the Schism of the Church, famine, civil war, and the decline of the guilds. The colleges were depopulated, and the professors merely aped the subtleties of the great thirteenth-century thinkers. The great teachers of the sixteenth century scored them. Erasmus wrote:

"They spend their time in questioning, dividing, distinguishing and defining. They divide the first part into three, of which the first part again is split in four, and so on. . . . Vulcan's chains cannot bind them, they cut the link with a distinction as with an axe. They will tell you through which crack Sin crept in to corrupt man and how Christ formed in a virgin's womb. . . . They will explain how God can be a woman or an ass, can assume the substance of the Devil or of a pumpkin, and if so, how such pumpkin can preach a sermon, work miracles or be crucified." [2]

It was a crisis of science, as deep as ours today, with philosophies of doubt and despair reflecting a crisis of culture and society. Eminent thinkers came to the conclusion that Reason could no longer cope with the complex reality of life. Academic erudition and philosophy failed to relax the qualms of their conscience.

PLATO AND THE QUEST FOR CERTAINTY

When Theophrastus arrived at Tübingen, his father's Alma Mater, he witnessed a lively discussion. The university had a twin faculty, of "old school" professors and "moderns" busily baiting each other. As every student was required to sign up with one of the two warring factions, Theophrastus joined the "old school" and, according to custom, swore lifelong allegiance to his teachers.

This fateful oath placed him at cross-purposes with the leaders of the Reform movement; for Luther, Calvin, and nearly all their followers were in the opposite camp, and Paracelsus never could stomach them. Most reformers followed the philosophy of a Franciscan friar, William of Occam (1290-1350), who may be called a critical disciple of Aristotle. Theophrastus, on the other hand, followed the school of Duns the Scot (1265-1308), another Franciscan, whose basic tenets were closer to Plato. The Occamites believed in Predestination, Paracelsus in Free Will. They supported the particularistic powers of the new national and city states; he favored World Government under an Emperor. They held that Faith alone could save a man's soul; he hoped to meet Socrates and Plato, redeemed by their immortal works and love, in the Christian heaven.

Plato and the Scot were considered more conservative. Their philosophy implied that, on the whole, the world was reasonable and harmonious. Among famous "Scotists," Dante probably is the best-known, and Theophrastus' thinking was formed by the austere world-view which we still admire in his *Divine Comedy*. Most advances in science, on the contrary, had been conducted under Aristotelian auspices. The contemporary Aristotelians found it difficult to reconcile Faith with Reason, essence with existence, soul with intellect. Their philosophy appealed to those who felt that the Christian theology needed adjustment to the changing conditions of life. Hence the affinity of the Reformation movements and the urban middle classes for the critical philosophy of Occam. Moreover, Aristotle's logic and metaphysics seemed to supply a good ground work for the scientific endeavors of the age, collecting and classifying data and somehow finding a pigeonhole for each creature in Creation.

Such plodding progress hardly appealed to the radicalism of Theophrastus. Like Vesalius, Giordano Bruno and Galileo after him, he felt attracted to Plato, to his Utopian soarings, his speculative assertiveness, his idealism. His problem was not that of the Empiricists. He yearned for evidence that man is not a stranger in the Universe, but has the power to understand it through the "Light of Nature." He wished to find certainty, not about particular facts but about the essence of all things. In his obstinate Swiss mind there was no room for Occam's subtle distinction between "being" and "essence"; with Duns Scotus, he was interested in "evidence," and with Plato he liked to think that that which is good and beautiful also is reasonable and real. Such a philosophy could fortify the individual in the belief that his personal judgment of the good and the sublime was the supreme authority, that he had the "Light of Nature" from God directly. This the Occamistic Lutherans denied, contending that man was in error constantly.

Thus a philosophy, originally conservative, was to become the instrument of a radical departure in the hands of Paracelsus. The "Light of Nature," he hoped to show, was in the hearts of men, not in books. This new feeling gave a new turn to old ideas: "Would we humans knew our hearts (*Gemüth*) in truth, nothing on earth would be impossible for us." [3]

"*Gemüth*" is a personal experience which the individual enjoys through Nature, not through erudition. The old scholastic philosophy assumed that the student was ignorant of what Nature was; he had to be taught the nature of Nature. Now students felt that they themselves knew what Nature meant to them. Turning the concept of Nature around, they converted what once had been a chain of orthodoxy into a weapon of criticism and free thought. Nature, they maintained, could be known outside the web of theological doctrines; it was "the book which God himself wrote"—no scripture and no deception.[4]

In the same vein, at the threshold of this age, Nicholas de Cusa (1401–64) wrote in his book *Idiota* ("The Layman," meaning the unlearned man):

> "*Orator:* How can you be led out of your ignorance to science, since you are a layman?
> "*Layman:* Not through your books, but God's.
> "*Orator:* Which are they?
> "*Layman:* Those which He wrote with His own fingers.
> "*Orator:* Where are they to be found?
> "*Layman:* Everywhere. . . ."[5]

The philosophy of de Cusa had a lasting influence on Theophrastus. The layman who made himself the protagonist of these new concepts demanded recognition for a new style of life. A new intelligentsia was arising among the middle classes, indifferent to the subtleties of monkish scholasticism, but eager to use intellectual powers in more creative ways. When they studied the freedom and elegance of ancient Athens or the vigor of ancient Rome, the punctilious discipline and ponderous dignity of medieval scholarship appeared purposeless pedantry—in the words of Luis Vives, a Spanish brother-in-arms of Paracelsus: "orthodoxy defending the citadel of ignorance."[6]

HUMANISM

Having rejected monkish science, Theophrastus looked around for other guidance. Fortunately, a friend of his father's had been elevated to high academic dignities. One-time teacher of humanities in Villach, now a famous humanist, Vadianus (Joachim von Waadt, 1484-1551) had become president (*Rector*) of the University of Vienna. It was natural for him to take the young Hohenheim under his wing. (Twenty years later he was again to extend his hospitality to the hunted Paracelsus.)

The Vienna faculty of science was one of the best in Europe. Its calendar experts had laid the foundations for the Copernican reform of astronomy. Here, at the "school of arts," Theophrastus, sixteen years old, enrolled in 1509 to learn the "four higher arts"—arithmetic, geometry, music and astrology. Just as today he is required to study chemistry, so, then, a student of medicine had to start his studies with astrology, the supposed harmonies of the heavenly spheres with the sublunar world. Scientists then believed that the members of the human body are governed by the planets, and Theophrastus was taught to determine a man's destiny from the constellation of the stars. He rebelled, however, against such schematic views. He denied the submission of man under rules which seemed to be abstract and contrary to his nature. "Human wisdom is so great that it has made the stars, the firmament, and the zodiac subject to man. . . . The sky must obey him like a little dog." [7]

His whole future work was to be an outcry against servitude to destiny and the limitations of intuition. Nature, as he understood it, was all the philosophy he needed; for "what is nature if not philosophy?" [8]

His unscientific optimism caused Theophrastus to turn his

back on academic learning, and, after graduating to the
baccalaureate, he wandered on. To receive the master's degree,
it would have been necessary for him to stay another two years.
But in 1511 the pestilence broke out in Vienna, and enroll-
ment at the University dropped to zero. Besides, Theophrastus
realized that the available science could not teach him what he
considered worth while. In his disparagements of scholastic
studies, he did not exempt Vienna: "That God created the
damned schoolmaster, procurator, apothecary, and monk to be
physicians, that is not [true]. They were created at Tübingen,
Leipzig, Vienna, and Ingolstadt." [9]

Dissatisfied with "philosophy" and determined to find another approach to learning, Theophrastus continued his wanderings in the company of the so-called "Roll-Brethren." They
were an offspring of the "Brothers of the Common Lot"—
scholares who cultivated a new form of piety very congenial to
Theophrastus. They, too, believed in the spontaneity of will
and taught that man can justify his existence through love, not
through faith, as Luther thought. Many looked up to de Cusa as
their spiritual father and to Erasmus as their leader. They also
rejected dogmatism and theological hair-splitting, preached
tolerance, organized popular Bible classes, lived in fraternal
communities, and developed charitable institutions. They
represented democratic ideas in the guise of apostolic
Christianity. Two quotations from Erasmus' works will illustrate their ways of thought:

"The yoke of Christ would be sweet if petty human institutions had not added to the burden."

"Would that people let Christ rule through the command
of His word, and not try to build their tyranny with human
decrees."

Theophrastus, it will be seen, took these doctrines most literally. At Erfurt, Theophrastus met the most advanced humanists of Germany, the brilliant Eobanus Hessus and the licentious Crotus Rubianus. They were sophisticated "deriders of God and men" and the hardest drinkers to be found at any university. (Theophrastus himself not only loved wine but was a connoisseur.) They knew the pagan authors by heart, and their teacher, Rufus Mutianus, had advocated the brotherhood of all men, with Christ's spirit being imparted to Jews, Greeks, Turks, and Germans alike. Paracelsus learned from him "not to adulate the coat or the beard of Christ. The true living God has neither beard nor coat." Mutianus also was the friend of Pico della Mirandola, the Florentine cabbalist whose doctrines Paracelsus was to echo in his works.

Like other humanists, whether pious scholars or pagans, they hated bigotry and ignorance. At the time when Theophrastus was in Erfurt, Eobanus Hessus and Crotus Rubianus were writing that immortal satire on the clergy, the *Letters of Obscure Men*.[10] Such license and irreverence, however, brought the humanists at Erfurt into bad repute. In 1513, a mob besieged the university, drove out the professors, and destroyed the library, which they considered the source of all evil influences.

The genial fellow-drinkers of Erfurt could hardly have quenched the metaphysical thirst of the young adept. Their learning held no key to the mysteries of Nature. The antique sources to which they pretended to return proved as dry as the books of the theologians. Their criticism was literary rather than scientific. Their learning produced eloquence rather than knowledge. At the age of nineteen, young Faustus had had enough of "philosophey." Summing up his experience with German universities, he said: "At all German schools you cannot learn as much as at the Frankfort Fair." [11]

CHAPTER 4

Hippocrates vs. Galen

A RENAISSANCE DOCTOR'S
STUDY OF MEDICINE

*Carefully peruse the books of
the Greek and Latin physicians,
not despising the Talmudists
and Cabbalists, and by frequent
anatomy get thee a perfect
knowledge of the microcosm
which is man.*

GARGANTUA TO PANTAGRUEL

Like Albrecht Dürer who pilgrimaged to
Florence and Rome to admire the new painting of Michelangelo;
like Nicholas Copernicus who went to Padua to study Achellini's
cosmography; like Andreas Vesalius who visited the master
anatomists at Padua, Theophrastus traveled to Italy to do his
graduate work. The Italians then were the most famous teachers.
They had at their command the science of the Ancients and of
the Arab and the Christian doctors. Only recently they had discovered the original works of Aristotle, Galen, and Celsus—he

whom Paracelsus sought to excel—and had republished them in beautiful editions, purged of the distortions they had suffered at the hands of medieval editors.

Galen (ca. 130-200 A.D.), a native of Pergamum, was the last great scientist of antiquity, a courtier of rank and the fashionable doctor of imperial Rome. He had endeared himself to the Emperor by concocting an antidote against all poisons, theriac, the most cherished drug of medieval medicine. Galen's admirers called him Paradoxopoeus—he who wrought miracles. He boasted that he had put Hippocrates in the shade. In dubbing Galen a fool and his disciples asses, ignoramuses, and swindlers, Paracelsus was only returning compliments which Galen had paid his predecessors.

In his anatomical lectures Galen used pigs and monkeys; but he did not own a human skeleton. The resulting errors were outweighed by his accurate observations. His very dogmatism, on the whole, was the best thing any science of antiquity could have bequeathed to the dogmatic centuries which followed. He systematized the whole of ancient medicine for medieval doctors.

Rediscovering this last of the ancients was a great experience for Paracelsus' contemporaries. Strengthened by the humanist revival, the Italian doctors felt that they were emancipating medicine from traditionalism and eclecticism. Moreover, Italian and Christian partisanship helped to sharpen the critical axe. During the Middle Ages, Arab culture had been more favorable to the sciences than Christian philosophy. Aristotle reached the West only through his Arab and Jewish disciples. Some schools of medicine in the sixteenth century still required students to learn Arabic, and the curriculum was equally divided between lectures based on Arab and on ancient texts. Averroës was a paramount authority in philosophy, and Avicenna—a Persian or Turk writing in Arabic (980–1037)—ruled over medicine. When Mondino de Luzzi (1246–1326), the great anatomist of the thirteenth century, wished to impress a finding of his on the students, he added "as Avicenna sayeth." Yet in the fifteenth century this same Mondino was found in error because he contradicted Galen. At Theophrastus' Alma Mater, at Tübingen, his works were forbidden. Times had changed; Rome was reborn.

Now the Arabs stood accused of having garbled and adulterated the pure teachings of Hippocrates and Galen. It became fashionable to speak scornfully not only of Arabism but to deprecate all advances since Galen. Forgetful of the scientific thirteenth century, scholars looked down on the "dark" age when people could neither read nor buy books, spoke coarse "hog's Latin" and admired "Gothic"—*i.e.*, barbarian—art.[1] For the first time since antiquity scholars dared acclaim their own century as more enlightened than its predecessor.

Great as it was, however, this movement did not immediately revive research. The very enthusiasm for Galen at first stifled experiment, substituting one orthodoxy for another. Lecturers were warned not to digress from the standard text[2] and students were not allowed to read books not specifically recommended. Teaching still consisted of almost uncritical recitations. Clinical instruction was almost entirely absent. Even at dissections, the professor referred to the book more often than to the corpse; it would happen that a certain bone was being removed from the back while Galen was being read to the effect that it is in the breast. Sculptors and painters were teaching their contemporaries to see reality in a new light, but science still relied on the books. Neither anatomy nor physiology made any significant progress.

THE FOUR HUMORS

The Ancients taught that the body contains four humors—the blood, the phlegm, the black bile, and the yellow bile, corresponding to the four tempers: sanguine, phlegmatic, melancholic, and choleric. An excess of phlegm produces the common cold; an excess of yellow bile causes jaundice; a sanguine person needs to be bled. All other diseases were traced to such imbalances of the humors. Cholera was named from its supposed origin in choleric temper.

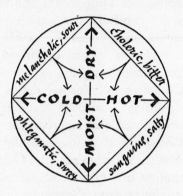

The four humors.

As the diagram shows, each of the humors was hot or cold, moist or dry. The doctors, therefore, prescribed "cold" medicines against "hot" diseases, "dry" remedies against "moist," according to the famous principle: *"Contrary cures contrary."* Students of medicine had to learn how cold or hot, moist or dry, each disease was, and pharmacy informed them which plants had the opposite properties. Thanks to the great Arab doctors, this schematic and oversimplified system had been modified but was still known as the Galenic system. Drugs based on it were called "Galenicals." They were mostly abstracted from herbs, in contrast to the so-called "dirt pharmacy"—concoctions from unicorn horn, ostrich feathers, egg shells, toadstools, excrements of rare animals, vipers' blood, "mummy" powder, and other magic remedies. (Galen, it must be said, was a much better man than would appear from the dogmatism of his followers and Paracelsus' diatribes.)

This mechanical model of disease and health faithfully reflects the rudimentary development of contemporary technology. The spinning wheel was invented during Paracelsus' lifetime. Apart from certain pieces of artillery, the non-mechanical loom, the windmill, and the clock were the most complicated machines known. Common technological experience was restricted to the action of simple tools—the push, the pull, the leverage, pressure, and rotation. The highest level of technical knowledge, embodied in the Gothic cathedrals, required no dynamic concepts.

This was the world in which doctors lived. Their ideas of a remedy were inspired by the technology of their daily life: moisture chases dryness, hot drives out cold. There was little that could help them conceive the idea of a working mechanism, still less of an organism where each part interacts with all others. The circulation of the blood could be discovered only in an age which had invented pumps. Paracelsus got his water from wells.

THE "SKIPPED" ANATOMY COURSE

The way in which medical instruction was given to Theophrastus and his fellow students may be seen on the title page of a text book, printed in Theophrastus' birth year. The lecturer, reading from a book, sits high above the students and above the operating table. He is obviously more concerned with what is in the book than in the dissection. A barber-surgeon performs the dissection and an assistant points to the incision (Plate II). Professors would not risk dirtying their hands or polluting themselves by the touch of intestines, like butchers. That was the barber's duty. Doctors neither applied dressings nor performed operations.

On graduating, the young doctor swore the oath of Hippocrates, pledging himself never to use cautery and knife. No respectable doctor would condescend to do the work of a surgeon or barber. Learned doctors were not even expected to see the patient. Albrecht Dürer, the painter, feeling pain in the region of the appendix, sent his doctor a sketch with a mark indicating "the place where I hurt." Probably he also sent his water along, "urine inspection" being the most favored technique of diagnosis. "Their ignorance cannot justify their fantastic theories. All they can do is to gaze at piss," charged Paracelsus.[3] In addition, doctors studied the patient's horoscope, established his "critical days," and the hour propitious for an operation. The operation, itself, was left to the surgeon or the barber. "The blind leading the blind" was a common joke among medical students.[4]

Theophrastus found nothing worth learning in an anatomy course. He always remained hostile to dissections, and he ridiculed the anatomists who stole corpses from the gallows: "They dissect thieves. The fools. After they have seen everything, they know less than before and into the bargain are soiled with the refuse and cadaver. Then they go to the mass instead of seeing their patients."[5]

This invective, in bad taste and unbecoming a scientist, shows that others, at the risk of their salvation, tried to see for themselves. Though forbidden by the Church, autopsies were not entirely unknown.

It sounds strange that Paracelsus, who preached "*experimentum*" to others, should have spoken so scornfully of dissections. Some have charged it to ignorance of anatomy. Paracelsus, however, gained fame as a surgeon; consequently it would be better to look for a different reason.

Anatomy, Paracelsus said, takes apart what belongs together. It obviously did not explain how the human organism *functions*. The physiology of the four-humor doctrine was altogether unrelated to anatomical knowledge. Before this cleavage could be closed, Paracelsus, obviously, had a good case for calling the anatomists "fragmentary." To anatomy he opposed his physiological concepts. In a nutshell, this controversy on anatomy contains the entire significance of Paracelsus' quarrel with the Galenic school. He sought an understanding of the human body as a functioning, living whole:

"You will learn nothing from the anatomy of the dead; it fails to show the true nature, its working, its essence, quality, being, and power. All that is essential to know is dead. The true anatomy has never been dealt with. It is that of the living body, not of the dead one. If you want to anatomize health and disease, you need a living body." [5]

THE NEW ARISTOTLE

But progress was under way. In the lively demonstration, reproduced in Plate III, everybody is interested. The professor, surrounded by the students, performs the operation himself. It is the title page of Vesalius' *Fabric of the Human Body*—the first modern anatomy, published in 1543, shortly after Paracelsus' death. In the fifty years between publication of these two pictures flanking Paracelsus' lifetime, mankind took a great leap toward modern science.

Most of this progress was the work of a generation of scholars and students who interpreted Aristotle in a new way. They were less interested in his metaphysical system than in his empirical method. At the very Alma Mater of Padua, which had been the stronghold of Aristotelian reaction up to the end of the fifteenth century, a galaxy of young doctors proclaimed the age of empirical research. Surgery became a dignified profession, anatomical studies no longer had to be conducted underground. In broad daylight, the medical school erected an operating amphitheater and twice a year invited notables and students to attend a public dissection. Certainly, it was a show rather than instruction, but prejudices were breaking down. Da Carpi boasted of having dissected a hundred human heads. But when his studies revealed muscles and bones not accounted for by his predecessors, he was far from "claiming the invention of any member which has not been mentioned by so many and so great experts." To tear the authorities down, he liked to quote, dead-pan, conflicting passages from classical textbooks. Others expressed their criticism in ingenious commentaries or blamed the translators.[6]

To anticipate the end of a development which Paracelsus did not live to see, Padua remained the Alma Mater of the great scientists who eventually shattered the world of Galen. Vesalius (1514-64), who contributed the first modern anatomy; Harvey (1578-1657), who discovered the circulation of the blood; Copernicus (1473-1543), who removed the earth from the center of the universe (severing thereby the human anatomy from its alleged relations to the zodiac; plate V); Galileo (1564-1642), who established the modern method of experiment— all were alumni of the empirical school of Padua.

All this, however, happened after Paracelsus' death. The shock which overthrew the medieval system of philosophy and medicine during his lifetime came from another direction, with the active participation of Paracelsus, in contrast to and in criticism of Aristotelianism.

REVOLUTION AT FERRARA

A rival school had been founded at Ferrara. In contrast to Aristotelian Padua, it was humanist and Platonist, closer to the Realist doctrines of Duns Scotus which Paracelsus had sworn to defend. It was obvious that he had to go there.

Ferrara, moreover, had an additional attraction for German students. The Duke d'Este maintained friendly relations with the Emperor, whose Germans were always to be found, in force, in the town, along with Swiss soldiers, wayfarers, diplomats, and scholars. Here, in the German House, Theophrastus met fellow students to whom later he was to dedicate his books —though some, we shall learn, received them with ill grace.

What splendor Ferrara meant to the poor student from Germany! The mighty Dukes d'Este, ruthless Renaissance princes, had made the town big and glamorous. They ruled over a larger population than the Pope. Their court was illuminated by the greatest lights of the century. Their Duchess was the beautiful Lucrezia Borgia, daughter of Pope Alexander and sister of the bloody Cesare. In her mature years, she was devoted to the promotion of the arts.

The University was progressive, and the pride of the medical school was old Dr. Niccolo Leoniceno (1428-1514). To him and his successor, Giovanni Manardi (1462-1536), Paracelsus owes more than to any other academic teacher. Leoniceno had specialized on the new and ravaging "love pestilence" or "French disease" to which, later on, Paracelsus turned his attention. His translations of Hippocrates and Galen led the battle against Avicenna and against slavish acceptance of authority. He said that doctors had eyes to see for themselves, the battle cry of Paracelsus for the rest of his life.

Stimulated by the revival of humanist studies, Leoniceno at-

tacked the Arab scholars, in particular, their garbled editions
of Galen and Hippocrates. Once on the trail, however, he became painfully aware of inconsistencies in the works of his beloved ancient authors themselves. Leoniceno did not attack
Galen or Aristotle directly. He chose as his target Pliny, the
Roman naturalist. Today we know this classic author as an uncritical collector of factual reports and tall tales; but, at that
time, he was revered as the encyclopedist of antiquity. Pliny
was the authority for the belief that magicians could transmit
diseases with the aid of a waxen image, and that a menstruating
woman had harmful effects upon all life around her. He had
seen with his own eyes, so he says, the birth of cinnabar from
the blood shed on the sand by an elephant and a dragon locked
in deadly combat. Pliny's authority was so great that other
authors, as late as the fifteenth century, reported that they
themselves had seen this, too.

Leoniceno undermined Pliny's reputation.[6] Confidence in
the old books was shaken even though the students were required to learn them by heart.

Once more, Theophrastus discovered that books were not
to be trusted implicitly. Besides, he was not used to the rapid
succession of new theories and the textbook revisions taken for
granted today. Uncritical at heart, despite all his attacks on
textbooks, he would have liked to find some book which contained all the truth. After his disenchantment with theological
certitude at Tübingen, this new disillusion shook his belief
in the certainty of science. Had he taken too seriously the
Devil's sarcastic advice to Faustus' student?

> Write it down with ink and pen,
> You need not further study then.

His fury toward the learned books smacks of disappointed
love. His later onslaughts on Galen and Avicenna cannot be ex-

plained by the zeal of the innovator alone. Leoniceno and Manardi had made the discovery for him; he had little more to do than translate into German what he had learned in Italy.

HIPPOCRATES

Not anatomy alone, all science seemed to be contradictory and doomed to failure. The complaint, taken up later by the authors of the Faustus poems, that "we cannot know for certain," rings through Paracelsus' works in many contexts.

> "Their doctoring has given people the idea that all medicine is a fraud and a hoax. Peasants know more than they. Isn't it a shame that a municipal doctor with a salary should not be able to care for his patients, whereas others, who have not studied medicine, are?" [7]

In Ferrara, however, Theophrastus found friends and teachers of the same opinion. Moreover a tradition of non-"fragmentary" medicine existed among the Platonists in friendly Florence. Ficino (1433-1499), who had translated and republished Plato's works, is one of the few philosophers whom Paracelsus praised without qualification; significantly, he called him a "great physician," though Ficino is little known as a doctor. Another Platonist and cabbalist of whom Paracelsus thought highly was Pico della Mirandola, the friend and correspondent of Rufus Mutianus. The works of these authors were available at Ferrara, and disciples of their Florentine Academy taught there. Incidentally, Ficino and Pico had their ideological roots in masonic or pious fraternities similar to those "Brothers of the Common Lot" with whom Theophrastus had wandered.

Furthermore the teacher of Leoniceno, and his predecessor in the chair, was Michael Savonarola, grandfather of Fra Girolamo, the saintly dictator of Florence. Savonarola had criticized

Arab and Galenic medicine, recommended the study of Hippocrates, and developed a system of his own which influenced the thinking of Paracelsus. His point of view was bio-physical, in contrast to anatomical studies. Like Hippocrates, he emphasized the patient's constitution, was wary of schematic theories, and trusted *"the healing forces of nature."* Treatment, he said, must be given to the whole organism of the patient, not merely to the diseased member; and he went as far as to say that pulling a tooth does not cure the toothache. This view is known in literature as "wholism."

Here was an idea which later was to prove fertile. It had grown in the circle of Florentine and Ferrarese Platonists, nourished in magic and cabbalistic ideas so different from the analytical and anatomical approach of Aristotelian Padua. Who would produce revolutionary results first, those who studied the parts or those who directly reached for the whole?

It took Theophrastus a long detour to find out, for his opposition to organized studies led him away from all schools. Goethe echoes him when he has the Devil, disguised as professor, tell the student:

> All dull and gray is theory,
> But green is life's all-golden tree.[8]

figure I

"The Alchymist." A Rembrandt etching known also as
"Dr. Faustus watching the appearance of the sign of the Holy Spirit."
(The sign shows Christian and Arab symbols.)

figure 2

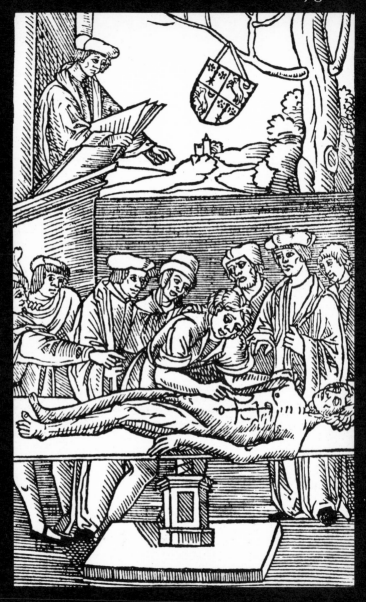

*Mondino lecturing. Woodcut from the title page
of his* Anathomia.

figure 3

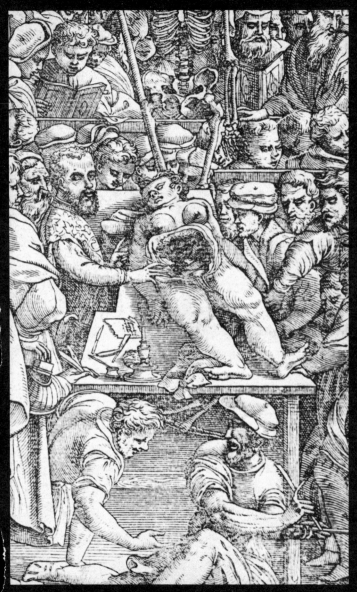

*Vesalius lecturing. From the title page
of his* Fabrica.

figure 4

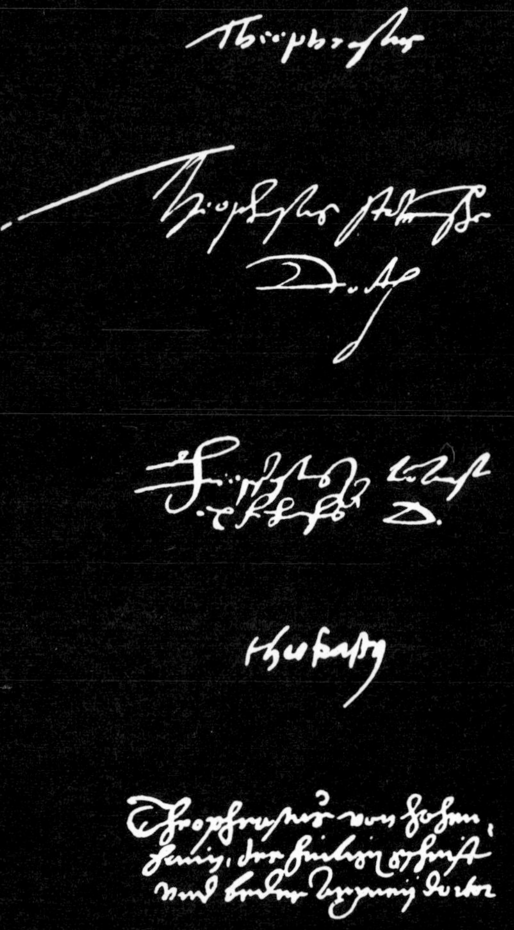

Paracelsus' signatures. The bottom specimen
says: "Theophrastus von Hohenheim, Doctor of Holy Scripture
and of both medicines." Reproduced from Sudhoff's
edition of Paracelsus' works.

CHAPTER 5

Quack Doctor

PRINCE OF THE
MEDICAL MONARCHY

*My accusers complain that I
have not entered the temple of
knowledge through the right
door. But which one is the truly
legitimate door—Galen and Avicenna, or Nature? I have entered through the door of Nature. Her light, not the lamp of
an apothecary's shop, has illuminated my way.*

PARACELSUS

An unforeseen event precipitated Theo-
phrastus' decision to interrupt his studies. In the war between the
German Emperor and the French king, Ferrara was the Emperor's ally, sending Swiss mercenaries into the field. In 1515, at
Marignano, French artillery killed eight thousand Swiss, and the
Emperor Maximilian lost his claims in northern Italy. With Ferrara supine at the feet of King Francis, it became embarrassing
for a Swiss and a German to remain there.

Theophrastus joined his compatriots in their flight south—

not even pausing in Rome—to find shelter in the ranks of another Hapsburg army, operating near Naples. The Emperor's grandson, Charles, King of Spain, had invaded southern Italy to restore the balance of power against Francis. As a surgeon in this army, Theophrastus secured his first employment and his first practical experience in his profession.

Scalpels. From an old textbook on surgery.

Surgery still was hazardous and rudimentary. Paracelsus reports with horror how once, at Friaul, he "chanced into a soldiers' brawl; and in a public house one man's ear was chopped off. A barber was called and he stuck the ear on with some mortar. . . . The ear, however, fell off soon, dripping with blood and pus." [1]

Barbers still performed most minor operations, and surgeons were little better than "barbers of the long robe." Their instruments were as crude as their techniques. Operations were performed without benefit of anaesthesia and asepsis. Wounds were treated with a branding iron. The ligature, although known by the ancients, was not used until Paré (1510-90) reintroduced it shortly after Paracelsus' death. To stop bleeding, surgeons padded the wound with moss, or scorched it with scalding oil. Their dressing ointment was concocted of cow dung, viper fat, feathers, and other unsavory substances. Wounds, it was thought, must suppurate, and the victims of this treatment had to face gangrene and wound fever. Paracelsus raged against these practices. He insisted that wounds be kept clean. "If you prevent infection, Nature will heal the wound all by herself." [2]

A disciple of Hippocrates and the elder Savonarola, he had confidence in the self-healing power of the body. Unfortunately, however, his own trust in nature was not shared by his fellow-surgeons. How was he to convince them that wounds be left alone? A strange superstition of medieval folk medicine came to the rescue—the practice of "weapon ointment," *i.e.*, the belief that a wound balm is most effective when applied not to the wound but to the sword that made it. This certainly was "magic." Ignorant of antisepsis, Paracelsus was unable to give a rational explanation of its working. But he used it, and this method of sparing the wound saved the lives of numbers of soldiers in three European wars.

The painful procedures of medieval surgery inflicted added traumatic experiences upon the patients. In all his later cures, Paracelsus tried to avoid operations. He consistently opposed the advice of "fragmentary" doctors to amputate. He even refused to remove bullets from the flesh, much to the misery of his patients. The theory of weapon ointment, obviously, could not work in the case of bullet wounds, and treatment remained inadequate. Surgical care, therefore, continued to be an ungratifying occupation.

Wounds were only a small part of an army surgeon's worries. Epidemics took more lives than weapons. Wherever the armies went, typhoid fever, dysentery, cholera and other plagues marched along. The most dreaded was the new scourge which was neither cancer nor ulcer, neither leprosy nor smallpox, and to which every nation gave the name of its enemy. The Spanish stigmatized it as "the French disease"; the French cursed it as *"morbus Germanicus."* The name by which it is known today, syphilis, came into use after 1530.

Leoniceno had written on the new disease, and now Theophrastus had an opportunity to check medical theory with the facts. Syphilis then was incurable and the young medicus saw all his high expectations come to naught. Under the shock of failure, Theophrastus despaired of his ability to help the patients—"you injure ten while saving one," he exclaimed. It discouraged him from persisting in his medical studies altogether. "Often I decided to leave the art alone. I pondered that it is all uncertain and deceitful. I abandoned it again and again and treated it with indignation." [3]

Paracelsus' confession of professional qualms has found its way into the Faustus books, culminating in Goethe's famous rendering of Faustus' self-recrimination:

> Our medicine made the patients sick,
> Yet no one asked: Who did recover?
> Worse than the pest we killed, the poison
> To thousands with these hands I gave.
> They perished, yet the murderer earns praise.

FOLK MEDICINE

If Theophrastus had needed an eye-opener, the shock of his Italian failure must have provided it. When he recovered, he swore never again to admit defeat. "God has not permitted any disease without providing a remedy." [4] He refused to believe patients doomed just because the books did not provide a treatment. A doctor by nature and of nature, he could not help trying to heal the sick with unproved medicines, studying the reactions of the body and, in his own words, "following the disease as the cow follows the crib." [5]

It was ridiculous to think that medicine should be powerless. Did not case histories prove the authorities wrong? While some diseases defied medicine, inexplicable cures belied it. Not medicine, but Galen and Avicenna were bankrupt. The idea that medicine is all patchwork did not suit him at all. Rather would he believe that he had not yet found the right kind of medicine. Were there no other avenues to health?

One such approach was folk medicine. Old women, necromancers, barbers, shepherds, and peasants knew many things which apparently had been overlooked by the learned doctors. Barbers, the common man's doctors, knew the art of healing not from books but through the Light of Nature or by a tradition handed down from the ancient magi. "Before there was medicine, doctors were called magi. Manifold things were revealed to them, but much of it was lost. That's why in these matters so much experience is wanting." [6]

The realm of folk medicine ranges from wound spells to love potions and the medicinal qualities in the local flora. The use of some of these roots and plants—stimulants, purgatives, emetics, etc.—is hallowed by centuries of experience. Others have proved worthless despite such long usage. Some are outright superstitious. The value of Paracelsus' return to these treasures was mostly negative. It helped him discredit the complicated concoctions of Galenic medicine. In addition, most remedies of folk medicine are *specific*—a principle about which we shall have to say more in the following section.

Agrippa von Nettesheim, Paracelsus' contemporary and brother-in-arms, thus contrasts folk and academic physicians and their medicines:

> "Physicians recommend themselves by splendid costumes, rings and jewels, tedious travels, a strange country of origin, and a strange religion. They are shameless in praising their medicines and cures, observe times and hours according to the astrological calendar, hang amulets and charms on the patient.
>
> "Simple and native medicines are altogether neglected in favor of foreign drugs. Also, medicines are mixed in such enormous numbers that the effect of one is canceled by the action of another, and none can foresee what such abominable mixtures will achieve." [7]

In a few instances, Paracelsus was critical of folklore. He did not believe in mandrakes, for example. Yet he never rejected experience, however superstitious. The following case is characteristic. Paracelsus had operated on a boy's hand and, apparently due to the uncleanliness in contemporary operating rooms, the wound became infected. The boy's father sued for damages when the hand remained swollen and rigid, but Paracelsus pleaded that judgment be deferred, hoping that the swelling would subside. Eventually, hard-pressed by the court, he ordered live earthworms placed on the wound, and—it worked. Thereafter, Paracelsus recommended earthworm cures against blood poisoning.

Paracelsus' procedure here reveals the shortcomings of his age rather than his own. He resorted to the folk remedy after all the others had failed; then hastened to conclusions which were not disproved until the nineteenth century.

THE DIRT PHARMACY

Thumbing through Paracelsus' surgical works, the modern reader finds a repellent collection of superstitions, practical folk remedies, and medieval prescriptions. *"Theriacum"* (treacle) or *"mitridatum"* was a cure-all concocted of viper's fat and fifty other worthless ingredients. The idea was that the viper, itself impervious to poison, must immunize the body to which it is applied. A stand-by of medieval pharmacy, it was so highly regarded that in Venice, for instance, it was solemnly cooked once a year on St. Mark's Square. "Unicorn horn," in reality a narwhal tooth, was supposed to prevent food poisoning. Pope Clemens presented one to the French Dauphin. And we have already spoken about "weapon ointment."

Above all, "mummy powder" was a substance which pharmacists were expected to carry. Genuine Egyptian mummy being rare, an ersatz was prepared of birds stuffed with spices and then pulverized. Paracelsus did not think much of this substitute. He insisted that the mummy should be human. Two kinds of mummy, he thought, were particularly effective: that of a Saint and that of a healthy young person who had recently drowned or been killed by a fall. He also recommended thieves cut down from the gallows or beheaded rebels. Having died in full vigor, their flesh, still radiating life power, might regenerate the failing spirits of the sick. Relics of Saints owed their healing power to the fact that their mummy continued to radiate. It was well known that a Saint's carcass does not stink—proof enough of its curative powers.

All this obviously is magic at its worst, and Paracelsus had no share in overcoming this stage of medicine. On the contrary, he drew heartily on superstitions, the dirt pharmacy, and folk remedies. He treated frost blisters with "children's hair boiled by a red-haired person." He recommended "live toads" against bubonic pustules. On foul wounds he heaped "three handfuls of steamed pigeons' dung." For hemorrhage, he prescribed "moss grown on a skull." In reviewing these prescriptions, one may assume that part of his cures he owed to his reluctance to prescribe. A few of his empirical remedies can be justified by modern knowledge. Frog's eggs, for instance, contain iodine, and Paracelsus used them as a disinfectant, though he could not possibly know what "*arcanum*" he was employing.

THE "ARCANA"

Neither surgery nor the wisdom of witches and magi, however, could lead medicine out of the blind alley where the Galenists had left it. Paracelsus might have been a genius of a healer, but he would hardly be remembered as a great innovator if his sole merit had been a revival of folk prescriptions. His boast, that he had learned from folk doctors, was a strong way of formulating his challenge to academic medicine. Actually, he neither glorified folk medicine nor did he make any greater use of its prescriptions than his rivals. The most orthodox Galenists relied on dirt pharmacy. Paracelsus was not distinguished from them by his practice but by his refusal to disown it in his theory.

Paracelsus' approach was entirely experimental and empirical. He prescribed whatever experience had proved effective. The word empirical, which we use advisedly, had two special meanings in the parlance of contemporary doctors. Both, we shall find, fit Paracelsus.

An empiricist, first, was a practitioner without academic standing who had picked up his knowledge of medicine outside the colleges. They were the lowly ones of medicine, students whose education had been cut short; adventurers who treated the sick at country fairs; itinerant peddlers of wonder drugs; and alchemists who believed that they had found the Elixir. Some, perhaps, were naturally talented. But, on the whole, they practiced by rote and rarely lingered to see the effects of their remedies.

Among these empiricists, however, were a number who experimented in a rather different way. They tested the properties of stones and metals, prescribed certain new drugs which, in some cases, achieved cures where Galenic remedies failed. Some may have been mere quacks. Others were probing toward a new medicine, based on chemical studies.

Very few learned doctors took the empiric remedies seriously. Most scholars despised them. Melanchthon thus characterized them:

> "Empiricists are without education, but have picked up a few remedies in apothecary and barber shops. From rhetoric, however, they borrow certain other arts and make extravagant promises which detract from the reputation of regular physicians. They pretend that their predictions are derived from the stars. . . . They learned their remedies from magicians and Jews, or from barbers and mid-wives." [8]

Melanchthon had a low opinion of Paracelsus because of his impiety. Like any bigot, the famous Reformation leader and humanist combined the charge of quackery with the accusation of sorcery. Paradoxically, he held against Paracelsus the very empiricism in which the latter glorified.

The truth is more complex than Melanchthon realized. Bona fide empiricists did not find their medicines in pharmacies. They were experimenters who studied new drugs, then unknown to doctors and pharmacists alike, the so-called *arcana* or chemical medicines. Enraged apothecaries warred against this threatening competition. These remedies did not contain the costly ingredients of medieval pharmacy. They were known as "simple" recipes, though for a different reason. Since ancient times, doctors had recognized a few remedies which, in contrast to the "Galenicals," do not act on the "humors," but on the body or the disease directly. They were supposed to have a "specific virtue." Paracelsus, therefore, called doctors who applied them *"specifici."* The Arabs knew a number of such specifics.

Here now is an interesting lineage: Aulus Cornelius Celsus, the ancient Roman doctor to whom Paracelsus alluded in his pen-name, considered himself a disciple of Hippocrates. He did not use remedies according to their place in the table of humors, like Galen, but divided them into groups according to their *specific* virtues—purgative, diaphoretic, diuretic, emetic, narcotic, etc. These classifications reappeared in the works of some Arab doctors, but the elder Savonarola was the first to establish a list of forty such specific effects. Savonarola, moreover, was the teacher of Leoniceno, and Leoniceno of Paracelsus.

However, the Arabs and Savonarola had been satisfied with a catalogue—*"This will purge, that will constipate,"* Paracelsus was to mock it. He went one step further; he asked why this is so. He wondered what makes an herb purgative.

"It does not matter that rhubarb is a purgative. The question is: What is it that purges? Not the answer: Rhubarb purges; but the answer: What is the corpus that purges? Names have no virtues; substances have." [9]

Substance, here, means the medicinal force which is hidden in the herb, and which Paracelsus later called *"arcanum,"* the secret power. This question marks the transition from empiricism to chemo-therapy [see also p. 127].

THE MISSING DIPLOMA

Paracelsus turned into a passionate empiricist. Later in his career and after his death, his detractors accused him of belonging to that "sect." They held against him his failure to obtain the doctor's degree at Ferrara. Indeed, to the chagrin of his eulogists, no record of his graduation exists, and he was unable to show that important document when, later, his right to practice medicine was disputed. His posthumous advocates have ardently defended his title, and this quarrel has so agitated the scholars that the nub of the controversy has been overlooked —the fact, namely, that Paracelsus himself was proud of being an empiricist.

Defiantly, he retorted to the doctors that "I have been transplanted from your garden into another garden" [10]; for indeed, he had not remained in school long enough to take the examination. Like his father, Paracelsus never became an "M.D."; and he insisted that it was of no consequence:

"Doctors, what is the use of name, title, and school, unless we have the knowledge? . . . Whom do honors, the doctor's ring and cloak behoove but those who deserve them by their skill? . . . If disease puts us to the test, all our splendor, title, ring, and name will be as much help as a horse's tail." [11]

Not content with scorning professional attire and title, he even railed against the doctor's oath, the most sacred of the guild institutions: "They [the Nuremberg doctors who had questioned his competence] are sworn fools, and beware of such ———[obscenity] swindlers." [12]

The German word *Bescheisser* which he used here is one of his favorite epithets for the professional morals of his competitors. He also called them "accredited asses," "bloaters," "sharpers," and other names reflecting the social resentment of the free lance toward official practitioners. On the other hand, he dared them to deny that "in your (!) field"[13] he had worked more successful cures than they. Verily, he needed no rehabilitation from the charge of entering the temple of knowledge by a back door. He held his doctorate by the right of genius, not by grace of the faculty or the law of the land. "The art of healing makes a physician. The work makes the master and doctor—neither Emperor nor Pope, nor faculty privileges and university. For from them is hidden what makes a physician."[14]

On such grounds, Paracelsus did not hesitate to assume the title which the faculty had refused him. He was never meticulous with respect to procedure, jurisdictional rights and due form. In any field that he considered himself qualified, he bestowed upon himself the appropriate title. His *Interpretation of the Comet* (1531) was signed: "Professor of Medicine, Doctor of the Arts and Propagator of Philosophy." The signature on our facsimile reads: "Theophrastus, Doctor of Both Medicines [*i.e.*, surgery and physics] and of Holy Scripture," though he had less legal right to nominate himself doctor of theology than doctor of physic.[15] Perhaps he was a doctor of surgery, an infrequently used and socially disdained title. A surgeon was unable to swear the oath of Hippocrates, pledging him never to use cautery and knife.

"INTELLECTUAL VAGABONDS"

Only in Italy were barbers and druggists acquiring the right to swear the professional oath, and there, alone, professors themselves were beginning to perform operations. In Germany, the castes remained tightly partitioned. No surgeon could pass judgment on a physician's business. In some places, the surgeon was also the local hangman.

The doctor's degree, then, was not a matter of adding two letters to one's name. It conferred honors and status. Like the ordination of a priest, it elevated its bearer high above the crowd. When a doctor had been accredited by the faculty of medicine, he became a member of the upper classes. He had the right to ride on horseback, preceded by a valet, to wear a fur hat and a red robe. He was eligible to marry "quality" and his wife was exempt from the rules of modesty which governed the attire of burghers' wives. Admitted into the patrician guilds, along with grain and wool merchants and bankers, he was not supposed to associate with surgeons, to say nothing of doing their work. Surgeons had their own lesser guild.

Paracelsus' attack on the schools threatened to tear down the guild barriers. The doctors, therefore, did not ask themselves: Is Paracelsus right? Their reaction was: How can anyone be right who is not a doctor? Behind the authority of Galen and Avicenna, the privileged guild of learned doctors shut itself off from the new fountains of experience and knowledge. Of necessity, whosoever found fault with the school doctrines faced class prejudice and interest.

It is curious to note how this attitude has been taken over by modern Paracelsus worshippers. Proud to proclaim his genius, they nevertheless take pains to prove that their master was not an outsider.[16] The priests of the Paracelsus cult have their revolution behind them. The title of doctor, they think, would make their hero as respectable as they are themselves.[17] They choose to represent him as a fairy prince who temporarily assumed the shape of a frog. It embarrasses them to admit that his manners were rough and his rags not borrowed for show but the real rags of a real beggar.

The new prince of the medical monarchy, Paracelsus' own

description of himself, was by no means a prince *incognito*; he appropriated the title through a revolutionary act. Like that other great barber-surgeon, Ambroise Paré, Paracelsus was an outsider struggling for recognition. In another field their friends, the humanists, proclaimed the new principle of the liberal arts which elevated genius above social barriers. They denied that learning could be monopolized, and demonstrated that the kind of knowledge which can be monopolized is not all there is to be learned. Claiming that lay studies had opened purer sources of wisdom, a free intelligentsia asserted its right to teach and to practice the new truths. The idea of a renovation, therefore, came to be associated with a new class of spiritual leaders who developed a new approach to nature, held a new view of man's position in the universe, and used these concepts to pry open the closed shop of medieval learning. Professional pride and social resentment flare up when Paracelsus contrasts the empiricists with the haughty guild members:

"I praise the chemical physicians. They do not consort with idlers or go about in gorgeous satins, silks, and velvets, with gold rings on their hands. They tend their work by the fire patiently by day and night, seek their recreation in the laboratory, wear plain leathern dress and aprons of hide to wipe their hands. Sooty like blacksmiths, they make little show and do not gossip with their patients. Nor do they praise their remedies; for they well know that the work must praise the master and that chatter does not help the sick. But they busy themselves at learning the steps of alchemy— distillation, solution, putrefaction, extraction, calcination, reverberation, sublimation, fixation, separation, reduction, coagulation, tinction." [18]

The free artist, the free Platonic Academy at Florence, the freedom of medicine from guild barriers—all signs pointed up the same trend. Unorthodox thinking thrives in the climate of a socially independent *Bohème*, and new sources of wisdom or knowledge are tapped when new classes rise to the surface of society.

THE ARCH-MAGUS

Among the few learned men who sided with the rebellion against Galen was one whom, strangely enough, Paracelsus never met, although their paths must have crossed several times and although Paracelsus knew his works well. He was the famous Agrippa von Nettesheim (1486-1535), arch-magus of the age. Like Paracelsus, he dabbled in alchemy and the occult sciences, attacked the established science and the caste of its devotees in vigorous language, and was distrustful of pure reason. His troubled and wandering life also offers striking parallels with that of Paracelsus. Both were interested in alchemy, and both, not altogether accidentally, as we shall see, returned into the fold of the Catholic Church the same year.

Like Theophrastus, Agrippa has provided material for the Faustus saga. He actually was accused of having clandestine relations with an enormous dog—Faustus' poodle—which accompanied him everywhere and which, at his death, ran away "howling as only the Devil can howl." Like Faustus and other damned disciples of the Devil, Agrippa allegedly died with his face turned to the earth.

In real life, Agrippa was at times a wandering quack, at times a famous doctor and lawyer. He was personal physician to the Emperor Maximilian, the Duke of Savoy, and many noble families. He lectured at the orthodox University of Cologne and elsewhere, conducted diplomatic missions on behalf of mighty sovereigns, but was unable to settle down either as scholar or courtier. On several occasions he had to leave a town in great

hurry for unknown, allegedly dishonorable reasons. After he
had studied and taught all the science of his time, he wrote a
book, *On the Uncertainty and Vanity of the Arts and Sciences
and the Excellency of the Word of God.*

In the following chapters, we shall pause to consider the
unorthodox interests which for a while kept Paracelsus from
pursuing his medical career. As he himself testified, he was
ready to take up "other pursuits," probably alchemy or other
"magic" sciences.[19] Christopher Marlowe did nothing but ver-
sify the old sixteenth century book of Dr. Faustus when he
wrote:

> Philosophy is odious and obscure,
> Both Law and Physic are for petty wits;
> Divinity is basest of the three,
> Unpleasant, harsh, contemptible, and vile:
> 'Tis magic, magic that hath ravished me.

CHAPTER 6

The Necromancer

ON NYMPHS, GNOMES,
GIANTS, DWARFS,
INCUBI AND SUCCUBÆ,
STARS AND SIGNS

For good reasons did the ancient magicians express their prophecies in images rather than in writing. For who dare tell the naked truth to a king? I'd rather not—my reward might be hanging. No magus, astrologer, or chiromancer should tell his sovereign the naked truth. He should use images, allegories, figures, wondrous speech, or other hidden or roundabout ways.

PARACELSUS

Neither Theophrastus nor any of his contemporaries would have doubted the Devil any more than God. Angels appeared to persons who were worthy of God's grace, and demons tempted or tormented the faithful. Whatever occurrence could not be explained readily was attributed to hobgoblins who seemed to disregard the law of gravitation, the law of cause and effect, and the impenetrability of bodies. They produced freaks of nature at will, which people accepted. In nature "anything can happen."

Paracelsus had to accept as factual reports stories which would never pass today. Did not the milk really turn sour after a certain old hag passed by? And did not a dream announce the death of a relative? It was common knowledge that

"the air is full of demons as it is with flies in summer. Many men are forewarned by familiars in diverse shapes, such as crows and owls. . . . Demons teach, instruct, and inspire men; there never was a man of outstanding stature in any art or action who had no familiar spirit to guide him." [1]

Necromancy (magic based on communication with the dead), nigromancy (black magic), astrology, signatures (p. 80), and forms of divination such as geomantics, pyromantics, etc., which Paracelsus himself calls "uncertain or deceptive arts," all belonged to the heritage he shared with his contemporaries. At heart a medieval "magus," despite his great contributions to the progress of science, Paracelsus described practices still followed by spiritualists, anthroposophists, theosophists, and occultists today. He believed in "signs" and prophecies, mediumistic states, "action at a distance," removal of physical objects through spiritual powers, communication with the dead, divination, passage of matter through matter, telepathy, the healing powers of stones, charms, spells, and amulets, in number magic, astrology, and all the "mantic arts."

He maintained that the phoenix is born of a horse's carcass, that vermin originate from the putrefaction of organic matter, that a magnet, rubbed in leek, loses its power (nobody ever seemed to have tried it); that a dead man may be resurrected and live for six months if his body is planted in a certain way in the earth, a belief he shared with Francis Bacon; that human blood operates like a magnet on cattle and deer; that a spider hung around the neck is a protection against ague; that certain words have healing powers; that a waxen image of a man can convey to him or take from him any disease; that a pregnant woman can impress a picture upon her child's body; that a magus can make himself invisible; that a possessed person may be cured by perforating his skull; that a man with a red beard is unfit to be a doctor.

"Nails and hair, needles, bristles, pieces of glass, and many other things have been pulled out of the bodies of some patients, and the physicians stood there helpless and did not know what to do. Had they understood their business, they would have known that these things had been brought into the body by the power of the evil imagination of a sorcerer, and they might have put one of the extracted articles into an oak tree, on the side of the rising sun, and that article would have acted like a magnet to attract the evil influence, and it would have cured the patient." [2]

Paracelsus was sure that he had these reports on good authority. In some cases he interviewed the patient, a victim of a swindler or of his own hallucinations.

However, he was no uncritical believer. When his own experience was at variance with tradition, he registered his skepticism. He doubted that water can be found with the aid of dowsing rods. He never cast a nativity and condemned all "judicial" astrology, *i.e.*, the prediction of personal fate from the constellation of the stars at a certain date. At times he denounced superstitions which he had elsewhere endorsed. We shall try to find out what led him into these contradictions.

"FORTUNE"

Superstition, in the opinion of Paracelsus, is every belief in freaks and whims of nature, every "explanation" of wonderful events through supernatural forces, every assertion that demons, saints, or even God himself interferes with the eternal course of nature. On the contrary, science, or magic, as he preferred to call it, is the belief that all natural phenomena, however strange, have a cause in nature herself and are determined by immutable laws, accessible to investigation by experiment and to understanding by the human reason.

The oddities we have reported and other strange beliefs which he shared with his contemporaries are not superstitions in the true sense of the word. They are errors of observation, uncritical acceptance of reports at second hand, or wishful thinking. They never are irrational. To illustrate our point, we shall pause to consider two notions which played a significant role in Renaissance philosophy—fortune and providence. Paracelsus rejected one, but accepted the other. What was the difference? "What else is fortune but that we keep order in the knowledge of Nature. What is misfortune but that we fall out with Nature? If Nature goes right, it's good luck; if she goes wrong, it's bad luck." [3]

Thus he pitted his own interpretation of Luck against the favorite goddess of Renaissance authors like Machiavelli—Fortuna, whose wheel arbitrarily elevates and crushes man. Paracelsus continued: "There is no such person called Luck who does to people whatever she feels like doing. Good and bad luck are not like wind and snow, but should be known by the reason of nature." [3]

Dotting his i's as usual, he added that "Misfortune is ignorance, Fortune is knowledge." [3] We shall find that formula again when we go into the meaning of magic. Suffice it here to emphasize the point on which Paracelsus was in agreement with the humanist tradition of Thomas Aquinas, that *knowledge gives power*, hence fortune is knowledge. As man acquires mastery of Nature, he frees himself from the thraldom of circumstance and accident.

This beautiful idea was deeply rooted in ancient magic and can be pursued through the ages until its expression, in our day, in the utopias of technocracy and in Marxian philosophy. The wise man foresees how Nature will behave and harnesses her forces. Magic still joins in her lap science and technology.

Luther and Calvin accepted the pagan concept of fortune. What they called Providence also was a blind force. Man's helplessness under its whims only served to point up his utter lack of power and his need of salvation. In Paracelsus' interpretation, Providence was not blind, but most rational, almost calculable. It was another name for something similar to our "laws of nature." It is almost correct to say that Providence is that which can be foreseen.

Of course, Paracelsus did not formulate laws of nature as we do. He rather entertained the magic belief, which some call "superstitious," that one great law governed all Nature. Although this great law was substantially the astrological pattern he had rejected as a student, the nuance in which he differed seemed to make all the difference in the world.

THE STARS

No belief was as popular in the sixteenth century as astrology, among intellectuals as well as the masses. Paracelsus would not give an enema or bleed a patient when the moon was in the wrong constellation. In prescribing charms and amulets he consulted the Zodiac; and he attributed the bad "humor" of a patient to a harmful exudation of his planet. At the same time, his criticism of astrology was outspoken.

"The stars determine nothing, incline nothing, suggest nothing; we are as free from them as they are from us." [4]

"The stars and all the firmament cannot affect our body,

nor our color, beauty and gestures, nor our virtues and vices.
. . . The course of Saturnus can neither prolong nor
shorten a man's life." [5]

Both quotations are from his early works. Toward the end he
became less uncompromising and went so far as to outline a
system of astrological determinations:

> "There is no governing power but predestination, so that
> nothing can remain concealed. . . . In order to give you an
> example of what I mean, know that the Sun governs the
> crown, the scepter, the throne, and all royal majesty and
> power, all glory, wealth, treasures, decorum, and vanity of
> this world. The Moon is sovereign over farming, navigation,
> travel, and everything that pertains thereto. . . ." [6]

Can these statements be reconciled? Planetary signs were used
in three different contexts: chemical, meteorological, and psychological. The influence of the stars on climate and weather
was generally accepted, with the seasons dependent upon stellar
"exhalations"; today we would say radiations. In turn, the climate influences a person's "humors"; and thus, astrology served
to analyze a person's character. Since psychology did not yet
exist, it was convenient to characterize and classify people by
their "stars." But Paracelsus no longer sought such stars in the
firmament; he merely used their names as sign-posts. "Had the
moon never been in the sky," he wrote, "there still would be
people who partake of her nature." [7] Likewise, he spoke of Saturnine men, Jovian men, solar men, etc. His friend Beham illus-
trated these character types in beautiful drawings. Dürer's famous "Melancholia" represents a Saturnine character—that of
the Emperor Maximilian. The "stars," therefore, stand for the
lower instincts, talents, and particularly the passions:

"Heaven is master of brutes (*Vieh*), not of man. For if heaven makes a man mild or patient, we say he has a lamb's mind or is like the dear sun; thus the sun governs sheep, not men. Beasts are dependent upon the stars. . . . He who rages does so like a dog, not as a man; he who murders is murderous like a bear. . . . Thus heaven is master over such men who are like brutes and live like brutes. . . . But man ought to be a man, not a brute." [8]

The most damnable and damaging passions are those of war and power. They subject man to the blind forces of Fate. A wise man need not follow them, Paracelsus taught: "It is said that a wise man rules over the stars. This does not mean that he rules over the influences which come from the stars in the sky, but that he rules over the powers which exist in his own constitution." [9]

Paracelsus believed in free will, like Erasmus, Pico della Mirandola, and the other great humanists, who for that reason were never able to agree with the Protestant doctrine of predestination. A calendar verse of 1508 said:

> All the Planets' complexion
> Over nobody holds sway
> If he wants not to obey,
> Because of the great liberty
> Which God gave to humanity.

In his astrological calendars Paracelsus warned against trusting the stars. The Church likewise assumed scientific value in astrological knowledge, but frowned upon nativities and prophecies. Its position had been defined by its greatest scientist, Albertus Magnus:

"Astrologers are able to foretell the future because people are used to follow their urges and passions, and consequently

their actions are determined by astral influences. This en-
ables astrologers to prophesy events which depend on the
actions of the multitude."

Assuming influences of the stars upon the body, since each
star was supposed to exude a particular kind of vapor, Paracelsus went on to explain why one affects the head, another the
liver, and so on, for each organ according to its susceptibility
to specific poisons.

Astrology, as accepted by Albertus Magnus and Paracelsus,
was an attempt to understand character structure in terms of a
universal law. Moreover, it was then the most perfect example
of a mathematical science. Although it remained vague about
the relations of cause and effect, it did picture the universe as
a self-regulating mechanism. Far from being superstitious, the
astrological world view rather excluded those freaks of nature
which are the basis of superstitious practices. Astrology was a
step in the direction of a scientific philosophy. Its concepts were
incompatible with belief in demons and other non-natural
causes of diseases. A biologist who studied the body as a working whole and a functioning system could not possibly, at the
same time, admit that a demon might invade it, that it could
be a spirit after death, that it could be in two places simultaneously, and the like.

DEMONS

Yet, here was a great difficulty. It was held to be common
knowledge that demons and ghosts populate nature. Their appearance was recorded in the most authoritative books. They
were held responsible for everything out of the ordinary, and
for many commonplace events, too. Paracelsus himself had
manifold proof of their mischievous works. In his own psy-

chiatric practice, he encountered the spirit *Afernoch* (p. 109) which caused melancholia. Some of his patients were tortured by *succubae*. Miners with whom he worked were plagued by gnomes which guarded subterranean treasures. All nature, tree and spring, marsh and mountain, was the haunt of a host of monsters, ghoulish or friendly, neither men nor beasts, not quite spirit nor quite corporeal—what was the nature of these irritating creatures?

Paracelsus wrote volumes to prove that Nature can take care of herself without any outside assistance. He ridiculed the belief that ghosts can reappear, talk to people, walk, make noises, or disclose the future. Yet, would he deny that they were real? Such modern skepticism would not have occurred to Paracelsus or, for that matter, to any Christian of his time. To reconcile the contradiction, he devised some interesting and clever rationalizations. Ghosts are neither body nor soul but a certain reflection which he called *evestrum*, utterly ineffectual shadows which had no body nor any power that a person might fear.

Clearly, Paracelsus was seeking a scientific alibi for appearances he was unable to explain. He tried to define a realm, neither "spiritual" nor "corporeal," where the so-called supernatural could exist without interfering with nature.

His demons are real, but they do not exist like human beings, nor are they responsible for miracles or sorcery. They live in their own realm. This thesis is expounded in a charming little book on the elemental spirits [10] which testifies to Paracelsus' love of nature and to his great humanity. All the leprechauns, dwarfs, giants, salamanders, gnomes, nymphs, sylphs, dryads— all the children of the human imagination are there, performing their pranks. Paracelsus describes their appearance and their habits, traces their origin, tracks them to their lairs and explains how they can appear to man and why God made them.

Lovingly he embraces them as brothers and sisters in the Creation, and vehemently denies that they are instruments of the
Devil or work any evil. Incidentally, he takes time out for a
gallant defense of a certain nymph who had married one von
Staufenberg but later was repudiated by him as a witch. When
he took another wife,

> "she gave him the sign . . . during the banquet, and three
> days later, he was dead. . . . If she had been a ghost, from
> where would she have taken blood and flesh? If she had been
> a devil, where would she have hidden the devil's marks? . . .
> She was a woman . . . in honor, not in dishonor, and this is
> why she wanted duty and loyalty to be maintained. Since
> they were not . . . God permitted her the punishment that
> is appropriate for adultery, and permitted her to be her own
> judge, since the world repudiated her as a spirit or devil." [11]

This is the sole instance in the book where an elemental spirit
is reported to have done evil to a man, and here the nymph acted
as a human being. Otherwise, strangely, the elemental spirits are
not the cause of anything. They might warn a person of a danger, but they are not its agents. In their rare actions they use a
force of nature or induce a human being to use it. The Devil himself is powerless to work miracles. If he plans mischief, he
must persuade a man to be his instrument.

> "The Devil can effect transmutation only to the extent that
> nature permits. His arts go as far as nature offers him a
> chance to operate. . . . We say erroneously: That was the
> work of the Devil. We should say: He did it with the power
> of natural craft." [12]

Black magic only reaches as far as nature. In the world view of
antiquity, the demons were powerful forces of nature. In the
medieval world view, they still were agents of evil. In

Paracelsus' view, they fill no functions whatever. Playful inventions of God's imagination, they praise His omnipotence in unison with man, beast and inanimate nature. They live in a realm apart and rarely make contact with people, and then only with the superstitious. There was a certain Melusine who believed she was a serpent. She

> "came from the nymphs to the humans on earth and lived there. But then, as *superstitio* seduces and vexes all beings, she went away from her people in her superstitious belief, to the places where the seduced people come who are bewitched in *superstitionibus* and spell-bound. Mind you, she [became a] serpent to the end of her life. . . . It is stupid, however, to consider such women ghosts and devils on the basis of such happenings and because they are not from Adam. It is holding God's works in low esteem to assume that they are rejected because they have *superstitiones.* Yet there are more *superstitiones* in the Roman Church than in all these women and witches. And so it may be a warning that if *superstitio* turns a man into a serpent, it also turns him into a devil. That is, if it happens to nymphs, it also happens to you in the Roman Church. That, is, you too will be transformed into such serpents, you who now are pretty and handsome, adorned with large diadems and jewels. In the end you will be a serpent and dragon, like Melusine and others of her kind." [13]

Melusine could be bewitched because she was superstitious. Paracelsus shifted the demons out of reality into the realm of imagination. He was less interested in the things demons can do than in their origin and in their ethical justification. Finally, he transposed the whole problem to psychology when he discussed nightmares, in an almost Freudian analysis. Nightmares were supposed to be the action of little monsters called *incubi* and *succubae.* Paracelsus explained their origin in sexual fantasy:

"*Incubi* are male, *succubae* female creatures. They are the outgrowths of an intense and lewd imagination of men and women, formed of the semen of those who commit the unnatural sin of Onan. Such semen that does not come into the proper *matrix*, will not produce anything good. Therefore the *incubi* and *succubae* grown out of corrupted seed are evil and useless; and Thomas Aquinas has made an error by mistaking such useless things for perfect ones. . . .

"This semen, born from imagination, may be taken away by spirits that wander about by night, and that may carry it to a place where they may hatch it out. There are spirits that may perform an *actus* with it, as may also be done by witches, and, in consequence of that *actus*, many curious monsters of horrible shapes may come into existence." [14]

The theory, of course, was ridiculous; but the question which Paracelsus asked was a scientific one. He probes for the origin of the useless monsters, and found it in—the imagination. A great insight appeared in the husk of a great superstition. Similarly, the method of Paracelsus' discussion was far in advance of any results he could possibly have obtained. He was not satisfied with describing a phenomenon about which he had but uncertain reports. He asked the scientific question: How is this phenomenon possible?

MAGIC AND SCIENCE

In Paracelsus' time, the public's belief in demons resembled our belief in gravitation or, say, vitamins, agents which supposedly occasion certain natural reactions. Scientists believed in astrology as today readers of popular science magazines believe in atoms and electrons, and for the same reason.

Paracelsus believed in demons, but denied them any powers; and in astrology, but thought that man can rise above it. He placed himself squarely across superstition and science. His most scientific approaches have since been discarded as mere superstitions, while several of his crudest superstitions have found justification in some new scientific discovery.

As a result discussion of his views became rather bewildering. We cannot decide what was superstition and what scientific observation, so long as we look at results, theories, theses, beliefs, or any *content*. Whether a particular opinion is scientific or superstitious depends on the *method* by which this insight was gained. Did it integrate the available experience? Was there any means of checking it through observation or experiment? Did it satisfy the laws of logic, and in particular, did it presuppose a reasonable relationship between cause and effect? Finally, did it assume a self-contained universe?

Such a reasonable assumption, for instance, was the alleged influence of the stars on epidemics. It happened to be erroneous, but it was not improbable. The assumptions of modern science often are less plausible. But the available data support them, as magic practices once were based on incomplete information about facts. Error is not superstition. Was it unreasonable to expect that a magnet might "attract" ulcers or that "radiating" mirrors and stones might disintegrate cancer? Often, a truly modern approach masked itself in the superstitious medieval terminology. Thus, Paracelsus used the word divination where he clearly had in mind prediction, a process of all scientific analysis.

"God has ordained that man should make divinations from nature, but not without a medium. The proper medium is the stars. Some think that God does things without any intermediary or that angels are the medium. Divination, however, is possible because man has an astral body besides his earthly body." [15]

The astral body here is the *locus* where the human mind is commensurate with that which it wants to know. Was this assumption reasonable? Paracelsus substituted a material of nature, the astral body, for the supernatural creature, the angel. Moreover, he denied that the astral body can be conjured and has senses. He condemned all exorcism and conjurings, as well as prayers, blessings, and consecration ceremonies. "Does lightning spare churches?" he asked.[16] He also condemned the hocus-pocus and abracadabra with which nigromancers exploited the gullible multitude.

Some impostors pretended that at their bidding a certain demon would heal an incurable disease. Though some worked occasional cures, Paracelsus denounced them: "Surreptitiously they used medicines." [17] Nor would he permit another kind of impostor to attribute to God what patently should be credited to Nature:

"Some patients were informed during their sleep what remedy they should use, and indeed were cured by such remedy. This, however, happened to Christians as well as to heathens, to Jews, Saracens, Mamelukes, Persians, and Egyptians; to good as well as to bad people. Hence I cannot believe that the revelation came from God directly, because there only is one God and all these people cannot have separate Gods. I believe that these adepts were illuminated by the eternal light of nature. But since that light has no speech, it causes *evestra* [ghosts] in the astral spheres of men during their sleep." [18]

The nonsense of this conclusion, though logically arrived at, is based on the misinformation in the premise. Paracelsus believed that people had such experiences. He states that this experience has been reported by people belonging to various denominations. He then proceeds to eliminate that which is accidental and offers a working hypothesis which would cover the general case. That is the classical scientific procedure to explain phenomena which seem to be established on good authority.

Paracelsus accepted the reports uncritically, but he felt the urge to explain them. He never was short of hypotheses. He was particularly fond of introducing material links where older theories accepted action at a distance or spiritualistic explanations. Thus, hypnosis and telepathy were "just magic" to his predecessors. Paracelsus suggested that a "magnetic fluid," resembling the "ether" of our Newtonian fathers, transmits the suggestive influences through the variation of its quantity and quality. The wording makes one think of waves.

So far so good. But why, it may be asked, did Paracelsus not reject the evestra, astral body, divination, and magic, altogether? If he was that close to the scientific approach, why did he not question all the alleged experiences of spiritism and occultism? That would have made him a modern man. He would have questioned what then appeared obvious to all; as though, today, someone were to deny that technological progress might make possible accurate weather forecasts. It is always easier to formulate a new theory than to deny "common" knowledge.

> "There are more things in heaven and earth
> Than are dreamt of in your philosophy."

Medieval magic had little in common with the doings of our various latter-day occultists. Rather, it anticipated modern technology. Experiments with the hidden forces of nature were designed to bring forth the science we know. Paracelsus and his disciples not only organized a vast research in chemistry and other fields which then seemed to border on occult phenomena; they also had quite a lucid and rational idea of what distinguishes superstition from science:

> "Natural magic is the use of true, natural causes to produce rare and unusual effects by methods neither superstitious nor diabolical. Although all natural science may be called magic, the name should apply only to that which resembles diabolical magic in the effects produced." [19]

CHAPTER 7

Microcosmos and Macrocosmos

FUNDAMENTALS OF MAGIC MEDICINE

*Man is superior to the stars if he
lives in the power of superior
wisdom. Such a person, being
master over heaven and earth,
by means of his will, is a magus,
and magic is not sorcery but
supreme wisdom.*

PARACELSUS

Since the teachings of the scholastics and the humanists had left him intellectually famished, Theophrastus turned to "other pursuits"—"hence I have taken to magic," says Goethe's Faust, borrowing the phrase from the sixteenth century *Book of Dr. Faustus*. Magic, Paracelsus explains in his *Sagacious Philosophy*, is command of the forces of nature. The magus is the wise man to whom Nature has taught her secrets. He knows the "signs" which reveal her powers. Kindly, she has made orchids in the shape of testicles, thus hinting that their juice will "restitute his lewdness to a man" [1] "just as she indicates the age of a stag by the ends of his antlers, and the influence of the stars by their names [*sic*]. Thus, she made liverwort and kidneywort, with leaves in the shape of the parts which they can cure." [2]

Similarly, black hellebore (Christmas flower) reveals its rejuvenating power by blossoming in wintertime. Paracelsus introduced this magic plant into European pharmacy and recommended it to patients over fifty years of age. (The dose he prescribed is just right to alleviate certain cases of arteriosclerosis, but the patient was cautioned to gather the flower under the full moon.)

Not all of Nature's hints were so straightforward. Others needed elaborate interpretation. Venereal disease, for instance, is acquired from venal girls. It is "signed," the magus says, by the god of the market, Mercury. A metal's name points to the same god. Hence mercury is the cure for syphilis. Such indications were called "*signatures*."

The magi assumed that names, colors, shapes, and numbers govern the relationships between the various parts of the world, notably those between man (the *microcosm*) and the universe (*macrocosm*). The "small world" repeats the "great world," trait by trait. Like the pattern of a wonderful piece of tapestry, it was assumed, the various phases of the creation reflect each other in manifold ways. The features of one's face, the lines in one's hand, or the flourishes of one's handwriting, many still believe, reveal his character. So astrology taught that a man's life repeats a pattern of heavenly events. Other, so-called "*mantic*" arts used stones, metals, flowers, letters and instruments to read the physiognomy of the universe. A comprehensive canon of these signatures was alleged to have been confided to Moses and secretly inscribed in the Bible. Whosoever could decipher its occult message could become as powerful as God. Scholars learned Hebrew to penetrate into these mysteries of *Cabbala* and find out whether they had the call. "Man is inspired with divine wisdom, gifted with divine arts. Therefore we shall be called gods and sons of the Almighty, for in us shineth the Light of Nature and the Light is God."[3]

THE MAGUS OF SPONHEIM

To obtain the key to these secrets, Theophrastus, on his way home, stopped at Würzburg. There a famous magus and alchemist had gathered an eager crowd of students; he was Johannes Heidenberg of Tritheim, called Trithemius (1467-1516), Abbot of Sponheim, an expert in Cabbala and occult sciences, but also a respected historian, a connoisseur of art and poetry, and a teacher of ethics. Like Raymond Lull, the great thirteenth century alchemist, he had invented a system to teach a layman any science or language in a few short lessons. He called it "steganography," cipher writing. He conversed with absent friends through telepathy, or so he said, and made other experiments which would have rendered the invention of the telephone, telegraph, and airplane superfluous. On the other hand, he denied that witches exist, and defended the victims of the Inquisition. He concealed his chemical knowledge in conjuring formulas.

As an enlightened man, Trithemius approved of all efforts to use the hidden forces of God's nature, so long as no demons were called in. This was legitimate, "white" magic. He despised sorcerers, who deceivingly used black magic. Ignorant of the real "work," he charged, they invoked supernatural agents to help them. Anybody could do that! Such a swindler, *e.g.*, a quack named Faustus, once tried to entertain him. The pious Abbot denounced him as a sorcerer whose art was derived from the Devil.

But alas! The web of legend entangled the good with the bad magi. The colorful character of Trithemius contributed at least one episode to the Faustus saga. Allegedly he called the ghost of Mary of Burgundy back for the benefit of her husband, the Emperor Maximilian—which the "Faustus Book" transformed into the conjuring of the Beautiful Helen.

This Abbot, so convinced of the existence of the Devil, also became the victim of bigotry. His superiors became suspicious of his ciphers and cryptogrammata. Nothing more offensive than a few prescriptions was concealed in his strange formulas, but the borderline between alchemy and sorcery was still dim in the minds of authority, and Trithemius, accused of black magic, was removed from his Abbey at Sponheim. This became a *cause célèbre* which agitated the world of letters.

In his autobiography, Paracelsus boasted of his connection with the famous man. Among his teachers, he wrote, "were many abbots [such as the one] of Sponheim . . . and bishops such as Erhard of Lavanttal. . . ." [4] One should think the reference is unequivocal. Educated contemporaries understood that Paracelsus here pointed to Trithemius, the Abbot of Sponheim. Not so his modern worshippers. Brushing aside their master's testimony, they have made heroic efforts to erase the magic Abbot from Paracelsus' life. They have drawn up itineraries to show that he had never been to Würzburg; and an ingenious theory attempts to prove that the person to whom Paracelsus refers by the name of Sponheim was his old teacher of Latin, the Abbot of Lavanttal. That cloister had once belonged to a count of Sponheim, and Paracelsus is assumed to have confused the two.[5] This theory is fantastic. It is true, however, that a date for Paracelsus' visit to Würzburg is difficult to establish.

The Trithemius issue is characteristic of that strange mixture of philistine respectability and eccentric bigotry which characterizes modern Paracelsus worshippers. Some seem to feel that a genius like Paracelsus need not be taught anything by others; some find it embarrassing to associate their hero with the fantastic experiments and speculations of Trithemius. They cannot deny, however, that Paracelsus knew the works of Trithemius, repeated many of his ideas in his own writings, and quite obviously considered him worth emulating. Occasionally, when he had made a startling discovery, he would exclaim, proudly though reverently: "Trithemius himself did not know that." [6]

Trithemius was a magus, to be sure, but so was Paracelsus. Both had been brought up in ideas which the twentieth century finds most difficult to understand. Yet, both found these ideas convenient tools in organizing their experience. Research had to discard magic before it could become science. But the two were far from being hostile forces. On the contrary, magic became the midwife of science.

A LESSON IN ALCHEMY

Instead of denying the sources from which Paracelsus' reform of science sprang, the historian should use it to gain new insights into the dual nature of his mind. He was a magus and a scientist at once. A quotation from Trithemius will illustrate the ambiguity which resulted from such amalgamation:

> "Studies generate knowledge; knowledge bears love; love
> —likeness; likeness—communion; communion—virtue; virtue
> —dignity; dignity—power; and power performs the miracle.
> This is the unique path to magic perfection, divine and
> natural, from which all superstitious and diabolical wizardry
> is totally separated and by which it is confounded." [7]

Few will recognize an alchemical recipe in this mystical process. Yet the initiated knew that "knowledge" is governed by the god Mercury, "love" by the goddess Venus, and so on. Moreover, the planet Mercury was identified with a metal, and Venus, also a planet, symbolized copper. In the same way, "power" was embodied in the sun, which symbolized gold—"philosophical gold," the end product of alchemy.

The seven steps which the pious Abbot enumerates, therefore, parallel the seven planetary spheres, each governing one of the seven metals. As the metal, "transmuted" or "purified" in the crucible, passes the seven stages from mercury to gold, the alchemist ascends from the first to the seventh heaven—from knowledge to power. Alchemy makes him more "perfect" because it brings his will into harmony with the universe. Incidentally, "power" should not be interpreted in any political or mechanistic sense. Rather, it is defined as a state of perfection where the world is harmoniously at peace with itself. This is the "miracle," or the "great work" of the Philosopher's Stone.

This sounds so utterly fantastic that most people today refuse to see any sense in such speculations. They would dismiss them as, at best, myths or archaic poetry. Such myths, however, dominated protoscientific thought for many centuries. They are responsible for the astronomical knowledge of the ancient Egyptians, for the geometrical discoveries of Pythagoras, for the art of counterpoint in Gregorian church hymns, and even for the first glimpses of mathematical physics at the time of Paracelsus. All that was progressive in magic, but also all that delayed the advance of science, is summed up in the proposition that "knowledge gives power."

Knowledge, Trithemius tells us, follows nature and confounds sorcery. Like the scientist, the magus rejects belief in demons. Nature, both believe, is self-sufficient and self-contained. Moreover, magi and scientists are agreed on one basic assumption: that Nature is governed by certain basic conditions of relatedness so binding and immutable that God Himself would not think of violating them. Today these relationships are called "laws of nature"—and here ends the agreement between magic and science.

The magi were satisfied with less than the rigid concepts of cause and effect that exist today. In place of gravitation they had "love". Water, for example, was supposed to run downhill because it longed to be united with the ocean. Instead of quantitative "laws," they had harmonies. They valued music as a preparation for the study of nature. The entire universe, they thought, is embodied in signs and numbers (God, of course, being the One). Through these signs, the elements of the upper world were related to the parts of the lower world. In particular, the planets and the signs of the zodiac had their counterparts in the members of the human body, in metals, in stones and flowers. Each sphere of the universe was in sympathy with all other parts, so that nothing could happen without being reflected or "signed" in the heavenly spheres, in the lines of the hand, in magic squares, in the relations between numbers, or in Scripture. Letters and ciphers had cosmological meaning besides being signs of words. (See Plate: The Zodiac Man.) "One thing is great; nothing is in heaven or on earth that is not in man." [8]

Mathematical geniuses wasted talents which might have been more usefully employed, on combinations of letters which would yield the "key." He who found it would be the master of all the secrets; he would "make apparent what had been occult" and "bring to perfection that which is imperfect." [9] Knowing all the harmonies, he would be reconciled with destiny, and through his consciousness Nature would be reconciled with herself. Thus knowledge ended in universal love. Paracelsus echoed Trithemius: "He who knows Nature will love her and obtain power to use her forces." [10]

"LIKE TO LIKE"

Applying these ideas to the practice of medicine, the magi rejected the Galenic principle that "contrary cures contrary"—hot drives out cold, moist drive out dry humors, etc. Folk doctors believed that "the iron that made the wound also will heal it," that a heart condition could be cured if the patient ate a bull's heart, that "like cures like." This famous maxim of unorthodox medicine was revived in the nineteenth century by Hahnemann, founder of the homoeopathtic school. With some reason, followers of this sect count among their spiritual ancestors Hippocrates and Paracelsus who taught that a poison, given in small doses, may be an antidote.

Originally, this idea had grown out of the fertile soil of German folklore. In the language which Paracelsus spoke, the word *gift* meant any potion, poison, medicine, or love-philter. "Poison is in everything, and no thing is without poison. The dosage makes it either a poison or a remedy." [11]

Notwithstanding similarities cited in their works, neither Hippocrates nor Paracelsus had much in common with Hahnemann. Their principle of "like to like" was based on the magic doctrine that "nothing is in heaven or earth that is not in man." [12] If a member of the human body was sick, the signature indicated which member of the Zodiac, which metal, stone, or herb was in sympathy with the disease. Paracelsus explicitly rejected at least one folkloristic idea: "Not heart of the pig or spleen of the cow will cure diseases of the heart and of the spleen. Limb to limb—that means: limb of the macrocosmos [must be applied] to limb of the microcosmos." [13]

An anemic person, for instance, needs iron. In alchemical terms, Paracelsus would have said: The limb of the body which is sick is blood. Blood is "signed" by Mars. So also is a limb of the universe—iron: Iron is the metal of Mars. There is an affinity of blood and iron. Hence, prescribe iron. "The star must fit the medicine. Cold to cold, hot to hot, that is the remedy. It must act on the disease as though a wife were given to a man." [14]

Paracelsus' view of the "like-to-like" principle was chemotherapeutical, based on the "simple" or "specific" recipes of empiricists rather than on homoeopathic conceptions. In the final count, his support of homoeopathy boils down to a question of terminology, as is evident in a curious proposal he made to rename the diseases, each after the remedy which cured it.

"They call diseases by names that have no hands nor feet. They say: This is cholera, this is melancholia, after the tempers. But who has seen *choleram* in nature? Who has found *melancholiam* in science? Who has recognized phlegm as an element? . . . The doctor should name the diseases by the way they are in nature. He should follow the disease as the cow follows the crib. Nature can be seen, speculation cannot be seen. The doctor can deal only with that which is visible. So he should not say cholera but: This is arsenicus, that is aluminosum. If you say: This is Melissa's disease, that is Saturn's, then you know the cure by the disease's name. Likewise, you say: This is a blood disease. How do you know it is the blood's fault? There are as many kinds of blood as there are trees in the wood." [15]

YOUNG ADEPT

Let us look at the influences which the century and special circumstances brought to bear on the young adept. At the end of his apprentice years, twenty-three years old, he remains as bewildered as when he started. He has rejected the philosophy and theology which his teachers had to offer; he has experi-

enced all the disappointments then possible in the art of healing. He has learned a few successful but unorthodox treatments.
He knows folk medicine, magic recipes, and chemical remedies
—but all highly experimental. Gropingly, searchingly, he tries
various doors, each just enough ajar to permit a glimpse into the
secrets of Nature; but none opens wide enough to reveal Nature
as a whole.

What would Theophrastus, at the threshold of his wander-
years as an adept, know about Nature? Was she as arbitrary and
inconsistent as pagan folklore assumed? Or a well-ordered, pur-
posefully governed Universe as Christian theology taught? Were
the stars instruments of blind destiny, or did they represent the
eternal rhythm and harmony of a universally valid law? More
particularly: was Nature to be found in something common to all
Creation, or did she manifest herself in infinite diversity? If the
first, was human Reason (with the help of God, of course) commensurate with Nature? If the second, was pure experience
capable of exhausting the wealth of created nature or fathom-
ing its depth? And applied to medicine: was man subject to the
omnipresent "humors," or was each man according to his constitution, birth auspices, and situation, susceptible to specific
disease, curable by specific remedies?

Magic proposed to solve the riddle of the One and the many.
Pious Abbot Trithemius, reared in the tradition of Renaissance
humanism, still appeared to hold the whole world in his grasp. A
universal Reason still seemed to promise power to the adepts of
the true philosophy. But his disciple Agrippa, as restless and
erring in his personal life as in his intellectual pursuits, no longer
saw the unity of the world in an all-embracing power of Reason.
Not through erudition, but partly through experience, partly
through faith and revelation, he hoped to know, though no
longer to understand. Though he was a "vagabond *scholar*,"
his attack on learning was that of a disillusioned savant.

Theophrastus, youngest of the three, had his disillusionment before he had a chance to be learned; his attack on the science of his teachers was that of an outsider.

However, the vision of Universal Reason was not lost. Paracelsus tried to close the gap between the One and the many. With Trithemius he agreed on the necessity of achieving unity between reason and existence, between man and the Universe, between God and the world. That makes him a humanist. On the other hand, he agreed with Agrippa that science is uncertain, that the universal law is difficult to establish except through special revelation, and that the Creation is diversified. That makes him a critic of humanism. We shall find him torn between the two throughout his career. Magic, he thought, would reconcile what was so patently irreconcilable.

CHAPTER 8

The Traveling Adept

A CHAPTER OF ADVENTURE

> *No man becomes master while*
> *he stays at home, nor finds a*
> *teacher behind the stove. Dis-*
> *eases wander here and there the*
> *whole length of the world. He*
> *who would understand them*
> *must wander, too.*
>
> PARACELSUS

I n 1517, while Dr. Martin Luther was nailing to the church door in Wittenberg the Theses which were to shake the world, Paracelsus set out on his great trip around the civilized world. He visited the great universities of Europe, met many celebrities, learned various trades, bathed in all spas, drank many wines, worked in several mines, took part in three major wars, and, so he claimed, cured hundreds of sick persons, the noble for honor and money, the poor for the sake of God.

"I traveled on to Granada and Lisbon through Spain, England, Brandenburg, Prussia, Lithuania, Poland, Hungary, Walachia, Transylvania, Croatia, Crain, and other lands not necessary to recount here." [1]

In this account of his travels, Paracelsus recalled insignificant provinces like Crain, on the Adriatic coast, but omitted such important kingdoms as Naples and Denmark. Though mighty sovereigns employed him, his services apparently were not of the kind he cared to record. He was a military surgeon in mercenary armies, a profession held in low esteem. However, when his enemies later charged that he had no right to practice medicine, he included these services in his angry reply:

"Why, in your opinion, should I not be a physician but merely a surgeon? Have I not cured eighteen princes in physica [*i.e.,* not through surgery] after you had given them up? In the wars of the Netherlands, Romagna, Naples, Venice, Denmark, and Holland, I restored many fever-stricken and healed forty different diseases. Now you say I should not be a physician, not qualified to refute your lies and denounce the abuses of the scribblers. And all my experience and industry should be counted a trifle? I have helped the sick more than you have in your profession [*in eurer Pflicht*]." [2]

Such outbursts confirm rather than refute the charge that Paracelsus' title of doctor stood on shaky grounds, and explain his ill repute. Consistently citing his "experience" to support his case against the medical guild, he frankly admitted that he had wandered with "necromancers, folk doctors, quacks, barbers, and witches." Some of his companions, he had to concede, had ended on the gallows. Nor was there any denying that he drank in taverns with teamsters and other wayfaring folk; and the suspicion never faded that this association was no mere slumming. If his cures seemed to point to forbidden arts, his friendships implied a secret society or sect. Perseveringly as he might defend himself: "I am writing as a Christian, I am no sorcerer, no pagan, no gypsy. . . . "[3] the stigma stuck to him. To this day he is generally known as a traveling medicine man who outdid all others in promoting his drugs, a vainglorious braggart whose "bombastic" (his family name!) style attracted congenial charlatans and mystics, while reputable students shunned his company.

Researchers have tried to unravel his meanderings. Checking and recording every place name in his writings, searching every archive,[4] they have contrived to fill some gaps in his autobiography. The result is an almost fantastic Odyssey. Nevertheless, considerable blanks remain. It still is difficult to reconstruct what Paracelsus did between 1517 and 1523. We know that he traveled thousands of miles; but how long he stayed in any given place and how he made his living, whom he met and what medical lore he picked up, can only be guessed.

Four great universities lay on Paracelsus' path West, Montpellier, in Provence, still the stronghold of Arab medicine, with disciples of Averroës and Avicenna in command; Seville in southern Spain, where Jewish and Moorish influences were still dominant; Salamanca, a most Catholic university with a great tradition and high standards; and, finally, the Sorbonne at Paris, Alma Mater of orthodoxy. Paracelsus found none to his liking. Nowhere did he stay long. At the Sorbonne he found that "the Parisian doctors despise all others; yet they are ignoramuses. They think their high necks and high judgment reach into heaven. . . . They don't know the art of experimenting."[5]

WARS AND MEDICINE

This was Paracelsus' last attempt at university study. In England, he ignored Oxford and Cambridge. Some say that he worked in a Cornwall mine. His knowledge of metallurgy won him influential patrons, and for some time we find him in the company of German and Flemish merchants who enjoyed, in London harbor, extra-territorial privileges for their wool, grain, and metal trade. A mission in their behalf sent him back to the Continent,[6] and while crossing the Channel, he wrote a prescription against seasickness which has been preserved.

In Flanders, again, Paracelsus maintained close contact with the burghers of the great trading centers.[6] When two Dutch provinces arose against their foreign sovereign (King Charles I of Spain, the future Emperor "on whose realm the sun never set"), Paracelsus accompanied the insurgent army as a surgeon. But the rebels were beaten, and Paracelsus traveled on, from Hansa town to Hansa town,[6] until he arrived in Copenhagen. Here fortune served him when King Christian's mother opportunely fell ill, apparently of melancholia. Paracelsus cured her and legend reports that the grateful old Queen secured him an important position at the Court. At the King's request he reorganized the pharmacies of the kingdom.

In 1520, when the Danes invaded Sweden, Paracelsus was appointed master surgeon in the King's army. Christian conquered all Scandinavia, and Paracelsus took his part of the spoils. A painting by Scorel, now in the Louvre, shows him in nobleman's attire wearing the doctor's miniver hat. He used his official position to inspect the copper mines in northern Sweden.

Soon, however, the Swedes shook off the Danish yoke. In the fall of 1520, Paracelsus was forced to flee across the Baltic Sea, to lands then dominated by the Teutonic Knights. (His grand-

father, we remember, had been an official of this order.) The
Knights, who had just been crushingly defeated by the burghers
of Danzig, had work for a surgeon. But Paracelsus did not stay
long with them. Adventure called when the Russian Grand
Duke, Basil, invited Western physicians, astrologers, architects,
and humanists to bring culture to his court. Paracelsus gladly
joined the caravan of adventurers, charlatans, humanists, and
scientists to Moscow. Almost immediately, however, the Tartars
raided the new Russian state, pillaged Moscow, and removed
the foreign scholars to their capital.

Medieval chivalry, or his medical skill, assured the prisoner a
lenient captivity. He had leisure to study the customs of the
tribesmen and in particular the magic rites of their medicine
men, the shamans. Some have conjectured that from them he
learned techniques of healing through faith and suggestion; or
even that he was initiated into secret shaman practices. No
evidence supports such fantasies. The only document extant
from that period discloses a more prosaic concern. Traversing
the Ukraine, Paracelsus was plagued by vermin. A lice powder,
concocted by him, is described in his works.[6]

In 1521 a Tartar prince took Paracelsus along with him on a
diplomatic mission to Constantinople. There he allegedly met
the magus who gave him the Philosopher's Stone. The kernel of
truth in this legend may be that Paracelsus acquired from the
magus the recipe for his much vaunted *laudanum* drug, probably an opiate.

Once in the Orient, it was natural for Paracelsus to visit the
Holy Land, but he did not stay long. On he went to Alexandria,
home of alchemy and occult heresies. He made an excursion
up the Nile River, along the Venetian trade road, "wandering
in the sweat of my brow" and frightened by "monsters so fearful
you would jump right back into your mother's womb" (a croco-
dile, a hippopotamus?).[7]

From then on, spotty records of Theophrastus' wanderings
turn up in the Balkan peninsula and the Greek islands, always
following Venetian trade routes, stopping at the outposts of the
vast empire which the crusaders had built for the lagoon merchants. Venice was still the great sea power in the Mediter-
ranean, but her might was challenged by Sultan Suleiman. The
Orders of crusading Knights garrisoned the advance bases of
Christian conquest, Cyprus and Rhodes. Paracelsus lived
through the terrible siege of Rhodes, where more people were
killed by malnutrition and cholera than by the Turks. The
island fell in 1522, and Paracelsus had a narrow escape from
capture. He was among the few who were evacuated the night
before the surrender. It has been suggested that he was in the
diplomatic service of the Venetians, for he continued to visit
places of strategic interest to that power. Some of the islands of
which he shows some knowledge hold a memorable place in the
history of science. Kos was the birthplace of Hippocrates,
father of Greek medicine; Samos, of Pythagoras, oldest of Oc-
cidental mystics; Lesbos, of Theophrastos of Eresos, Paracelsus'
namesake.

After a short visit to Venice, Theophrastus crossed the
Adriatic to the Dalmatian coast. There he stayed almost a year,
working in the mercury mines which belonged to the Venetians.

Early in 1524, he was back in his father's house at Villach.
He brought home the wonder drug laudanum and an enormous
sword from which he never after parted, not even in sleep. In
its hollow pommel he allegedly kept the laudanum, his greatest treasure.[8] He never used the sword for any other purpose,
having acquired a strong distaste for military action.

He also brought home experience which became the foundation of his doctrines in medicine and chemistry. He had gained
insight into the varied forms a disease can take under different

skies, had seen cures worked by doctors and medicine men who were ignorant of Galen, had learned how the Oriental doctors healed wounds without the benefit of viper's blood. He also had established contacts with chemists all over the world and had acquired knowledge of Oriental magic, myths, folklore, and science.

CHAPTER 9

Under the Brogue

PARACELSUS'
SOCIAL PHILOSOPHY

When Adam delved and Eve span,
Who was then the gentleman?

PEASANTS' SONG

Old Wilhelm von Hohenheim received his
son well in Villach. But Paracelsus could not settle down as a
physician in the shadow of the old doctor. He went on to near-by
Salzburg. History, however, again crossed his path. Paracelsus
had been absent from Germany for nearly ten years, and it is
time to deal with events which, in the meantime, had changed the
face of the Christian world.

Luther nailed his Theses to the Wittenberg church door.
The Pope answered with a bull which Luther burned in 1520.

Charles V was elected Holy Roman Emperor. Though this brought under his scepter all the lands of Germany, Spain, and the New World, he could not mend the broken unity of Christianity. At the Diet of Worms, Luther won a shining victory. In the meantime, Ulrich Zwingli, once a preacher at Einsiedeln, Theophrastus' birthplace, spread the Reformation to Switzerland. His more radical partisans, Oecolampadius and Haller, organized Protestant communities in Basle and Berne. Oecolampadius, a humanist and Brother of the Common Life, later became Paracelsus' sponsor. Two other evangelists, Carlstadt and Melanchthon, invaded Wittenberg at the head of an enraged mob, closed the cloisters, forced priests and nuns to marry, abolished mass, and distributed the endowments among the poor. Services were read in German.

Another rebellion, led by the weavers of Zwickau, soon spread all over central Germany. Its "prophets" came to Wittenberg to unite the two movements. Luther, alarmed by the spirits he had roused but not meant to release, emerged from his voluntary seclusion at Wartburg castle and hurried to Wittenberg to suppress the insurrection. Orthodox services were reintroduced in all Germany in 1522.

The times were out of joint. The impoverished knights of southern Germany had taken up the banner of insurrection. Although their movement collapsed ingloriously, it kept the spirit of insubordination alive, and no peace was in sight. Astrologers predicted a great Flood for 1524. At the appointed hour, the rich fled to the mountains. The weather remained fine, but—Thomas Muenzer had united peasants and small artisans under the brogue (the peasant's shoe used as an emblem for their flag). It was the last of the great democratic movements which flared up in all parts of Europe after the middle of the fourteenth century—"Poor Jacques" in France, "Poor Conrad" in Germany, "Jack" Cade in England.

Famine and high prices were the immediate causes of the revolt. In a wider perspective, however, the *Jacqueries* were but one aspect of social disintegration. The network of medieval society had lost its supports. Former redeeming features of feudal law were gone and its full weight bore down on the *"villeins."* Forced labor and tithes were increased while the lords enclosed the commons, depriving the peasants of their pasturelands. With the advance of territorial *seigniory*, backed by moneyed interests, the Emperor and the Pope lost their power to protect the people against the predatory overlords. Merchants, bankers, usurers—denounced by Luther— added new burdens. "The peasants' lot has become unbearable," wrote Trithemius.

THE SECOND COMING

Against oppression and exploitation the peasants sought sanctions in the Bible. Christ shed His precious blood for all men alike, says a pamphlet, implying that serfdom is incompatible with religion. In new translations of the Bible men found confirmation of their craving to be free and equal. The books of prophecies were read and—still more important— inflammatory illustrations explained them to the illiterate. As early as 1498, Albrecht Durer had issued his subversive broadsheets on the "Secret Revelation of St. John." His "Four Horsemen of the Apocalypse (see Plate VI) riding roughshod over humanity are King Death, War, Pestilence, and Famine in the garb of a merchant with scales and fur coat.

Prophets arose in all parts of the Empire, announcing the end of the world, the Second Coming, the Antichrist, and the onset of war, famine, and revolution. In the name of the Millennium, a great uprising was in the making.

To receive the new life in dignity, people admonished each

other to return to the paths of the divine law (rejecting the hated Roman law), confessed their sins and rededicated themselves through a second baptism. The traditional sacraments no longer were held sufficient, and the Church which administered them stood accused of alienating the Vicarship from Christ.

This was the climate of iconoclastic riots and Anabaptist ecstasies, a fanatical, heretical movement which had little in common with Luther's new national Church. It attracted the intelligentsia and the common people alike, for it combined demands for both social reform and intellectual freedom. Its purity and innocence enraptured the best minds. Melanchthon participated in its first actions. Erasmus upheld some of its basic tenets. Oecolampadius befriended its persecuted leaders. Together with intellectual vagabonds, the greatest artists of the age were active partisans, and the features of the rebel leaders have been preserved by Dürer, Beham, Holbein, Cranach and Riemenschneider. Paracelsus obviously had to join, at great cost to his career.

In 1524, the silly whim of a Countess, who forced her retainers to collect snails at harvest time, set off the new Peasants' War all over southern Germany. Thomas Muenzer gave it a political program: "The people want to be free and God wants to be their only master." Balthasar Hubmaier, a preacher in Waldshut, announced the abolition of all taxes, tithes, and interest, and taught that under the divine law the people had the right to depose the government. In the Tyrol, Michel Geismeyer drafted a "constitution" calling for the extermination of all "godless men who persecute the common man," a program subsequently carried out at Münster.

The final expression of the rebels' program were the famous Twelve Articles. We quote some which Paracelsus expanded in his writings.

1. The community shall have the right to select its pastor

and to depose him if he is unworthy. The pastor shall preach the Evangel without any supplement added by man.

2. No *tithe* shall be paid on cattle, for God gave all animals to man.

3. Serfdom is abolished; but the peasants are willing to obey the authorities which have been established by the will of God, in all decent and Christian matters.

4. The wood shall belong to the community, and Church property shall be returned to the peasantry. . . .

7. *Statute labor* shall not be increased; fines shall be determined by a jury; death taxes shall be abolished. . . .

The insurrection had seized practically all southern Germany, but the princes united to beat it down. In the battles of Koenigshofen and Frankenhausen the peasant armies were annihilated. Thomas Muenzer was captured and executed. In Salzburg and the Tyrol, the rebels held out longer but were finally defeated. The suppression which followed was the more ruthless and vindictive.

Sebastian Franck and others have testified that several thousand Anabaptists were executed. The Duke of Bavaria granted a special favor to those who recanted: they were beheaded, while the others died under the sadistic tortures so characteristic of a counter-revolution.

THE PARTISAN

In Salzburg, Paracelsus became implicated in the uprising. Although the documents revealing his share in the insurrection are incomplete and of uncertain date, this much is clear: he preached in taverns and voiced "un-Christian, heretical" ideas. Derisively he admitted that he "made the peasants rebellious so that they no longer pay tithes to you nor care for what you say. Mind, if my sermon were inspired by the Devil, they would follow you, not me. However, what I said has been inspired by the Holy Spirit; ergo it was the Gospel." [1]

He gave medical assistance to wounded rebels and seems to have acted as liaison, carrying messages from the peasants to the rebels in the city. His doctor's garb made it possible for him to pass through the lines of the Archbishop's army. But he took no part in battle.

As usual, the authorities resorted to any means to "convict the criminals," including the agent-provocateur and the frame-up. Paracelsus noted that "thousands are being executed these days." On Christmas Eve, 1527, all the men of Salzburg were arrested. Paracelsus, himself, barely escaped the hangman. Questioned and brought to trial, he established an alibi. Although he refused to inform on the peasants, he was spared the gallows, saved by his status and title, and probably by the fact that he had not borne arms. Expelled from Salzburg, he left in such haste that his belongings remained with his host, Wolfgang Büchel at the Kumpf Mill. An actuary's inventory listed a compass, a magnetic needle, a portrait of his father, several Oriental garments and fur-lined coats. Even his unguents were left behind.

During the following years of wandering, Paracelsus frequently stopped in Anabaptist towns. His protectors and sponsors were men like Oecolampadius and Vadianus, who gave asylum to Anabaptist fugitives. His social, political, and economic teachings are replicas of their theories. He lifted entire paragraphs from the writings of rebel leaders like Geismeyer, Muenzer and Jan von Leiden. In one of his astrological prognostications, a common form of political pamphlet, he repeated predictions which the furrier, Augustin Bader of Augsburg, had made in his Anabaptist prophecy for the same year: All secular and ecclesiastical authorities would be destroyed, the Turks would reach the Rhine, and an empire uniting Christians, Jews, Turks, and pagans would be established to end all empires.

CHRISTIAN SOCIALISM

Ever since moneyed interests invaded the relations between men, in the thirteenth century, people expected the coming of the Anti-Christ. A learned pamphleteer asked the Emperor to assume supreme power and prepare humanity for the Millennium. Others called poverty a blessed state, and exalted communal life as the natural social order. Contrary to modern socialists, medieval utopians did not look forward to the machine age, but backward to a Golden Age. They fought against competition, capital, and everything the nineteenth century was to call progress. Paracelsus subscribed to each of these ideas and to their idealization of the past.

> "Money is the Holy of Holies of the thieves. To take interest is contrary to the commands of God, and the crowd of merchants only disturbs peaceful intercourse of men. They are useless and nefarious. . . . The gifts of Heaven, water, and earth come from God; they ought to belong to the poor." [2]

More and more people, he thought, were being converted to his Christian ideals, and "perhaps that which now is budding will sprout into green herbs in time." However, what he regarded as a hopeful new sprout stemmed from the Catholic doctrine. Paracelsus was far from rejecting medieval society. Rather he sought to restore its ideals. In his sermon on the social order, he demanded common ownership of land, with periodical redistribution, as prescribed in Deuteronomy, equality of wages independent of the accidents of natural talents, artisans' coopera-

tives with a complicated accounting system to guarantee equality
of obligations and benefits, and abolition of private trade. A
monopoly of foreign trade was to assure the supply of imported
goods. This was a pet idea of Geismeyer's, and the whole concept is that of the Biblical socialism preached and practiced by
the Anabaptists. Wealth was to be shared, as the Gospel pre-
scribes.

> "If one earns so much that twenty could be satisfied, that is
> against brotherly love and against God's institutions. It forces
> others to be thieves and beggars. No inequality shall exist in
> the blessed life, no envy nor selfishness. The land shall be-
> long to all, and none shall be allowed to buy land. Every-
> body shall work." [3]

Like other revolutionary writers, Paracelsus deliberately confused heavenly and worldly bliss. The social revolution which
he described was supposed to make the world habitable for
angels. In his later writings, he never departed from a social
viewpoint. Even in his medical works he did not refrain from
lashing out at the rich:

> "No good can happen to the poor with the rich being what
> they are. They are bound together as with a chain. Learn, ye
> rich, to respect these chains. If you break your link, you will
> be cast aside. Learn, rich and poor, that all your diseases lie
> in the same hospital, the hospital of God." [4]

Likewise, in an astrological prognostication for the year 1539,
he prophesied that famine would break out again: "not from
heaven, however, but from people; it will not be the fault of the
crop, but the fault of the men who have power over it." [5]

Much as Paracelsus sympathized with the peasants, he had
controversies with their leaders. He criticized their attempts to
seize temporal power. When the rebels, failing to establish the

Kingdom of Heaven, sought compensation in the riches of the earth, he gave them friendly warning not to soil their movement with the temptations of power. In another astrological prognostication, he explained that the stars have no power over the peasants, but only over those who seek power and sit in court, and continued:

"Now judge for yourself, who is higher, the one who is subject to the stars or the one who is not under their dominion? Is there any among the learned who would not praise the peasants as blessed because they remain in their order? Everything that will afflict the peasant, has its cause in the fact that he leaves his order. . . . They will govern and make war, rule religion and the magistrates. Thereby they will lose their freedom and become subject to the stars. The peasants have submitted to the stars, and have been beaten by them. Whosoever trusts the stars, trusts a traitor." [6]

Nothing favorable was in the stars for the peasants. They had been beaten. It was folly to continue a struggle which, at best, could only lead to further degeneration of their movement, not to the liberation Paracelsus had in mind. *His* Lord had come to bring not the sword but peace.

"The Law is from the Devil, the Canon from Leviathan." [7]

AGAINST SECTARIANISM

Paracelsus also differed in points of doctrine. Like all sects, the Anabaptists had their ritual by which they recognized each other. Adult baptism determined whether one was to be saved or damned. Paracelsus thought as little of this sacrament as of any other ceremonial. "God blessed the water to quench the thirst and to breed fish, but not to serve as a sprinkling against the Devil." [8]

He who lives as a Christian, he taught, needs no sacrament. Although children and fools may benefit from a sacrament, it is wasted on a person who has sense enough to understand its significance. He denied that baptism has any but symbolic meaning.[9] But, always mixing the rational with the superstitious, he declared it necessary to baptize children.

The Anabaptists could not follow this argument. The deeper they went down in defeat, the more stubbornly they clung to dogma. Finally, as is often the case with defeated movements, the urge to assert themselves as "peculiar people" submerged the original motives. The movement disintegrated into sects which sought to outdo each other in eccentric bigotry. Religious folly and ecstasies became a sign of loyalty in some fraternities; others gave a literal interpretation to Christ's words that whores would be the first to enter the Kingdom; others were seized by "spirits."

Disgusted by these excesses of hysterical mass exaltation, Paracelsus charged that such practices do not originate in the spirit of religion but of sectarian neurosis:

> "They go into the fire on the strength of Faith and not on the strength of Truth. For to be a martyr, by the will of God, one needs a greater Cause than the number of times a person is baptized. To obtain this passport nobody has been ordered to die by God. If anybody should die on account of the Word, he ought to abound mightily in the Holy Spirit. . . . Blessed are they that die for their Faith, but to die for the articles of faith, that is to die for misbelief." [10]

Unlike Luther, he remained a friend of the unhappy sectarians. Compassion, scientific curiosity, and the doctor's inborn urge to help and to heal united in him and prevailed over the controversialist. Paracelsus treated the fanatics as sick persons. He described their symptoms clinically and prescribed remedies which will be discussed in Chapter 21 with his other psychiatric activity.

"Musica expels the spirit pythonis which belongs to witches and sorcerers and other malefactors. It also takes away the spirit Afernoch [Hebrew?] which inspires the Anabaptists and other melancholic sectarians who think they see the Heaven and God therein. All these are diseases of the brain and of reason." [11]

figure 5

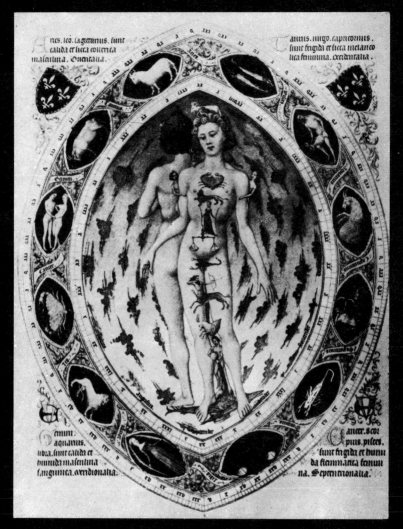

The Zodiac Man, an illustration from
Les Très Riches Heures du Duc de Berry. *Reproduced*
from Yearbook of the Warburg Institute.

figure 6 (following page)

Woodcut by Albrecht Durer: "Death, Pest, Hunger, and War.

figure 7

Liber de arte diſtillandi. de Simplicibus.

Das buch der rechten kunſt zů diſtilieren die eintzigē ding

von Hieronymo Brunſchwygk/Bürtig vñ wund artzot der keiſerlichē frÿē ſtatt ſtraßburg.

Title page of Hieronymus Brunschwig's Art of Distillation, *showing chemical instruments, ovens (athanors), and medicinal plants; also the alchemical symbols of the garden, the source, the basin (matrix), and the stag.*

CHAPTER 10

Aureolus

OF GOLD-MAKING
AND OTHER MYSTERIES

Evil is that which is finite.

CABBALA

Expelled from Salzburg, Theophrastus again took to the roads. Peddling his drugs and promising health and long life to young and old, he traveled up the Danube valley in southern Germany. Finally he found both employment and refuge at Neuburg Castle, a few miles west of Ingolstadt. There the Duke of Bavaria kept his archives. Since it was not his permanent residence, the property was at the disposal of his librarian and alchemist, Hans Kilian. Always short of money, the Duke was interested in metal research, hoping that one day his alchemist would make gold.

Paracelsus joined Kilian, and the two chemists spent a few months together, studying in the valuable library or experimenting in the basement, where the chemical kitchen was not far from the Duke's wine. Many notes which Paracelsus jotted down in the excitement of those hopeful moments have been preserved. Kilian filed them all and continued to collect Paracelsiana after his friend's death, thanks to which Neuburg Castle became a mine of chemical and other manuscripts for Paracelsus scholars.

Most of these alchemical writings are hard to interpret today. Paracelsus did not use his symbols consistently. Far from having any intention of making himself clear, he sought protection against spying and plagiary by deliberately omitting key factors from his formulas and prescriptions. At times he admitted that he was withholding the full truth, or hinted at a secret cypher. Typical is the following passage:

> "Do not take anything from the Lion but the Rose-Colored Blood, and from the Eagle only the White Gluten. Coagulate as the ancients have directed, and you will obtain the Tinctura Physicorum. If this is incomprehensible to you, however, remember that only he who seeks with all his heart will find." [1]

PIONEER OF CHEMISTRY

Adepts of the art, of course, could decipher this code. The lion symbolized a strong solvent; the eagle the process of sublimation. The red residue in this case probably was mercury oxide, and the white gluten may have been a metal chloride.[2] Knowing no elements, Paracelsus was unable to name the compounds which he produced in his alembic, and it is hard for us to identify the products of his experiments. Several times, however, he did come close to modern concepts. Thus he correctly stated that vitriols are made from metals whereas alums have "earth" for base. He recognized zinc as a metal although it is not malleable. After him, fusibility was sufficient to characterize a metal. He also described the properties of bismuth and "kobold" (goblin; cobalt) and made "bastards" of them. The technique of purifying and of alloying metals was no secret to one who had spent considerable time in mines and smelters.

Chemistry then was a technique rather than a science. As distinguished from alchemy, the study of the Universe, it was called "the art of distillation." Largely due to Paracelsus' efforts, this craft won recognition among the sciences. He was the first to use the word chemistry.

The transition is most interesting. Neither the kitchen recipes of practical distillation nor the speculations of alchemy could lead to a scientific view of chemical processes. Contrary to popular belief, chemistry is not alchemy minus gold-making. New conceptions were necessary before the drudgery over the chemical oven was illuminated with scientific insight. Or rather, familiar conceptions had to be rephrased and clarified. Adumbrating the modern idea of the element, Paracelsus turned the old concept of "quintessence" around.[3] Anticipating the modern classification of chemical substances, he divided the reagents into groups of substances which produce similar reactions.[4] Thus he marveled that a drop of vinegar can turn a barrel full of wine sour. Such a substance he called a "magisterium." Quite different from such a reaction, he found, is that of the "specifics," such as gall used to make ink, though neither the gall nor the vitriol has the properties of ink.[5] In the same way, he distinguished elixirs, quintessences, tinctures, mysterium. Although none of his actual classifications would satisfy a modern chemist, their principle made future research meaningful.

The art of distillation supplied "experience"; the tradition of alchemical speculation provided "reasoning": two pre-conditions for systematic research. Paracelsus proclaimed them in his famous program of the Basle lectures; and they governed his own experiments. Fantastic though some of them appear now, they helped conduct alchemical thinking into the channels of scientific chemistry.

THE GOLD-MAKER

Paracelsus scorned those "who have a golden mountain in their heads before they put their hands into the charcoal." He laughed at the so-called "multipliers" who, to quote Chaucer,

> Make them think at the least weye
> That a pound [of gold] we can make tweye.

Yet, the reputation of being a gold-maker clung to him. His enemies charged that the Devil had taught him the art. Editors of his works gave him the surname "Aureolus,"[6] the Golden One, and related stories like the following:

> Once Theophrastus had cured a farmer's wife in Ambras with one of his wonder drugs. After many years, he came along the same road again, and inadvertently entered the same farm. The woman recognized him and showed her grat-itude in such moving ways that the master was much affected by such goodness in a simple woman. He took a kitchen fork and smeared it with his yellow ointment. The fork changed into solid gold.[7]

The "gold," it will be seen presently, was copper, if the story be true at all. Another amusing story of gold-making came from his butler, "Franz":

"One day he said to me: 'Franz, we have no money,' and gave me a guilder, bidding me to go to the apothecary, get a pound of mercury and bring it to him. I did this, and he shook the mercury into a crucible, which he set upon four bricks, bidding me lay burning coals round about it and heap coals and coal dust upon them. After a long time he said: 'Our volatile slave may fly away from us, we must see what it is doing.' It was already smoking and flying away. He said, 'See, take hold of the mass with the pincers and cover the crucible. Put the fire out and let it stand.' Then after half an hour he said: 'We must now see what God has given us. Take off the lid.' This I did; but the fire was quite out and in the crucible all was solid. I said, 'It looks yellow like gold.' 'Yes,' he said, 'it will be gold.' I lifted it off, opened the crucible, which was now cold, and took out the lump. It was gold. Then he said: 'Take it and carry it to the goldsmith.' This I did; the goldsmith weighed it. It came to an ounce less than a pound. Then he fetched money in a flat purse."

Speaking of the substance Paracelsus used in the transformation, Franz says:

"There was a roll about the size of a big hazelnut, done up with red sealing wax, but what was inside I did not dare, being a young man, to ask my master. But I think that had I asked him he would have told me, for he always showed me liking." [8]

In another case, the metal was not mercury but common lead, and the victim was the mintmaster of the Duke of Württemberg. Is it possible that Paracelsus was a forger? Or did he believe that lead or mercury really changed into gold? Were goldsmiths and mintmasters so ignorant of their trade as to buy mercury or lead for gold, or is the whole story a legend?

Kolbenheyer and Stoddart maintain that Theophrastus, who was fond of practical jokes, was merely playing on the credulity of his servant. The truth, we suggest, is that Theophrastus knew how to color metals. Since color was supposed to be the seat of the essential quality in a metal, this art was highly appreciated and entirely legitimate. Goldsmiths paid high prices for "chemical gold" which the expert alone could distinguish from genuine gold. Paracelsus himself has given away the hoax in his *Greater Surgery Book*:

> "In chemical research very wonderful medicines have been made which prolong life . . . But after these come the gold-making tinctures transmuting metals. Thus one tincture colors metal. These discoveries have given rise to the idea that one substance can be transformed into another, so that a rough, coarse, and filthy substance can be transmuted into one that is pure, refined, and sound. Such results I have attained in various kinds, always in connection with attempts to change metals into gold and silver." [9]

THE MIRACLE OF "TRANSMUTATION"

Theophrastus received his instruction in this noble art at the best possible school, in the laboratory of an experienced chemist. In his autobiography he says:

> "Moreover, I gained great experience during a long period through the alchemists who have done research in such arts, notably the noble and firm Sigmund Füeger and many of his laboratory assistants." [10]

Sigmund Füeger was the Count of Füegen who owned large forest and mining privileges near the little town of Schwatz in the Tyrol. The timber furnished charcoal and the mines then yielded copper ore. They also carried veins of a new metal, zinc, which was brittle and formed brass in alloy with copper. Zinc had many uses in peace and war, and the count hoped to turn his subterranean wealth into money. The fantasies of alchemy were being crowded out by commercial metallurgy, with mine owners desirous of making money, not gold.

At Füeger's research laboratory, at the mouth of the mine, Paracelsus learned the techniques of metal chemistry—probably more than he could find in books. His fellow-chemists scorned the skulls, serpents, and other show-pieces of old-fashioned alchemy. They neither recited the Lord's prayer backward, nor did they pretend that occult powers were at their command. They had abandoned the search for gold because practical "transmutations" happened before their eyes. Instead of seeking the Philosopher's Stone, they used *aqua regia* (nitric acid and ammonia) to dissolve gold and *aqua fortis* (nitric acid) to separate out impurities. They also knew the secret of vitriol which "changed" common iron into pure copper. Paracelsus let the secret out many years later:

> "Vitriol makes copper out of iron. This is a natural virtue, not effected by the alchemist but by the vitriol through the alchemist. [!] It seems amazing that a metal should have the quality to disappear and to turn into another. It is as strange as turning a man into a woman. God has given a free hand to nature, though not to man. Therefore, in denying transmutation, Aristotle was foolish. Now I shall give you the prescription, so that in all parts of the German nation you will be able to turn iron into copper." [11]

In the course of this prescription, Paracelsus came as close to the concept of elements as anyone did before Robert Boyle formulated it.

"It is of the nature of the vitriol to become copper. . . .
for there is a unique, copper-like nature in it. Vice versa,
vitriol will change the quality in copper; for if copper is
broken by *aqua fortis*, the entire copper turns into vitriol.
. . . Whatever comes from copper gives a good vitriol." [12]

One would think that from such statements it was only a small
step to the insight that the copper is in the vitriol. Yet, it
took humanity another hundred and fifty years to make this
step. The great Isaac Newton (1642-1727) still thought it
wonderful that in Bohemia iron could be transmuted into copper. The truth, of course, is that the copper vitriol combines
with iron to make iron vitriol, while the copper which it contains precipitates out. The "miracle" Paracelsus performed
with the kitchen fork at Ambras may be explained by assuming
that a copper plating appeared on the iron.

Such triumphs made the Füeger technicians bolder. Transmutation of metals was a fact for them. Paracelsus believed that
common lead could be made into living quicksilver with the
help of borax. He did not doubt that all metals could be transmuted though, with respect to gold, "God has not revealed
the secret."

THE "QUINTESSENCE"

The Philosopher's Stone was a myth which alchemists utilized
to guard their trade secrets and to mystify rich sponsors.

"It is not proper to say much about the Philosopher's Stone
or to boast about its possession. The ancients have indicated
the recipe for those who have true understanding. However,
they used parables to keep unworthy persons from knowing
and misusing it." [13]

Yet there was something more to it. Whereas charlatans pretended that the Stone, if found, would enrich their masters and clients, the great researchers sought quite a different kind of wealth: the *Elixir* that perfects everything, reduces all substance to primal matter, and creates or prolongs life. These men, wise enough to leave gold-making alone, were dreaming of an even greater folly. They expected to distil in their pelicans, alembics, crucibles, and athanors the most perfect and most precious thing in the world, the soul, or, as Paracelsus occasionally says, "the chaos." "If you wish to succeed in such a work, you must separate spirit and life in nature, and make the astral soul in yourself tangible; then the substance of your soul will appear visibly."

Thus spake the wise Abbot Trithemius, concealing his meaning or unable to express it. We have seen, however, how he proposed to realize such fantastic aims. Paracelsus shared the strange and bold beliefs of his teacher, as did most of the astrologers and alchemists of his time. For he who was able to make this elixir would have eternal life and salvation.

A short reflection on the language of chemistry will reveal that the art of "making the soul tangible" need not have sounded utopian to Paracelsus. When we use the word "spirit of wine" for alcohol, we still follow the usage of alchemists. An essence (from the Latin *esse*, meaning *to be*) today means an extract. The alchemists taught that it was the "soul" of the substance, its innermost nature. The quintessence, says Paracelsus, is "nature fortified beyond its grade." Even today we use the word figuratively to mean the "spirit" of a doctrine or a poem or whatever we wish to summarize or reduce to its "essential" core.[14]

The art of distillation consisted in drawing the pure spirit, literally and concretely, out of the substance. In refining the im-

pure, complex, and material ore, the alchemists brought to
light what had been hidden in the slag, the pure, simple, essential tincture. The "spirit" was rather a material thing. The
Philosopher's Stone, that greatest mystery of ancient alchemy,
was the means to produce this spirit. Paracelsus explained it in
quite material terms, as though it were something like *aqua
fortis*:

> "The Stone is like the fire which purifies the rotten and
> soiled [*beschissen*] skin of the salamander and makes him
> to be born anew. It purifies the body of all its natural filth,
> with all new and young forces. . . . so that no fault remains
> in it. . . . All things which corrupt nature must yield before
> it." [15]

The transformation of a medieval concept into a modern law
was not yet complete. Nevertheless, the modern reader can observe how the meaning of "purity" is shifting from a philosophical to an empirical concept. The next chapter will show that
Paracelsus could make the notion of essence fertile precisely
because it still carried alchemistic connotations. To do that, he
had to put it on its feet whereas, with Trithemius, it had stood
on its head.

CHAPTER II

The Elixir of Long Life

INTRODUCING

CHEMOTHERAPY

> *In experiments theories or arguments do not count. Therefore, we pray you not to oppose the method of experiment but to follow it without prejudice. . . . Every experiment is like a weapon which must be used in its particular way—a spear to thrust, a club to strike. Experimenting requires a man who knows when to thrust and when to strike, each according to need and fashion.*
>
> PARACELSUS

Experimenting is an exacting pastime, and Paracelsus spared neither himself nor his neighbors. Wherever he stopped on his pilgrimage, he brewed his drugs on the charcoal under the chimney, right beside the hostess's soup. When he was in the mood he amused the guests with alchemical jugglery. More often he scared them. And he was apt to use his friends and neighbors as guinea-pigs to test a certain "spirit." One ruthless experiment is recorded by the pen of the victim, his amanuensis Oporinus:

"His kitchen blazed with constant fire; his *alcali, oleum sublimati, rex praecipiti,* arsenic oil, *crocus martis,* or his miraculous *opoldeltoch* or God knows what concoction. Once he nearly killed me. He told me to look at the spirit in his alembic and pushed my nose close to it so that the smoke came into my mouth and nose. I fainted from the virulent vapor. . . . Only when he sprinkled water on me did I come to. . . . He pretended that he could prophesy great things and knew great secrets and mysteries. So I never dared to peep into his affairs, for I was scared." [1]

A spirit Paracelsus naïvely credited with extraordinary powers was vitriol. It not only turned iron into copper, but also restored their "spirit" to mental patients. Paracelsus recommended it particularly against epilepsy.[2] Such prescriptions show that Paracelsus had a very material conception of the "soul." When he wished to impress his definition of "essence" upon his readers, he said that the soul is in the body much the way that milk is in the cow. After death, he noted, "a man's chaos goes into the air," [3] "chaos" being equivalent to essence, or gas.

Paracelsus was fond of coining terms with magical and alchemical connotations, and in at least one case, this habit inspired him to a great innovation in chemical conceptions. Observing the brown "spirit" which arose from his pelican (oxide of nitrogen) or the white "spirit" of stannic chloride (which Libavius later called *spiritus fumans*), he called it "chaos"—which van Helmont, a hundred years later, transformed into our word "gas". To the older alchemists "chaos" was the unorganized, primeval state of matter which contained all substances before the Creation. "*Omnis creatio est separatio*"—from this chaos all final substances issued through a process of sorting out, not, as we think, through a process of building up. In one of those breath-taking flashes of genius which still leave modern readers bewildered, Paracelsus used this word for the "quintessence" or "soul" of substances, and defined it as the airy or gaseous condition of matter.

Before his time, alchemists referred to gaseous substances as "sulfur." "Sulfur of mercury" was not a sulfur compound of mercury but mercury vapor. Great confusion resulted, and no progress was possible before chemists defined their conceptions more sharply.

> "Common sulfur should not be considered the soul of metals. It is not inflammable and cannot be destroyed, but is a fire itself. Indeed, it is nothing but the *Quintessence Sulphuris* which has been extracted with *spiritus vini* from reverberated sulfur, and it appears red and opaque like a ruby. This is a great and magnificent aid to transmute all white metals and to coagulate *mercurium vivum* into solid gold. Let this be recommended to your attention as a great treasure—and so you should be satisfied with no more about transmutation." [4]

Pathetic difficulties beset those who departed from the traditional line of thought. Pioneers constantly relapsed into the old speculations. In the just-quoted passage, Paracelsus first seems to wipe out all reminiscences of alchemical sulfur; but in the very next sentence he reels off in the train of Trithemian mystifications. Although, in the light of his disciple's progress, Trithemius' enraptured hope of "distilling the soul" almost begins to make sense, the stumbling back and forth between magic and science continues.

THE FOUNTAIN OF YOUTH

Nevertheless, something new was arising out of the confusion, and the transition from alchemy to chemistry becomes quasi-palpable in Paracelsus' great new idea—to reverse the process of alchemy. The aim of the older adepts had been to purify the impure, returning from the complicated, fragmentary, or corrupted condition of finished materials to the simple, essential beauty of the primeval unity. Paracelsus, himself, was far from repudiating the fascinating idea that "alchemy makes perfect that which was imperfect." [5] However, he found increasing pleasure in emphasizing that perfection may be interpreted either way—alchemy transforms crude materials into finished products just as it reduces impure substances to essences. He expressed this idea in numerous variations and never tired of citing homely examples, such as cooking and baking, the extraction of metals, or the concoction of a drug.

> "Medicines were created by God. But He did not prepare them completely. They are hidden in the slag. It is a matter of removing the slag from the medicine. For all things have been created in *Prima Materia*. Then follows *Vulcanus* who made them into *Ultima Materia*, through the art of alchemy. This is the art of separating the useful from the useless." [6]

Any "ultimate matter" may serve as "primal matter" in another process. Chemistry works both ways, building up and breaking down, synthetically and analytically. This was new.

The older alchemists had endeavored to reverse the process of Creation. They sought to return to pure quintessence and virtues which had been with God "before the beginning and uncreated." This primeval essence, they thought, was the fountain of eternal youth. He who found it would be reconciled with the Universe and be reborn like the Phoenix with whose image they symbolized the rejuvenated "gold." To distil the great "*nostrum* to cure all evil and heal all disease," that simply meant to return to the primeval unity of microcosmos and macrocosmos.

Paracelsus had little doubt that such a "nostrum" could be found. On the other hand he was realistic enough to see that the way of the alchemists was not the most promising. Instead of undoing the unperfected work of God, he would rather carry it further to its completion.

> "Doctors, I advise you to use alchemy in preparing *magnalia*, *mysteria*, *arcana*, and to separate the pure from the impurities so that you may obtain a perfect medicine. God did not choose to give us the medicines prepared. He wants us to cook them ourselves." [7]

Alchemy taught that the "heavenly substances" are so perfect that they make other things perfect and "restore corrupted matter to purity." Paracelsus believed that such substances might be found and that they would restore health to the diseased body. As an alchemist, he was seeking the great nostrum which cures all evil, the fountain of youth which reinstils life into the exhausted flesh. As a chemist he distilled his "Azoth of the Red Lion" [8] and *Mercurius Vivus*. He claimed cures of cancer, syphilis, hydrophobia, epilepsy, and other incurable diseases through his *Tinctura physicorum*, and hinted that his *Perlatum Auri* might preserve youth.[9]

> "Although certainly our medicines do not give eternal youth and heavenly harmony, nevertheless they are heavenly in relation to our body and preserve it. Their signatures are more wonderful than our reason can make out." [10]

THE ARCH-WISDOM

Generations of alchemists and quack doctors had promised to find nothing less than the cure of all evils—the Elixir, the great nostrum. Paracelsus was one of them, not less bold and not less impatient to help the sick. But he was also a chemist and an experimenter. He studied the miraculous actions of the elixir, the *tinctura physicorum* (doctors' tincture), and the *mercurius vitae* (mercury of life.)[11] He distilled "spirits" and experimented with "*magnalia, magisteria,* elixirs, quintessences, and tinctures." His finding was that there is no one remedy to end all sickness. Frankly he bid his confreres give up the search for the most perfect substance, whether it be gold, the Elixir, or the Philosopher's Stone, and instead, with the aid of chemistry, to discover a specific remedy for each disease.

"Don't make gold, make medicines."[12] With these words he formulated a program for two sciences. At Neuburg he wrote a book the like of which had never been seen before, a textbook of chemistry for doctors. Nobody had yet thought of the two sciences jointly. Was there anything in common between the transmutation of matter and human health? Magic had the answer.

The book makes no pretense to new findings. Contrary to his usual bravado, Paracelsus here followed the established lines of adept philosophy and scarcely made a single statement unacceptable to his teachers of alchemy. Underlining his orthodoxy, he called his book "*Archidoxa,*" the Arch-wisdom. However, in explaining the nature of chemical reactions and the effects of man-made drugs on the human body, he introduced new principles which were to become fertile. We remember that Paracelsus was not satisfied with the knowledge that this herb will purge, that one will constipate. He asked the decisive question: What makes rhubarb a purgative? What is the "virtue" which purges? "Nobody has seen medicine. The corpus would not be necessary were it not necessary for us to see the medicine. Without the body we could not. However, the healing power is not in the body (the mass from which the medicine is distilled). It is in the virtue; that is the Quintessence which constitutes an ounce in twenty pounds." [13]

This ounce is the "virtue" of the medicine or its "spirit." Paracelsus also called it the quintessence which remains when the four elements are taken away. He insisted that this quintessence is "not an essence above the four elements," but a subtle "chaos," invisible to the human eye and so concentrated that "nature has been fortified beyond its grade"; and so powerful that once he exclaimed: "That is an element!" [14]

Of course, neither Paracelsus nor any of his contemporaries spoke of elements in the modern sense. Somewhat helplessly he struggled with notions approaching it but did not know how to express his ideas. It remained "a great mystery" how chemical substances seemed to live, to react on others, to attack, and to preserve themselves. But the action was there, undeniably, and it had to be used and explained:

> "No one shall say that metals are dead matter. On the contrary, their salt, sulfur and quintessence have a great power to activate human life." [15]

The "hidden power which preserves" he called *elixir*, and likened it to a balm; the hidden power which "can change us, bring about transmutations, can renovate and restore us," [16] he called *arcanum*. Above, we have translated this term by "medicine," which is somewhat incorrect. "Arcanum," Paracelsus explains, is that "immaterial talent" of substances which embodies their "virtue." Today, it is called the effective principle of a remedy, its medicinal value. In the *Arch-wisdom*, he still called "arcanum" any hidden virtue. Later, he used it for medicines specifically.

> "There is an arcanum for each thing. Hence: like to like.
> . . . The art of the doctor is in the *arcana*. Heat will be heat,

cold will be cold; water remains water, and fire remains fire. These elements cannot be changed. Don't say: Hot drives out cold; contrary cures contrary. In medicine it should be: *Arcanum* is contrary to disease, and disease is contrary to health; the two drive each other out." [17]

With his doctrine of chemical remedies Paracelsus challenged both the Galenic system of tempers and the search for the cure-all.

Seven arcana were known since the earliest times: iron, salt-peter, liver of sulfur (ammonia of sulfur), sodium bicarbonate, sulphuric acid, red and black *pulvis solaris* (compounds of mercury and antimony). Paracelsus widened the field of application and generalized its theory. He added new arcana to the list, such as flower of sulfur, calomel, blue vitriol, and several compounds of zinc, arsenic, and lead. Zinc ointment is the only one of his original prescriptions still in use.

No evidence supports the claim that Paracelsus was the first to use mercury, arsenic, and antimony.[18] Although it is immaterial how many arcana or which ones he introduced, this question still divides his adulators and his critics. His apologists would have a better case, had they stressed the point on which Paracelsus himself put so much store: He was among the first who tried to determine scientific dosage and he was vividly aware of the fact that his strong arcana could best be introduced into the human body with digestible herbs, or even in the form of herbs if the signature indicated them. "The right dosis makes the difference between a poison and an arcanum." [19]

Others had used chemical remedies, and others again, centuries later, found the correct formulas. But Paracelsus set forth the program for research and established "chemical medicine" as a new principle. With him, chemotherapy no longer was a matter of mere experience, "this will cure that." He introduced a basic assumption on the ground of which cures were to become possible with chemical remedies.

"Man derives from matter, and matter is the whole Universe. Each thing in one man is like each thing in another. Man is made out of the whole. All he eats out of the great world becomes a part of him, and he maintains himself by that which he is made of. The healing substances in the outer world help the members in the inner world. The great world, hence, has all the human properties, parts, and members a man has. A son is different from his father by his soul, but in science they are not separated. Heaven and earth, air and water are in man, and man is one with heaven, fire, earth, and water. When we administer a medicine, we administer the whole world, with all its virtues." [20]

Magic here is turning into science, alchemical speculation into a principle of biochemical research. Certainly, the "mercury of life" still is the alchemist's "mother of metals," and symbolical of *materia prima* and *mumia* (see Appendix D). This confusion, however, has turned into an insight: Out of magic correspondences between the macrocosmos and the microcosmos, Paracelsus derives the metabolism between the two. Man and the Universe are related chemically. Hence, his diseases are susceptible of treatment with chemical remedies.

Starting from these principles, Paracelsus later will declare, in his lecture on *Long Life*: "Life is nothing but an embalmed mumia, with the mortal body preserved from putrefaction by some solution of salts." [21]

There also he communicated to posterity his recipe for long life:

"RECEPTUM CONSERVATIONIS
AD DUAS VEL TRES AETATES,
in viris et mulieribus:
Rp: florum sectarum unc. 1
  foliorum danrae unc. 5
    essentiarum auro perlarum ana unc. semis
      quintae essentiae croci
        chelidoniae
          melissae ana drachm. 5."[22]

CHAPTER 12

This Side of the Miraculous

INTRODUCING
BIOCHEMISTRY

People have neglected to study the secret forces and invisible radiations. They have been satisfied with relating miraculous facts. Nature has, within itself, forces visible and invisible, bodies visible and invisible, and all are natural.

PARACELSUS

U p and down the lands of southern Germany, Paracelsus applied his new science. In wayside hostels and in palaces his art won fame, his cures were called miraculous. He was asked to see patients whom other doctors had given up. In Ingolstadt he cured a girl paralyzed since birth (the episode has been narrated in our Introduction), but another patient, Petrus de Burkardis, died "suffocated *in asthmate*." In Rottweil, he cured the Abbess of Zinzilla. Patients called him to Stuttgart, to Ulm, and to the duchy of Baden.

Margrave Philip, the ruler of that little country, suffered from a diarrhetic condition which his doctors thus far had failed to cure. Here was a great opportunity for Paracelsus to gain fame among the mighty. Introduced to the court, he promised to cure the ailing sovereign. Belligerently he told the court doctors they did not have the first notion of medicine and he intended to teach them their place. The resulting clash and the humiliation in which it culminated initiated a long series of disasters, all following an identical pattern: initial success, intrigues which Paracelsus was too impetuous to ignore and too inexpert to cope with, and finally flight in disgrace.

The cure, described later in this chapter, took some time, as Paracelsus had expected; but the court doctors challenged him to show results.

> "I do not know at once what ails the patient, but I need time to find out. That they diagnose immediately is their foolishness; in the end the first diagnosis proves wrong and from day to day they know less . . . whereas I, from day to day, approach closer to the truth." [1]

The delay, which he thought essential, was his undoing. While the Margrave was slowly recovering, he grew impatient, and the court doctors saw an opportunity to discredit Paracelsus. They claimed that he had taken over as his the remedy they had recommended. The Margrave obviously could not know that timing and dosage were Paracelsus' well-guarded secret. He felt well enough to get rid of the boisterous surgeon, and Paracelsus was dismissed without fee or gratitude. "The Margrave is a worse cheat than the Jew Manasse," he noted, and announced that he would shame his enemies, the Galenic doctors, when the principles of his healing successes would be made known:

"They [the court doctors] assumed to do what I had proposed to do, and they believed they had counterfeited my secret. Just wait till you see what I wrote and what they wrote; then it will be clear who learned from whom. They defeated themselves: they published it before it was ripe."[2]

THE FIVE DISEASES

Paracelsus undertook to demonstrate that he knew more about disease than his enemies. No longer was the diploma the controversial point. He asked the question: Is the Galenic approach the only right door to the knowledge of nature? He studied Nature. Was not her realm far greater than academic medicine dared to admit? Or rather, could not diseases originate in various realms? If so, were they not susceptible to more than one treatment?

The humoral pathology, he proposed to show, was but one of five major approaches, and the Galenic guild but a small minority in the great field of medicine. He distinguished five causes of disease, his famous "five principles" (*Entia*)—they also might be called powers or realms.

1. *Ens Astri* (the influence of the stars; meteorology).
2. *Ens Veneni* (poisoning; disturbances of the metabolism).
3. *Ens Naturale* (the constitution of the patient, his humors, his hereditary traits).
4. *Ens Spirituale* (diseases originating in mental derangements).
5. *Ens Dei* (diseases sent by God, incurable diseases.)

Analogously, five kinds of doctors are competent to heal them. Disinclined to systematizing as he was, Paracelsus did not care to state how the five categories of doctors were supposed to fit the five kinds of diseases. Apparently the two methods of enumerating overlap.

1. *Naturales* treat contrary with contrary.
2. *Specifici* or empiricists use specific remedies (page 56).
3. *Characterales* or magi know cabbalistic remedies and treat "like with like."
4. *Spiritales* use chemical drugs (notably in connection with mental diseases).
5. "Christ and the Apostles."

It is all neatly explained in his little book "*Volumen Paramirum*," the first of the so-called Para-works which he esteemed as his major contribution to the study of man. We may translate "Paramirum" as "Beyond the Miraculous" or "Toward the Understanding of the Wonders." A few remarks shall be devoted to each of the five *Entia*, except the *Ens Spirituale* which will be discussed more fully in Chapter 22.

ENVIRONMENT AND HEREDITY

Paracelsus denied that the stars influence man directly, and he laughed at the idea that diseases, too, have a horoscope. His *Ens Astri* is concerned mainly with the material "exhalations" of the stars which poison the air and may produce epidemics or wars. However, this meteorological environment (or *Mysterium*) is all-pervading and may produce any systemic disease. Treatment is not to be undertaken while the offending star is in the ascendant.[3]

In the chapter on "Nature" he even made a stronger point against astrology. Traditional medicine discerned "critical days," derived from the horoscope of the disease. Paracelsus rejected this. The crisis, according to him, was determined by the "natural cycle of the body." Natural diseases originate in the patient's "complexion," in his constitution, or in the elements. Accordingly, they might be temperamental, chronic, or acute.

The humors, which were the basis of Galenic medicine, also belong in this category; but are they the whole? To know a patient's constitution, the doctor needs to understand a good deal more than the mechanical model of the four liquors battling each other in his body. What about hereditary traits? Do they not determine the diseases he is susceptible to? "A man's mother is his ascendent and planet." [4] Paracelsus was among the first to emphasize hereditary factors.

"Suppose a child was born under the luckiest stars and received the richest gifts, but in his character he develops qualities which run counter to these gifts. Who is to blame? The blood which comes by generation." [5]

Among the many arguments which pious thinkers had advanced against astrology, the biological principle of heredity had rarely been invoked. Paracelsus not only stated it with strength and clarity, he made it the basis of his biology. Biological heredity was a marvel of nature. Not before it was recognized as a law of nature could the living plasm be understood as the foundation of all animate nature.

Paracelsus, placing the study of life on this foundation, made biology autonomous. Henceforth, a person might be called "saturnine" or "mercurial" because he is so "constellated"; the term, however, referred to the flesh and blood, not to the star.

Biology became a self-sufficient science. For the first time since antiquity, it became possible to study life without constantly referring back to erratic and miraculous interventions of the supernatural powers. De-mystifying the mysteries, Paracelsus strove to understand all nature as subject to "natural forces only."

"LIFE POWER"

The biochemical point of view is triumphant notably in the discussion of food poisoning, where Paracelsus develops the theory of metabolism, with a clarity never achieved before. The human body, he suggests, may be likened to a chemical kitchen. The cook—an alchemist—transforms food into hair, bones, fat, etc., and rejects that which the body cannot assimilate. Alchemy, he says elsewhere, "makes bread become blood, though there was no blood in the bread; likewise, we do not have to eat hair to grow a beard." [6]

"*Archeus*," or life power, is the name of this alchemist who separates the poison from the nourishing elements. A pig's *archeus* must be smarter than a man's, for pigs eat many things that might harm them.

"The ox eats grass; man eats the ox; every creature has its proper food. The peacock eats lizards and snakes, animals in their own right but improper food for any other except peacocks.

"Likewise, man needs his own food, and the alchemist in him separates the poison from the good in the food. . . . He takes the good and changes it into a tincture which he sends through the body to nourish the flesh. The alchemist works and cooks in the stomach.

"Let a man eat a piece of meat containing both bad and good properties. When the meat reaches the stomach, there is the alchemist to divide the good from the bad. What does not belong to health he casts away, and sends the good to where it is needed. . . . Thus the body is maintained so that nothing poisonous shall harm it." [7]

But the *Archeus* may fail to digest the food, either because the flesh's regenerative power is weakening or because the food was improper. Then undigested matter will seek an outlet from the body or, failing to find one, will turn into poison. The doctor's task is to help the *Archeus* digest the food, and the poison to find a way out of the body, or to assist the flesh in expelling the poisonous substance. All "specific" medicines help in one of these ways. This is how Paracelsus cured the Margrave of Baden. He purged him. Instead of fighting "contrary with contrary," diarrhea with constipating agents, he prescribed in terms of metabolism. The prescription to purge, in such cases, remained in use for several centuries.

Paracelsus allowed his patients all food, on the theory that a diseased body must not be starved and weakened. On the contrary, the *Archeus* must be stimulated to work harder so that his life power can overcome the poison in the body. Oporinus, already quoted before, gives a picturesque account of how Paracelsus used his arcana in practical therapy:

"In curing ulcers he almost did miracles in cases which had been given up by others. He never forbade the patients food or drink. On the contrary, he drank with them all night and, as he said, cured them with their stomachs full. He used precipitate powder with theriacum or mithridatum or cherry juice, made into pills to purge.

"He had pills which he called laudanum and which had the form of mice excrements, but he used them only in cases of extreme emergency. He boasted that with these pills he could wake up the dead, and indeed he proved that patients who seemed to be dead suddenly arose." [8]

THE BODY MIGHTILY CONSTITUTED

In his lectures, Paracelsus later enlarged on the concept of *Archeus*, the primeval power which assures life to every individual. Not only human beings, but animals and plants, even spirits, gnomes, metals, and stones each has its *Archeus*. The *Archeus* is a force of nature, the chief link between the blind matter of which man is made and the personality which determines his "complexion." *Here is the first endeavor to understand the individual as a biological unit.* The patient no longer is the battlefield where the humors fight it out. Each individual has his constitution, his life cycle, and, moreover, his own prime mover. Man, the individual molecule of the Universe, is the root of the creation. He is a prime force himself. This great and novel notion of nature makes it unnecessary for God Himself to supervise every meal in person.

The body as a constituted biological unit, fulfilling its particular predestination, functions as an independent cosmos. So new was this idea that the consequences frightened Paracelsus. Stammering and groping, he vainly tried to explain it to himself. The weight of his own traditional scientific learning pulled him back. He could only give hints of his idea which he still strove to understand.

> "You call man a microcosmos, and that is right. But you don't know how to interpret it and we shall do it for you. Just as the sky has its constellations, so man is constellated in himself mightily. Just as the firmament is self-governed and not subject to any creature, so man's firmament is not subject to anything that has been created. Heaven and earth are one, man is something else. . . . Thus you shall understand that man has in himself his firmament, his planets, conjunctions, constellations, aspects, sidera, and the like. . . . The body gives food to itself. Some members need food from the outside, but something is in the body that is fed through the firmament in the body. The food which we eat is like the manure in the field; it makes it fertile and

maintains its substance. But life, intelligence, and spirits, that comes from the firmament. . . ." [9]

What a pathetic endeavor to jump one's shadow! "Something in the body is fed through its firmament"—here is the birth of a new biological concept, and all Paracelsus can do to help his readers is to give them an astrological analogy in terms which he had just condemned. (It is only natural that the passage is again followed by new protestations and warnings not to interpret it in an astrological sense.) That "something," obviously, is the vital power, or the living memory of the cell which Paracelsus, of course, did not suspect and with which the scientists of this century are still struggling. He called it either firmament or Archeus.

A shortcoming of language frustrated a grand feat of human intelligence. Biology was not yet born. All Paracelsus could do, at this stage of development, was to impress upon his reader, in the unsuitable terms of astrology and "predestination," the idea of a self-contained and self-regulating cosmos, a particular human being with a certain complexion, subject to the law of organic changes, and mightily constellated in himself—not in the sky!

PREDESTINATION

Biology could not become a science as long as man was considered exempt from its laws. In this first of his medical works, Paracelsus somewhat impishly asked the question: "Why should all creatures be subject to the laws of nature, but man alone have humors?" In his last, *The Doctors' Labyrinth*, he will answer calmly: "That which causes a tree to rot also will cause a man to rot." But he had not yet developed that far. In *Volumen Paramirum*, he did not conceive life as process, but rather as a cycle, determined by Predestination. But his understanding of that term was different from the one dear to the Reformers.

Aging, for instance, was part of the cycle, and no doctor could help when the end had come: "Even a child who dies a few hours after birth has fulfilled a complete cycle," [10] and "No herb has grown against death—only against disease." [11]

No fixed rule, therefore, applies to all patients of all ages and climates. Each individual has his personal balance of tempers which is normal for him, and his personal predestination.

The same idea prevails in the chapter on the diseases which may have been sent by God, and which neither priest nor doctor will cure, except if God changes His mind. "At His appointed time," [12] as Mary Baker Eddy was to repeat, God will allow the doctor to meet the patient, and the cure will be proof that the treatment was willed by God. "For the art of the real physician comes from God, and likewise the dosage, the practice, and method." [13] Consistently enough, Paracelsus ends this chapter with the complaint that "pagan doctors, be they Christians or unbelievers, work against Nature," while the believer leaves the cure to time and season.

Predestination, as Paracelsus understood the term, contained little notion of "cause and effect," the concept on which nineteenth century determinism is based. Immediate causes probably could be visualized more conveniently in terms of astrology or of demons. In trying to overcome these standbys of medieval physics, Paracelsus needed some new concept to de-mystify the mystery of the individual. The idea of a closed system, obeying its own law and hurrying toward its appointed end, apparently had been borrowed from the macrocosmos concept. The microcosmos no longer reflected the macrocosmos, it became a macrocosmos itself.

This magic idea helped Paracelsus to liberate himself from the conceptions he had inherited from medieval philosophy.

He later modified it considerably and proceeded to new and more inclusive conceptions. But he never gave it up completely. It was a circuitous way of establishing the identity of the individual, subject to a law of nature, but, nevertheless, independent and self-sufficient. This much the concept of predestination did for Paracelsus. It could not guarantee him the freedom of the individual and, therefore, he had to seek further before he reached a new philosophical guidepost. We shall see him return to the question under different circumstances and beset by considerably more qualms than he had anticipated.

CHAPTER 13

Call to Office

**DOCTORS AND
POLITICS**

*The cure comes from the medi-
cine, and the art of medicine
originates in charity. Hence, to
be cured is not a work of Faith,
but one of sympathy.*

PARACELSUS

From these two medical chapters, we return to
Theophrastus' life story. In 1526, Paracelsus went to Strasbourg
and bought his citizenship. As "doctor of both medicines," he was
received in the Guild of the Alfalfa, a patrician organization
which admitted doctors, millers, grain merchants, and manu-
facturers of starch.

Strasbourg was then a center of humanist studies. Its printing press was one of the best in Germany, and Paracelsus
sought a publisher for his *Volumen Paramirum*. Near by, at

Schlettstadt, the Brethren of the Common Lot maintained a famous school which counted among its alumni some well-known mystics, friends of Paracelsus' friends.

Moreover, at Strasbourg, alone in all Germany, surgeons had acquired equal rights with physicians. The school of surgery was under the direction of Hieronymus Brunswick and Hans von Gerstorff, celebrated surgeons of their time. Brunswick wrote the first chemical textbook in the vernacular. Another innovator was Dr. Vendelinus Hock. He lectured in German for barbers and surgeons and dissected in public. Confident of his reputation, Paracelsus also expected to teach at the school of surgery.

These hopes were immediately shattered. Dr. Hock challenged the intruder to a public discussion of anatomy, a subject Paracelsus hated and with which he had little experience. Shamed by his failure to answer Hock's questions, he stole out of the lecture room.[1] This academic setback in no wise diminished Paracelsus' popularity as a physician. On the contrary, a gratifying call came to him from "abroad," a city seventy miles away.

At Basle, the publisher Froben lay ill with a malignant infection of the leg. The doctors proposed amputation, a dangerous procedure at that time. The news alarmed the whole republic of the learned, for Froben was not only an important citizen of Basle but also acted as a father to the humanist writers. On his publishing staff were some of the most promising young artists. His sickness distressed the whole milieu in which Paracelsus was living. Mutual friends suggested that the famous doctor see the famous patient.

Paracelsus went to Basle, lived in Froben's house and cured the leg without amputation. This success was to influence his career.

PRINCE OF THE HUMANISTS

On the upper floor of Froben's house lived the man whose name the literate mentioned with the deepest devotion, Erasmus of Rotterdam, "prince of the humanists." He was the foremost Latin authority, the most accomplished writer, the sharpest wit, and a pious Christian as well. At first considered a friend of the Reformation, he soon fell out with Luther and his sectarian zealots. His religion was that of "Christ, Socrates, Plato, and Seneca." The gospel of love, humanity, idealism, and tolerance meant more to him than theological hair-splitting. Of humble birth himself, he felt for the common man and hated feudal lords and princes. This eminent man, however, was conceited and hypochondriacal. It was natural for him to consult the doctor who had cured his friend and patron. The *consilium* which Paracelsus wrote for him, almost his only diagnosis that has been preserved, is amazingly orthodox in content.

Despite the affinity of their opinions on many matters, Erasmus and Paracelsus differed in almost all other respects. One was the most refined Latinist, the other sought to make his coarse Swiss dialect a language of science. One was fastidiously neat; the other wore an alchemist's smeared apron. One was a master of innuendo, the other given to outspoken abuse. One was the most balanced mind of his time, scrupulously weighing each word, the other a mystic, rash of judgment and fond of speculation. The one lived with books, the other considered life the only book of value.

Necessarily their relations were cool. Their correspondence, which has been preserved, discloses no mutual interest. Paracelsus' letter is a sober diagnosis of Erasmus' ailment; Erasmus' reply is a fine specimen of contemporary epistolary art:

"To Theophrastus, the highly expert doctor of Medicine, Erasmus sends his greetings. Perhaps it is not out of place to wish perpetual health of the soul to the doctor who heals our bodily ailments. I am amazed to see how well you know me to the marrow although you saw me only once. I know that the riddles [in which you speak] are verily true, not from any knowledge of medicine, which art I never studied, but from my sensations of the disease. In fact I did feel pain in the liver although I could not guess the seat of the evil. I could see the liver troubles in my urine for several years. As for the third item in your diagnosis, I cannot understand it but it seems likely to me. At present I have no time for a cure, indeed I have no time either to be sick or to die, for I am engaged in exacting studies. However, if you know something [besides dissolution of the body] that might give me relief, please let me know it; and I wish you would explain to me briefly that which you have alluded to and prescribe a medicine for me. I cannot offer any compensation adequate to your art, but I promise to bear gratitude toward you. You have brought back from hell Froben, who is my other half. If you restore my health, too, you will give us back to each other. Let Fortune retain you in Basle, and I hope you will be able to read this hastily written letter." [2]

A POLITICAL APPOINTMENT

Erasmus exercised a tempering influence on the Reformation party in Basle. He hated intolerance and bigotry, and when the Reformers proposed to suppress Catholic services, Erasmus encouraged the aldermen to hold out for freedom of worship. The ensuing struggle drew Paracelsus into local politics.

At the head of the Basle reformation was Oecolampadius (Heusgen), a fighting preacher and humanist, a friend of

Zwingli and a protector of Anabaptist fugitives. He preached "according to Scripture only" and tried to introduce into all parish services a German liturgy which he had composed. Although no radical himself, he frequently defended the right of Anabaptist and peasant leaders to be heard. He deemed their doctrines worthy of discussion, though he did not accept them. The sacraments, he said, ought to be held sacred, not for their own sake but for the good of the community; and God, he taught, being unknowable Himself, should be worshipped in one's neighbor,—doctrines which Paracelsus was to develop in his own way.[3]

In 1526, Oecolampadius was near the height of his career. His position was almost as strong as Savonarola's had been in Florence. Three years later his partisans, the small craftsmen, were to demonstrate before the town hall, demanding retirement of the Catholic Aldermen and election of new guild provosts out of their own number.

When Paracelsus came to Basle, the Protestant majority was working to dislodge Catholicism from its stronghold, the University. An opportunity presented itself when a member of the medical faculty, Dr. Wonecker, "uttered fresh words against the Reformation." This professor's salary was paid by the city because he also served as a municipal doctor. When the Evangelical majority of the Town Council summarily struck him off the payroll, they assumed that they also had cancelled Dr. Wonecker's teaching license. However, they had underestimated liberal opinion in the town. Men like Erasmus stood up for academic freedom and united with the Catholic opposition in denying the Council's right to dismiss a professor. The Reformation party, finding itself in an unpleasant tangle, sought an "out."

In this strained situation Oecolampadius' political mind used Paracelsus to solve the deadlock. Although Paracelsus had never joined the Evangelical faction, the two men were of similar mold. Paracelsus' explosive personality could hardly fail to attract a fighter like Oecolampadius. On the other hand, Paracelsus had not repudiated the Church. Having just rendered the town an important service, he was respected among middle-of the-roaders. The Catholics could hardly oppose such a man if he were appointed to Dr. Wonecker's position.

Thus it came to pass that Paracelsus was offered the office of a municipal doctor and professor at Basle, which he promptly accepted.

The Faculty, however, was in no mood to compromise. Determined to fight against a nomination which had been imposed on the University, the doctors insisted on the academic custom of "colloquy," the public test of a new professor's qualification. Under ordinary circumstances this was a mere matter of form. The challenger whom the professors designated to debate Paracelsus, however, was Vendelinus Hock, victor of the Strasbourg discussion. This boded ill, and the Reformation party feared for their candidate. A legal excuse to dodge the disputation was easy to find. Since the Aldermen had created the position their appointment need not be validated by any academic formality. Paracelsus did not go to the colloquy. In fact he ignored the Faculty altogether.

But these legalistic antics backfired. Having never applied to the Faculty, Paracelsus never received its confirmation. He was not treated as a member and enjoyed none of its academic status and privileges. Strictly speaking, he was a city official with a lecturing assignment—a detail which became important in subsequent developments.

The majority of the Aldermen had accepted Paracelsus in the expectation that he would mediate, not that he would fight. They were ready to bring some pressure to bear on the Faculty, but not to disregard all accepted form and procedure. They were not revolutionaries. Their idea of the appointment was to add dignity and respectability to their Reformation, not to inflame the controversy. They hesitated to challenge the established rules of the learned community and wished to avoid a decision on matters of principle.

In the looming fight, therefore, the cards were stacked against Paracelsus. A mighty faction was against him, and by his undiplomatic approach he had failed to reconcile the undecided ones. Soon it became evident that he did not even mean to serve the faction which might have supported him, but was interested only in delivering his own, self-chosen message. Instead of helping the Reformation party, he embarrassed it.

CHAPTER 14

The Challenge

PARACELSUS·AT THE
HEIGHT OF HIS CAREER

> *Heretic is a title of honor, for
> truth always starts by being
> called heresy.*

> SEBASTIAN FRANCK

At Basle, at the age of thirty-three, Paracelsus was at the height of his career, and had an opportunity, that was never to occur again, to teach and to carry out the reform of medicine in an official capacity. But he wasted it. With a sovereign disdain for tact, he neglected to make the courtesy calls on his colleagues which academic custom required and which any newcomer would wish to make. Nor did he conform with the necessary formalities of University registration. He did not ask the Dean to enter his name in the register; he failed to present his diploma to the Faculty; he did not invite his colleagues to a disputation. Instead of discussing his intended lecture with the department, he published a program for the students over the heads of the Faculty.

This "intimation," given here in full, contains his famous formula, *"experimentum et ratiocinium."*

"Theophrastus Bombast of Hohenheim, doctor of both medicines and professor, greetings to the students of medicine. Of all disciplines medicine alone, through the grace of God and according to the opinion of authors divine and profane, is recognized as a sacred art. Yet, few doctors today practice it with success and therefore the time has come to bring it back to its former dignity, to cleanse it from the leaven of the barbarians, and to purge their errors. We shall do so not by strictly adhering to the rules of the ancients, but exclusively by studying nature and using the experience which we have gained in long years of practice. Who does not know that most contemporary doctors fail because they slavishly abide by the precepts of Avicenna, Galen, and Hippocrates, as though these were Apollo's oracles from which it is not allowed to digress by a finger's breadth. If it pleases God, this way may lead to splendid titles, but does not make a true doctor. What a doctor needs is not eloquence or knowledge of language and of books, illustrious though they be, but profound knowledge of Nature and her works. The task of a rhetorician is to bring the judge over to his opinion. The doctor must know the causes and symptoms of the disease and use his judgment to prescribe the right medicine.

"Thanks to the liberal allowance the gentlemen of Basle have granted for that purpose, I shall explain the textbooks which I have written on surgery and pathology, every day for two hours, for the greatest benefit of the audience, as an introduction to my healing methods. I do not compile them from excerpts of Hippocrates or Galen. In ceaseless toil I created them anew upon the foundation of experience, the supreme teacher of all things. If I want to prove anything I shall not do so by quoting authorities, but *by experiment and by reasoning thereupon.* If, therefore, dear reader, you should feel the impulse to enter into those divine mysteries, if within a brief lapse of time you should want to fathom the depths of medicine, then come to me at Basle and you will find much more than I can say here in a few words.

To express myself more plainly, let me say here, by way of example, that I do not believe in the ancient doctrine of complexions and humors which has been falsely supposed to account for all diseases. It is because of these doctrines that so few physicians have correct views of disease, its origins and its course. I bid you, do not pass a premature judgment on Theophrastus until you have heard him. Farewell, and come with a good will to study our attempt to reform medicine.

"Basle, June 5, 1527." [1]

The Faculty was outraged. It solemnly advised the University that Paracelsus' students would not be admitted to take examination and could not be graduated. This refusal had a semblance of legal justification. Paracelsus had invited barbers, alchemists, and others who lacked academic background to attend his lecture. Privileges were in danger of being trodden upon should the self-taught be admitted to equal rank with accredited students.

The Dean turned the tables on the city. If the University had no jurisdiction over the course, it need not make its facilities available. Paracelsus received no lecture room on the campus.

ACTOR, GLUTTON, TEACHER, AND SCHOLAR

Thirty students (twenty-two more than had registered in the preceding year) assembled in the off-campus hall where Paracelsus was forced to conduct his course. The opening session was as theatrical as the mountebank could hope to make it. Paracelsus appeared at the lectern in a professor's robe, paused, and tore the robe off. With a grandiose gesture, he flung it out into the room and proceeded to lecture in the sooty apron of the alchemist, to the applause of his friends, the barber-surgeons and itinerant *scholares*.

After this piece of showmanship, however, he set to work in earnest. He lectured throughout the summer term and the winter term 1527-1528. His subjects were pathology and therapeutics, pharmacology, diagnostic through the examination of the pulse and the urine, purgation, venesection, injuries and disorders requiring surgery. He delivered the medical lectures in a Latin version prepared by his secretary Oporinus, but in his surgical lectures he used German. The only subject he treated in the traditional way, by explaining a text, were the aphorisms of Hippocrates.

In addition to teaching, he saw patients, inspected pharmacies, gave personal consultations to his students, wrote essays and pamphlets, experimented in his chemical kitchen, and drank with his friends. How he spent his day is reported in a letter by Oporinus:

". . . As to Paracelsus, he has been dead for a long time and I should hate to speak against the spirit of his death (as the saying goes). While he was living I knew him so well that I should not desire again to live with such a man.

Apart from his miraculous and fortunate cures in all kinds of sickness, I have noticed in him neither scholarship nor piety of any kind. It makes me wonder to see all the publications which, they say, were written by him or left by him but which I would not have dreamt of ascribing to him. The two years I passed in his company he spent in drinking and gluttony, day and night. He could not be found sober, an hour or two together, in particular after his departure from Basle. In Alsace, noblemen, peasants and their womenfolk adulated him like a second Aesculapius. Nevertheless, when he was most drunk and came home to dictate to me, he was so consistent and logical that a sober man could not have improved upon his manuscripts. I had to translate them into Latin and there are several books which I and others thus translated. All night, as long as I stayed with him, he never undressed, which I attributed to his drunkenness. Often he would come home tipsy, after midnight, throw himself on his bed in his clothes wearing his sword which he said he had obtained from a hangman. He had hardly time to fall asleep when he rose, drew his sword like a madman, threw it on the ground or against the wall, so that sometimes I was afraid he would kill me. I would need many days to tell what I had to put up with. . . ."

[The excerpt omitted here will be found on p. 122.]

". . . He was a spendthrift, so that sometimes he had not a penny left, yet the next day would show me a full purse. I often wondered where he got it. Every month he had a new coat made for him, and gave away his old one to the first comer; but usually it was so dirty that I never wanted one. . . .

"I never heard him pray or inquire after the Evangelical doctrine which then was practiced in our town. He not only despised our good preacher, but threatened that one day, as he had done to Hippocrates and Galen, he would set Luther's and the Pope's heads right. He also said that none so far who had written about the Holy Scriptures had grasped their right meaning. I don't know how much more nonsense he said which I would be ashamed to relate here. . . ." [A paragraph, omitted here, will be found on p. 137.]

"He did not care for women and I believe he never had doings with any. In the beginning he was very modest, so that up to his twenty-fifth year, I believe he never touched wine. Later on he learned how to drink and even challenged an inn full of peasants to drink with him and drank them under the table, now and then putting his finger in his mouth like a swine."[2]

Dr. Johan Weyer (Wierus), who had requested this information on Paracelsus, inserted it in his work on *The Magic of Demons*. Wierus' approach to the problem of witchcraft has earned him the fame of being the first to publish a book on psychiatry. However, he was well aware that Paracelsus had preceded him in this field and appeared pleased to have a rival disparaged. Posterity, however, has discerned, in this damaging letter, involuntary tributes to Paracelsus' genius, his fanatical zeal, and the unrelenting energy which made him an exacting master. His secretaries could not keep up with the stream of his lectures and manuscripts. Paracelsus' obsession with his work is confirmed by other witnesses:

"It is true that he enjoyed drinking. But, on the other hand, when he had undertaken anything he scarcely ate or drank until he had finished his work, and then, when he felt free, he became mightily merry."[3]

The testimony of Paracelsus' butler Franz, whose report on goldmaking we have cited above, contradicts Oporinus. According to Franz, Paracelsus' conduct was exemplary, and he praised his professional skill, his generosity, and philanthropic practices. Franz reports:

> "He gave a florin to a cantor in Basle who was his patient, to buy some food and wine. I also know that he cured lepers, dropsicals, epileptics, syphilitics, and podagra [gout] patients, besides innumerable other diseases. The Galenic doctors could not do likewise, and envied the honors he earned." [4]

Oporinus, himself, admired Paracelsus as a doctor and teacher. When his master had to leave Basle, he followed him, and so great was his loyalty that Paracelsus mentioned him in his book on syphilis as his "faithful Oporinus" who stood by him when others betrayed him. Oporinus little deserved the honor. When he wrote his letter, in 1555, he believed that Paracelsus' prestige was buried with him. A few years later, however, the Paracelsus revival was well under way, and Oporinus, who in the meantime had fallen out with Wierus, wrote to Paracelsus' disciple Toxites that his unfavorable remarks had been published without his intention and knowledge. As an excuse he said that he had not realized Paracelsus' importance. Oporinus was to win fame as publisher of Vesalius' *Fabrica*; later he became a professor in Basle.

AVICENNA AT THE STAKE

On the 24th day of June, 1527, Paracelsus staged the symbolical act which marked the zenith of his career and which has gone down in history under his signature. It was St. John's Day, traditionally given over to commencement celebrations and the students' Midsummer Night's antics. On such occasions peaceable citizens stayed home behind shutters. Into the St. John's Fire went rubbish and bric-a-brac, whatever students no longer needed or did not like. And many a prince, cleric or unpopular professor was burned in effigy by the hooting students. Three hundred years later, German students threw into the St. John's Fire the uniform of a Prussian policeman, a pigtail, and other paraphernalia of the *ancien régime* in Germany.

On this St. John's Day of 1527, they built a beautiful fire. Theophrastus came to join in the merry-making. Behind him, his students dragged a heavy volume, the *Summa* of the books on medical science, the venerable *Canon* of Avicenna. At his command they hurled it into the fire.

A brief controversial note is in place here, too. Sudhoff, ever anxious to preserve the Master's respectability, has tried to make the famous incident appear innocuous. The gist of his argument is that the Canon was too heavy to be carried to the fire. He assumes that Paracelsus had a much smaller book, the Summa Jacobi de Partibus *(published in 1521), under his arm, and when he saw the students hooting around the fire, a whim of the moment impelled him to throw the book into the flames. This assumption almost refutes itself. If the incident had happened as Sudhoff construes it, nobody would have noticed or found it worth while to report or to dwell on it.*

Nor was the act a whim of the moment. Everything we know about Paracelsus' character and the elated feelings which possessed him at the height of his career supports the assumption that he deliberately chose the heaviest volume for the symbolic burning. His own report asks for no extenuation: "I threw into the St. John's Fire the Summa of the books, so that all the misfortune might go up in the air with the smoke. Thus the realm of medicine has been purged." [5]

THE FRIENDS

Froben had gathered an illustrious company in his circle at Basle. Among his editors were such well-known humanists as Mark Heiland and Urs Graf. The younger Holbein also served on his staff, and a drawing by him, dated at Basle, is supposed to represent Paracelsus [see plate XI].[6]

Like Paracelsus this circle was interested in the philosophy of Plato. The Professor of Hebrew at the University was Sebastian Muenster, a disciple of the arch-astrologer Stofler. Muenster advised Paracelsus in matters of astronomy and geography and interpreted for him Hebrew Cabbalistic texts. Moreover, Muenster had advanced pedagogical views which Paracelsus shared. He, too, advocated the education of laymen, and wrote his astrological textbooks in German.

Among his closest friends were the wealthy merchant brothers Amerbach. They were interested in the humanities and in science, and active champions of the Reformation although they opposed the idea of a schism. In this and in their political outlook Paracelsus agreed with the humanist circle more than with Oecolampadius. The Amerbachs stood by his side to the last, and one of them took his lectures down in the classroom—a valuable source since Paracelsus' own notes are lost.

In addition to friends, lectures, books, experiments, patients, and the supervision of pharmacies and bathhouses, Paracelsus had his disciples to concern him. Paracelsus was their friend and protector. Some, being barbers, had no academic standing, but took part in his experiments and in his drinking. Their ribald spirit is reflected in a parody of his "intimation," apparently written by one of his students.

"*Valentinus ab Riso* greets the reader; this is about Theophrastum and his writings. He was born at Einsiedeln in Switzerland and the *Athenienses* call him the Great Paracelsus. For he has written 230 books on philosophy, 40 on medicine, 12 on government, 7 on mathematics and astrology, and 66 about secret and magic arts. He also has combined three works in a book he calls Theophrastia. The first is *Archidoxa* in which he teaches how to separate the pure from the impure; the other *Parasarchum*, in which he treats *de summo bono in æternitate;* the third *Carboantes,* in which he deals with transformations in substance and essence. Gellius Zemeus wrote of this German Theophrastus as follows: 'There is a young man now in Germany the like of whom cannot be found in the whole world and who has written so excellently on philosophy, medicine, astronomy, and of Common Good and Right that I cannot believe otherwise. He has it either through innate influence or through an indescribable grace of God, if not through the intercession of evil spirits. For nobody knows what Theophrastus may think mean and improper.' I cannot remember having read anything more scholarly. Therefore, dear reader, receive these writings with good grace and do not fear to hold them higher than the ancients although they are thought to be novel. Vale." [7]

A more malicious lampoon was to follow.

CHAPTER 15

"Cacophrastus"

THE TURNING
OF THE TIDE

*So I have traveled throughout
the land and was a pilgrim all
my life, alone and a stranger
feeling alien. Then Thou hast
made grow in me Thine art
under the breath of the terrible
storm in me.*

PARACELSUS

As municipal doctor, Paracelsus was also
supervisor of pharmacies, barber shops, and bath-houses. He
immediately proceeded to take energetic steps against abuses,
filth, and negligence. An old ordinance prescribed that pharmacies must be inspected periodically, that medicines must be
fresh and conform strictly to prescription, and that no pharmacist could be a doctor as well. Paracelsus used this decree to
reorganize the public health system, to dust the shelves of the
pharmacies, and to throw out the horrors sold as remedies.

Again, Paracelsus had the law on his side, but showed poor political judgment in his use of it. Having antagonized the town fathers and the doctors, he now stirred up the pharmacists. He first criticized abuses, such as the employment of children, unlicensed, or inexperienced persons in pharmacies. Pressing for closer supervision and broader powers for the municipal doctor, Paracelsus apparently sought to supervise the prescriptions of other doctors.

Resistance against his summary measures ran high. Intrigues, pin-pricks, and passive disobedience made difficulties for the municipal doctor. Finally, weary of pleading and threatening, Paracelsus sent the Aldermen the following letter:

"Honorable, austere, pious, provident, generous, wise, gracious, and favorable gentlemen who have appointed me as a physician and ordinarius:

"It has come to my knowledge that doctors and other physicians who reside here have commented unbecomingly in the streets and cloisters on the status which I received through your kindness. This does great damage to my practice and my patients. They boast they are the faculty and dean and that your appointment of me, a foreigner, is without right and merit; so that I would rather not have followed the honorable call of your austere, gracious wisdom.

"With the help of God, I have cured invalids whom the ignorance of other doctors almost maimed and I think that I should deserve honor instead of infamy. Your austere, honorable wisdom has appointed me physician and professor; you are my superiors, masters, faculty and dean, not they; and I should be entitled to graduate my disciples to be doctors as behooves a full professor.

"Should the other doctors have power to prevent that, I

should not have abandoned [good positions with] princes and cities. If such is not the case, I humbly entreat your austere, honorable wisdom to make public the liberties of my status [*i.e.,*] privileges and rights.

"Furthermore, necessity compels me to insist, in the interest of my patients, that pharmacies be inspected at reasonable intervals so as to abolish abuses which are doing great damage. Pharmacists should be sworn in and their performance be controlled by the municipal doctor. Persons who are not licensed should be forbidden practice.

"Item, no pharmacist should act in collusion with any doctor." [1]

THE SHADE OF GALEN

Instead of gently prodding the reluctant Protestant party, Paracelsus appears to have delivered an ultimatum to the Aldermen who, on their part, appear to have found the demanding reformer a little tiresome. His complaint was merely filed away.

To make matters worse, Theophrastus' opponents had gathered support among his students. Some apparently kept the other camp informed of everything that went on at his lectures—his violent attacks on Galen, his boasts of outdoing all previous doctors, his unorthodox theories and the strange terms which he introduced. These were compiled in a poem, or rather a squib, which one day was nailed to the church door and to the entrance of the lecture hall. Written in dog-Latin, it purported to be a defense of Galen, speaking from Hades against the new pretender to the kingdom of Hippocrates. He calls him Cacophrastus, which has an obscene connotation in German.

"THE SHADE OF GALEN
AGAINST THEOPHRASTUS, OR RATHER CACO-
PHRASTUS

"Listen, you detractor of my glorious name:
A talker, you say, an idiot am I? Of chemistry
I can claim not the feeblest experience?
Unbearable! Have I not known the commonest simples,
Such as onions and garlic? [A bantering allusion to Para-
   celsus' commendation of folk medicine]
Hellebore I send you to cure your brains. [Hellebore was
   used against mania]
True, I don't know your mad, alchemical vaporings [*the
   "spirits"*];
I know not what Ares may be, nor what Yliadus,
Nor Archeus which you say preserves life.
All Africa bears not such fabulous fantasies.
Would you try to measure your wits with mine?
You who dodged the answer to Wendolin's [Hock's] well-
   reasoned word?
You are not worthy of carrying Hippocrates' piss-pot,
Or to feed my swine.
Your pinions fell from the wings of a crow,
Your glory is borrowed.
I say you shall lose what your cunning tongue won for you.
And your words of deceit will bring you to poverty's pain.
What will you do, madman, when you are found out?
I suggest you hang yourself.
"Let us live," he says, "we can always wander.
If imposture fails, some other adventure will succeed.
What if a second Athens, a Universe now I proclaim?
Not one of the audience I speak to can so much as guess
   what I mean."

The Stygian law here forbids me to speak further today.
Enough, reader and friend, fare thee well!

> "Out of Hell." [2]

Nothing could be more characteristic of Paracelsus than his
immediate reaction. To ferret out the culprit, he ordered an
investigation among the students, one of whom, it was clear,
must be the author of the lampoon. More even than charges of
plagiarism, the suspicion that a traitor was among his audience
hurt Theophrastus deeply. Always vacillating between overconfidence and suspicion, he demanded unconditional loyalty
from anyone with whom he dealt.

Particularly painful was the obscene surname—enough to un-
dermine the authority of any professor and town official. The
epithet raced from mouth to mouth. The "Caco"-phrastus seems
to have stuck for quite a while and Paracelsus never got over it.
Three years later he remembered it when he wrote his
Paragranum: "I uncovered these secrets and then they thought
they had penetrated into the wisdom of India and of Plato; and
they were so impertinent as to think they themselves were
Theophrastus and called me Cacophrastus." [3]

A MAN OF MANY
QUARRELS

Unable to see the humorous side of the affair, Paracelsus
despatched another letter to the Aldermen, this time making a
quite unreasonable request. He asked the City Council to find
the trouble-makers and punish them. Imagine a professor who
calls on the police to discipline his students!

The Aldermen had no mind to interfere with the academic
freedom of discussion and satire. With the delicate problem of
Paracelsus' status on their hands, it would have been most un-

wise for them to assume jurisdiction over his students. That would have played into the hands of the Faculty, providing proof of its contention that Paracelsus' lectures had nothing to do with the University. Those who wished to secure Paracelsus' students their right to graduate had to let Paracelsus fight it out alone.

But the unhappy professor utterly lacked political insight. He felt victimized and thought the whole town was in the plot against him. Disregarding the fact that his interests and those of the Town Council were identical, he only understood that they failed to support him. His legalistic stubbornness alienated whatever friends he had in the Council, and made difficulties for his other supporters.

His attire and his manners did not make things easier. His broad-brimmed teamster's hat, his sooty apron and soiled coat, and his drinking excesses little accorded with academic dignity. To this add his arrogant, dictatorial speeches, which even his disciples found extravagant.

It is true that Renaissance writers were lavish with self-praise. Nifo, the atheist philosopher, claimed that he "had written so accurately of nature that among Latin writers for the past thousand years I am not the least"; Carpi (p. 42) asserted that "even envy will love me after death." Paracelsus made them all look pale by a claim of a new kind. He not only vaunted the good job he was doing; he also asked to be considered a genius subject to no law but his own dynamism. Notorious is the passage from *Paragranum*, where he exclaimed:

"You shall follow me, you Avicenna, Galen, Rhazes, you Gentlemen of Paris, Montpellier, Germany, Belgium, and Vienna. . . . You who inhabit the islands of the sea, you likewise, Dalmatians, Athenians, thou Arab, thou Jew, thou Greek—none shall stay in a corner and have the dogs piss at him—all shall follow me, and the monarchy of medicine shall be mine. . . . How do you like Cacophrastum? This dirt you shall eat! All the universities and all the old writers put together are less talented than my a . . ." [4]

And the polished humanists on Froben's upper floor can only have shrugged their shoulders over Paracelsus' apologia for his manners:

"I know I am not the kind that speaks to each only that which might please him; I am not used to giving submissive answers to arrogant questions. I know my ways, and I do not wish to change them; neither could I change my nature. I am a rough man, born in a rough country. I have been brought up among pines, and I may have inherited some knots. That which seems polite to me may appear as unpolished to another, and what seems silk in my eyes may seem homespun to you." [5]

The "knots" were rather tough, and Paracelsus made no effort to polish them down. In speaking of doctors and pharmacists he used the German words *Bescheisser*, *Arschkratzer*, and *Betrueger*. Ignorance is the least of the printable characteristics which he always was ready to ascribe to his enemies.

It is true that slander was then as customary in academic pamphlets as it is in legislatures today. The art of irony and understatement, just invented by Erasmus, had not yet taken hold. Even the serene Copernicus called his detractors "babblers." An astronomer-critic of the Alfonsine tables was attacked as "cacostrologer." Theophrastus found little comfort in this fellow-victim, but took Luther's advice to "use a tough axe on coarse wood." Yet, he was sensitive to pin-pricks, and as irritable as he was arrogant.

MISFORTUNE

All this made Paracelsus feel that his position in Basle might become untenable. He thought, however, that only lack of Protestant zeal kept the Council from going his way with greater determination. Assuming that they would react to pressure from higher authorities, he tried to enlist the help of the Reformation leaders in Zurich. During the vacation recess he made a dash to that center of Zwinglian politics.

In Zurich he looked up Dr. Klauser, a fellow-student of Ferrara, but he soon made other contacts, too. A roistering crowd invaded the inns and Hohenheim, at their head, did his bit of drinking. As a pleasure trip, it was a success.

But in his hopes of support from the Swiss reformers, he was disappointed. He had a session with Heinrich Bullinger, Zwingli's closest friend and successor. The impression he made on this grave gentleman is preserved in a letter:

"I had several religious and theological discussions with Hohenheim. If there was a trace of orthodoxy I failed to notice it. Instead, he talked a lot of magic of his own invention. Had you seen him, you would not have suspected a doctor in his appearance. He rather looked like a teamster; and with such people, indeed, he liked best to associate. When he lived at the Stork Inn here, he always watched out for teamsters, and then he drank and ate with them, dirty as he was. When he had drunk enough, he would go to sleep on the first bench and sleep himself sober. In short, he was an extremely dirty, unclean man. He did not attend mass, nor did he seem to care much for any other divine things." [6]

Nor did Christopher Klauser prove a loyal friend. Paracelsus naïvely equated fellow-drinker with comrade-in-arms. He sent Klauser one of his lectures "so that you can get it into print."

Klauser, however, made a marginal note on it, "fantasy and lies," and never answered. In his pamphlet against the practice of urine inspection, published two years later, he wrote:

"I know Hohenheim, whom you may call an obscurantist rather than a Lutheran. I wonder whether he had knowledge of nature. He knows some tricks, notably in surgery, and he is more conversant with the alchemical sophistry. I also saw what he did in Basle, which was some madness and ignorance." [7]

Then the blow fell. While Paracelsus was in Zurich, Froben rode to the Frankfort fair, ignoring his doctor's advice, and died there of a stroke. Paracelsus, on returning, found the situation completely changed, and immediately wrote to his Zurich friends: "While I was in Zurich I lost my best friend, whom I had left here in good health. . . . Therefore, dear fellows, be careful; death is always around the corner. . . . Farewell and remember me well." [8]

He also wrote an obituary which he read to his "dear *combibones*" (fellow-drinkers) when he resumed the lectures. His patient's death deprived Paracelsus of his strongest support in Basle. Moreover, it temporarily submerged the fame which Froben's almost miraculous recovery had won him. The Basle doctors and the Faculty did not conceal their satisfaction. They obtained from the Aldermen an order to investigate the causes of Froben's death. All doctors could be held responsible for the health of their patients. An unfriendly jury might indict Paracelsus for murder through negligence.

FLIGHT

The drama, however, ended in a farce. The Catholic party set a trap for Paracelsus.[9] One canon, Cornelius von Liechtenfels,

pretended to suffer from an incurable disease and promised a
hundred guilders for a cure. No doctor would take him on,
despite the sensationally high reward. Eventually he called on
Paracelsus, who walked into the trap. "Within three days" he
cured the canon with a few pills of his laudanum. Being restored to full possession of his powers, the canon sent
Theophrastus six guilders, contending that this was sufficient
remuneration for so little work. The irritable genius took this
affront with ill grace. He jotted down in his notebook, "Never
to accept a clergyman as a patient again, be he ever so sick."

Then he sued the canon, demanding the promised fee. To
his consternation, the court ruled in favor of the fraudulent
patient. Paracelsus had been disobeyed, ridiculed, intrigued
against and insulted outright; he had been cheated and now he
was denied justice. His personal dignity was at stake. He could
no longer be sure that people were not laughing behind his
back. His overconfidence turned into suspicion, and he found
enemies wherever he looked—among the magistrates, the
Evangelical party, the humanists. Something, he felt, had to be
done to force his real or sham friends to take sides.

It might have been wiser to delay the showdown, to keep his
mouth shut while he could line up supporters and maneuver
himself into a more advantageous position. But Paracelsus always placed principles above expediency. He was so obsessed
that he could not distinguish between his personal honor and
the dignity of his ideals. His sense of justice and his respect for
decency and truth had been wounded no less than his self-
respect and pride. His compulsion to express his indignation
was stronger than his desire to maintain his position. Disregarding Amerbach's advice to lie low, he launched upon a contest
with the city of Basle.

In a rancorous lampoon which took its cue from the
Cacophrastus squib, he let go against the corruption of the

clergy and the connivance of the magistrates. Sparing no established authority, he alienated the remaining citizens whom he had not yet antagonized.

Although the pamphlet was anonymous, it was easy to identify the author. The faithful Amerbach begged him to apologize. Paracelsus took it as only a further proof of his isolation: even his friend did not seem to understand what was at stake. He was through with Basle, and he wanted no appeasers. Amerbach could do nothing for him.

The City Council's patience was exhausted. A bill of attainder was drawn up, and all Amerbach could obtain was a stay of execution for one night. While the police got ready to fetch the culprit, Amerbach knocked at Paracelsus' house and told him all was over. He must flee in the dark.

Paracelsus left his belongings with Oporinus, and escaped to Neuenburg where his friends owned a country seat. The younger Amerbach was spending his honeymoon there, and although he found Paracelsus' company amusing, there may have been one too many. So, Paracelsus proceeded to Colmar in Alsace, where his friend Dr. Fries gave him shelter and obtained for him from the town fathers a temporary permit to stay.

CHAPTER 16

Poisons, Bankers, and Pests

"WHERE MY
MISERY STARTED"

Bravely have I stood in fight
And have no cause for rue,
For though I lost my battle
The world knows I was true.

HUTTEN'S EPITAPH

D r. Lorenz Fries, of Colmar, an alumnus of
Vienna and a friend of Agrippa's, was among the rare medical
scholars who wrote in the vernacular. He was interested in
physiognomics and other arts then reckoned as "mantic," and he
cast nativities. His favorite remedies were cat and goose fat
and bones, though none of the other horrors of medieval medicine was entirely missing. He promoted his books with extravagant claims such as: "If you follow my instructions, your memory will be that of a god, not that of a man."

This friend and colleague gave Paracelsus asylum after his flight from Basle. But they soon quarreled over medical doctrine and education. In 1530 Fries published a defense of Avicenna, and in 1531 he inserted in his *Practica* an oblique censure of "charlatans and empirics who have little knowledge and no degrees." Fries asserted that he venerated a bone of Avicenna more than all the relics of Christian saints. Yet he was one of the first to call Paracelsus a necromancer, and to say that his magic came from the devil.

While Paracelsus tried to settle in Colmar, a letter from Amerbach informed him that his affair in Basle could not be straightened out easily. In his answer, Paracelsus offered no suggestions. He seemed to have given up Basle. Spitefully, he informed his friend that his large practice in Colmar made it impossible for him to accept Amerbach's kind invitation to visit him at his farm at Neuenburg.

Oporinus rejoined his master; other disciples followed; and soon the merry crowd was together again. The circle was enlarged by the pharmacist, Dr. Melchior Dorss, and other such notables. Despite his eccentricities and his horseplay, Paracelsus was a good mixer. Two town officials, well respected in humanist circles, Konrad Wickram and Hieronymus Boner, also joined this round table. To each he dedicated a book written in Colmar, one on surgical disorders, the other on syphilis.

News of Paracelsus' involvements, however, had reached Colmar together with his person. The town authorities took no chances. Giving him a temporary permit to stay, they did not grant him domicile, nor a permit to publish the book on syphilis which he expected would bring him fame.

No extension having been granted, Paracelsus again had to seek a refuge. Leaving his belongings with Dr. Dorss, he traveled to Esslingen, a small town in Württemberg where the Hohenheims owned a house. He sojourned there awhile and had Oporinus bring his instruments from Basle, after his house "*Am Rheinsprung*," in Basle, had been sold to the gold-maker Thurneyser, who was glad to acquire Theophrastus' chemical installations.

In Esslingen Paracelsus seems to have studied astronomical problems. A few hundred years later, when his house was renovated, the chimney and roof were found covered with astrological signs. But of the chemical apparatus nothing had survived except a hammer.

Again, however, Paracelsus' hope of settling down was frustrated. What embarrassments arose in Esslingen are not known, but before long Paracelsus was once more on his way. He later remarked: "My misfortune, which began at Esslingen, was confirmed at Nuremberg."

CONTEST AT NUREMBERG

This center of trade, of art, and of religious strife was the next station. Sebastian Franck noted in his *Chronica of Our Times and Bible of History*:

> "Item Dr. Theophrastus ab Hohenheim, a physician and astronomer. Anno 1529, said doctor came to our town; a peculiar and wondrous man. He laughs at the doctors and scribes of the medical faculty. They say he burned Avicenna at the University of Basle, and he stands alone against nearly the whole medical guild. He uses his own judicial physics and has contrarieties with many; his practice is against all, and he is another Lucian, so to speak."

So everybody was forewarned about Paracelsus. The doctors of Nuremberg proposed a debate with the challenger, but again he declined. Instead, he asked them to refer to him a patient whom they had given up as incurable, preferably a spyhilitic, for he placed much hope in his studies of that terrible new scourge. The guild seized upon this chance to silence their opponent; syphilis, they knew, was incurable.

Outside the gates of Nuremberg, fifteen patients were isolated in a "leper hospital." Leprosy was the common name for elephantiasis, syphilis, and similar loathsome skin diseases which at that time were not differentiated. Paracelsus himself thought the syphilis germ sprang from the intercourse of a "French leper with an impudent whore who had venereal bubas" and who forthwith infected her customers.

The provident town fathers of Nuremberg protected the citizens from contagion by quarantining such patients. Paracelsus was placed in charge of the prison hospital, and to the amazement of everybody, he cured nine of the fifteen inmates. Sudhoff found the record of this feat in the archives of Nuremberg. But no case histories have been preserved, and since leprosy still is considered incurable, it must be assumed that Paracelsus rid some syphilitics of their symptoms.

The victory, however, did not bring him the acclaim he had expected. He made only one convert, Dr. Magenbuch, who addressed him, in humanist fashion, as "my doctor and poet." The rest of the medical guild, on the contrary, was up in arms. For Paracelsus, not content to have nailed down their incompetence, denounced their opulence, inveighed against their "buxom fat wives," accused them of cheating (*bescheissen*) the public, and incited the populace against them. Finally he forgot all counsel of political expediency and openly attacked the dominant Lutheran faction.

Had Paracelsus been interested in medical matters alone, it would have been the part of wisdom to ally himself with the local Lutherans. Nuremberg, one of the richest towns in Germany, world famous for its churches and art treasures, was a stronghold of the Reformation. Its famed native sons included Hans Sachs the Meistersinger, Albrecht Dürer, and many patricians whom Dürer's brush immortalized. Dürer was not too happy with the Protestant merchants—witness his mordant portrait of Willibald Pirkheimer—and other artists were even more outspoken in their criticism of Lutheran politics. The brothers Beham, known among the "little masters" of the graphic arts, were warned to stop their "atheistic propaganda." Paracelsus boasted of being their friend and was an active partisan of the radical sect which beset the dominant faction. Though a stranger, he injected himself into local politics and intervened in an issue then agitating the public, the so-called Carthusian prophecies.

A series of politico-religious frescoes had been discovered at the Carthusian Cloister at Nuremberg. Using the current mystic and magic symbols, the artless work prophesied the end of the Pope, of the clergy, the princes, the merchants, of hate and greed, and the advent of the Kingdom of Christ. The Lutherans used these prophecies to justify their régime. Paracelsus challenged their contention. "Christian prophecy concerns the Last Judgment; so says magic." The symbols predicted the apocalypsis, not the substitution of a Lutheran hierarchy for a Popish one, "of unmarried whores by married ones." With unveiled allusion to the Lutheran emphasis on "the word" he proclaimed: "Not he is a disciple of Christ who merely invokes His word." [1]

This was hardly likely to persuade the town fathers and guild masters to respect Paracelsus' medical position.

It was in this setting that he published his first pamphlet about syphilis, and incited a controversy which has become famous in the epic history of medicine's campaign against venereal disease.

THE "FRENCH" DISEASE

Syphilis was a new disease; the literature about its nature and treatment was hardly thirty years old. Contemporary astrologers surmised that the conjunction of three planets in 1494 was responsible for its epidemic appearance. The truth seems to be that Spanish sailors brought the scourge from the West Indies to Europe. But some say that the biblical "leprosy" was a form of syphilis.

In those days the disease was merciless. The spirochetae had not been domesticated in the human body, and produced painful and disfiguring ulcers. The flesh was literally eaten away from the bones. Famous men, among them a pope, befouled the air with the stench of suppuration. The venereal character of the infection had been recognized very early, and the disease was the more odious, as it was taken as a divine punishment for sexual license. Virtuous Germans were quick to saddle the French with the responsibility for this plague; yet its most celebrated victim was the ardent German patriot, humanist, and satirist, Ulrich von Hutten. He was consumed by one of the most virulent forms of the disease. During a temporary remission of the attacks, which he attributed to treatments with guaiac wood, he wrote a pamphlet in praise of this medicine. Soon afterwards he died, for the treatment was futile. Paracelsus wrote a small tract ridiculing both von Hutten and the remedy, as a prelude to the big battle that was to follow.

Guaiac is a bush found in the West Indies. It also was called "holy wood," since the native medicine men used its smoke for fumigating. Today it still serves as a cough relief. Faithful to the doctrine of signatures, European doctors believed that an Indian wood ought to cure an Indian disease. They put their patients in closed chambers and nearly suffocated them in the biting guaiac vapors. Some doctors also used guaiac preparations internally.

The wonder wood had become a fad with the medical profession. It was in general use to treat ulcers, and its import had become so profitable that the mighty Fuggers of Augsburg obtained the monopoly for its sale, in exchange for the loan which financed Charles V's election to the Emperor's throne.

Practical men that they were, the Fuggers cut influential doctors in on the business. Thus the Dean of the Leipzig Faculty of Medicine, Heinrich Stromer, owned shares in guaiac cargoes of Fugger's West Indian ships. (Shares were not held in company assets, but in individual trading voyages.) This unimportant investment of an unimportant doctor was to affect the career of Paracelsus and the course of medical history. For Paracelsus' pamphlet against guaiac treatment antagonized not only Protestant doctors but Catholic merchants as well.

The guaiac pamphlet was followed by an *Essay on the French Disease*, with the characteristic subtitle, *About Impostors*. Again the whole medical faculty and guild were taken to task. Only the first chapter of this book was printed in 1529. The two remaining chapters were ready to go to press, when the censor forbade the printing. What had made the authorities fearful of medical books? Was it Paracelsus' threat to ruin the guaiac trade?

DISEASE AND BUSINESS

The profitable business was threatened by formidable competition: empirical doctors and quacksalvers, whom many desperate patients consulted, prescribed mercury or mercury compounds, and some academic doctors supported them. Mercury treatment was given internally and externally. It was extremely painful and quite as futile as the guaiac treatment. The mercury burned the ulcers away, but with them the flesh, too. Patients who were rid of syphilis symptoms died of mercury poisoning. Paracelsus inveighed against both treatments:

"You say even Theophrastus can't help this patient. That the lead club fell down on you: who could put such murder straight again? This patient you have smoked fifteen times. That one you have balmed fifteen times. Another you have washed fifteen times. And the fourth you led around in the [guaiac] wood. This one you made swallow a quarter pound of mercury, another half a pound or a pound or even a pound and a half. This one has it in his marrow, another in his veins. There it is in a corpse; there a living man goes around with it. There it is in powdered form; there it is sublimated, calcinated, resolved, precipitated, and so on. Who could cover up such a felony?" [2]

The fact that neither wood nor mercury were effecting any cures only made the controversy between their proponents more heated. Syphilis became a test case between empiricists and academicians, "metalists" and "herbalists," "chemical doctors" and "Galenists." Their dogmatism retarded research; and the commercial interests involved added fuel to the fire.

By the time Paracelsus was ready to write about syphilis, mercury had been discredited. Nevertheless, he came out on the side of "metalism." He declared that the disease was "mercurial" (page 80); hence, wood could produce no results. On the other hand, he excoriated the mercurialists, attributing their failure not to the mercury but to their indiscriminate and clumsy use of it. He proposed to find prescriptions which would cure the ulcers without emaciating the patient, thus promising to bring mercury back into medical favor.

Unfortunately, it so happened that in 1528-29 the Fuggers

were not interested in the sale of mercury. One Ambrosius Hoechstetter had cornered the market and the Fuggers were bearish toward the metal. They were losing money as its price went up. Being then at the height of their power—the Emperor had just paid his debts by issuing an ordinance lifting the ban on usury—the Fuggers could take swift action against this quarrelsome witch doctor and errant quack from Einsiedeln who was deprecating the value of their wonder wood and whose fantastic theories threatened to send the price of mercury still higher. They were determined to prevent publication of his pamphlet.

Thus, the embattled little Swiss doctor faced the biggest bankers of his time. All he owned was a chemical kitchen and his pen and knowledge; they owned thirty million dollars—an imposing sum at a time when the mighty French King's military budget did not exceed $250,000.

The first round, we saw, went against Paracelsus. But he did not give up. He persuaded another publisher, Friedrich Peypus, to print an underground edition. It appeared to be a good proposition; but science was poorly served. The composition was done in haste; Paracelsus, forced to go into hiding, was unable to read proof.

The *Three Chapters on the French Disease*, dated 1529, appeared in 1530, with a dedication to Lazarus Spengler, secretary of the Aldermen. The uproar it caused in Nuremberg is easy to imagine. Paracelsus had to run. From Beratzhausen, he wrote to Magenbuch:

"When the ulcer subsides, I shall return to Nuremberg, in order to face these men as a man and to enjoy your friendship. But the earth has not created me as one of the settled. My father did not engender me as a resident. I readily make a country my fatherland; but I leave it as readily."

Paracelsus had staked much on this publication. It was to provide proof of his competence and reopen the way to the print shops. For it was to be followed by a more exhaustive work, *Eight Books on the Origin and Causes of the French Disease.*

A PLEA FOR FREE RESEARCH

Again, the Aldermen forbade publication of any book by Paracelsus. Spengler and other friends interceded for him and obtained a compromise—the book was to be submitted to a medical authority to advise the city on its merits. Accordingly, the manuscript was sent to the medical faculty of Leipzig, whose Dean was none other than Dr. Stromer, the Fuggers' business partner in guaiac. Inevitably the Leipzig doctors despatched a devastating judgment to Nuremberg, declaring that Paracelsus, being neither a doctor nor a physician, was not qualified to write on medical matters, and that his book was without merit.

This decision reached Paracelsus when he was already on his way to the Danube. His first reaction was a draft of a letter, as harsh as the worthy citizens deserved:

"To the honorable, provident, wise Mayor and Aldermen of the laudable city of Nuremberg, my favorable masters: You have no jurisdiction over the printing press. Why should you assume to judge my work? You have no understanding in these matters." [3]

Then he reminded them of the Evangelical truth which he was defending and which should benefit the common man:

"I do not speak blasphemy or calumny against anybody. There are others who revile all authority, secular and clerical, noble and common, in print and otherwise, and it is being tolerated. I do not do that. I only denounce the abuses of medicine in order to protect the common man from robbery." [3]

And quite properly he concluded with a plea for the freedom of the press and of research:

> "If the school has anything to say against me, let us have it out in open discussion. But that cannot prejudice the right to print. That is why you print. Whosoever interferes with the press, he interferes with truth as long as the defendant has not been defeated in open discussion. You have no right to judge or disallow publication before a discussion has taken place." [8]

This time, however, a good friend dissuaded him from sending it and the letter which he finally despatched to the Aldermen was more politic. He reminded them of the honors he had won in the good town with earlier publications. He asserted that his intentions were the best, his concern only that of the "poor patients." He humbly entreated them to postpone their decisions until they had heard his side. Though not a Protestant, he particularly stressed the Evangelical freedom of the burghers and their reputation as protectors of the truth. Finally, he demanded a disputation on the merits of the case: "Let those who doubted the truth of his statements meet him in open discussion which, as formerly, so now, he will willingly attend." [3]

FROM PARACELSUS TO EHRLICH

The great book on syphilis was never printed in Paracelsus' lifetime. Authorities agree that it contains the best clinical description of syphilis available at that time. Paracelsus not only recognized all the internal and external ravages of the disease, he recognized that it could be contracted only by contact. He spared his patients the cruel purgations, salivation, hunger and sweat cures, but sent them to sulfur baths and gave them mercury balms in much diluted form.

A summary of Paracelsus' views will show how deeply the Leipzig faculty erred. His approach was chemotherapy. He did not apply "mercury," but a specified quantity of a particular compound. As the reader knows, for centuries doctors, pharmacists, and chemists unavailingly sought a remedy until, in 1909, Ehrlich found Salvarsan, an arsenic compound. Unnumbered thousands died before this help was available. Until the twentieth century, remedies could bring but temporary relief. Paracelsus obviously was on the right track in his notion that the success of any cure depends on the quantity and composition of the compound. He was the first to emphasize such "dosage." In his recipes and prescriptions he pointed out that metallic "arcana" are most efficacious when given in herbs and juices which contain the metal. He there used the word "arcanum" almost as "element" is used today. He warned, again and again, that the "impostors" did not know how to apply the metallic arcanum.

In another case, recommending iron against "poverty of blood," he was careful to add: "But we should choose a plant which contains iron in etherealized condition, which is preferable to metallic iron." [4]

The question was how to introduce the arcanum into the body. This is what the "impostors" did not know how to do and it is this task which Paracelsus set for future generations of researchers. That is his merit, not the alleged invention of the mercury cure or his "metalism." His contemporaries used mercury as a cauterizing agent, much as one uses a knife, to burn the ulcer away. Paracelsus used it biochemically, as an antitoxin or "arcanum" to combat the poison. Of course, he had no idea of the syphilis bacillus, though he occasionally spoke of the "germs" of the disease.[5] Based on his assumptions, however, he was able to supply a fairly rational theory and to indicate a treatment which would not harm the patient. Indeed, syphilis became the test case for the theory of chemical drugs.

The Fuggers soon rectified their initial error and got their hands on the mercury monopoly. Had Paracelsus sought to publish his syphilis tract a year or two later, the Fuggers might have paid the printing costs. By that time, he was interested in other and greater things. He was writing the sequels to his *Paramiric Essays*, outlining the fully developed theory of bio-physiology. But he was now alone.—At some turning point in these turbulences, Oporinus had bolted.

CHAPTER 17

Doctors and People

"AGAINST THE GRAIN"

The true ground of medicine is love.

PARACELSUS

Optimistically, Paracelsus assumed that his letter would appease the town fathers of Nuremberg. While waiting to be recalled with honors, he used his involuntary vacation at Beratzhausen for literary work. The second "Paramiric" essay, developing the biochemical theory of metabolism, was almost ready when the answer of the Aldermen reached him. The "No" was final; the battle was lost.

Furiously, and in a frenzy of impotent resentment, Paracelsus interrupted his work to compose the most consummate abuse of the medical guild ever written. The venerable authors of antiquity received their share along with the contemporaneous "*Bescheisser*" and their overdressed wives. Unable to forget the slur he had received at Basle, he took it out on "Cacoaristotle" and "Cacoplinius," and threatened to burn in lye "your Aesculapium, Avicennam, and Galenum until only their hindmost *faeces* are left." Calling them "cuckolds" and "lackeys" he prophesied: "How will you *cornutes* fare when Cacophrastus will be the prince of the monarchy? You *calefactores* will be the chimney sweepers." [1]

Paragranum is the title of the little pamphlet—*Against the Grain*, or, as others interpret it, *The Ground of the Grain*. It is his best-known work, for despite the usual confusion of detail the outline is simple, the style lively, and his basic teachings are put in a nutshell.

Polemizing against ignorance and dogmatism, Paracelsus develops the fundamentals of the new medicine. He answers the renewed charge that he lacks diplomas with a question: "What makes a doctor?" On four pillars, he says, rests the whole art of healing:

Philosophy (roughly corresponding to what today is called natural science).

Astronomy (in contrast to astrology, this includes characterology, psycho-somatic dynamics, and psycho-climatology, or that indeterminate universe of knowledge which, for want of a better name, may be called anthropology, or psychology).

Alchemy (including biochemistry and pharmacology).

Virtue (the professional skill of the doctor, his experience and his psychological ability to mobilize the patient's vital forces).

Philosophy and astrology were prerequisites of medical studies at all universities. The emphasis on chemistry was new. Even the chapter on astronomy is full of chemical references. Paracelsus, who believed in preparing his prescriptions himself, poured biting irony on the doctors who had to take advice from pharmacists.

"Like apprentices they ask: 'Master, what is this?' And when the apothecary tells them the name, they say: 'Dear me, is that so? I have read so much about it, but I would not have recognized it.' Isn't it a shame that you should be taught by a Jack Brewpunch?" [2]

Alchemy, he thought, would help him accomplish the revolution of medicine on both levels, scientific and moral. Hence his constant confusion of two different charges. The doctors were immoral because they despised chemistry, and they were ignorant because they lacked "virtue." Among other achievements, the Philosopher's Stone was to restore the ethical code of the guild.

"You feel safe when the magistrates support you; but that prop will tumble down. Don't trust your Galen and Avicenna. The Stone will be crushed and the Heaven [*i.e.*, alchemy and astronomy] will make new doctors who know the four elements, magic and Cabbala. They will be *adepts* and *archei*. They will be chemists and possess the quintessence. They shall have arcana, the tinctures, and the mysteries. Where will you flee before such a revolution? Who will paint your wives' thin lips and their sharp noses?" [3]

THE MAGUS

Among the four pillars on which the art of medicine rests, therefore, "virtue shall remain with the doctor until death, to hold together the other three columns." [4] Like each plant and metallic remedy, the doctor, too, must have a specific virtue. He must be intimate with nature. He must have the intuition which is necessary to understand the patient, his body, his disease. He must have the "feel" and the "touch" which make it possible for him to be in sympathetic communication with the patient's spirits. In short, the doctor must have the abilities of a medium. His highly sensitive wisdom "follows the disease as the cow follows the crib" and tracks down the signature of the remedy as a hound tracks game. (Such belief in communication between patient and doctor was not unusual. Doctors always made sure their own horoscope was not averse to the patient's.) Paracelsus despised the "impostors" who copied his prescriptions but failed to understand the patient from within. They were lacking in "virtue" and could not help the patient except in routine cases.

The good doctor has a certain power of suggestion. His therapeutic success largely depends on his ability to inspire the patient with confidence and mobilize his will to health. Paracelsus, himself, relied heavily on his authority over the patient's mind. He recommended chastity and fasting to heighten diagnostic sensitiveness and to intensify one's hypnotic power. That is what Oriental medicine men had taught him.

Few famous healers could avoid being considered mystery men. Theophrastus allowed his disciples to attribute his cures to secret knowledge, and like other medieval doctors he encouraged the belief that he possessed extraordinary powers. For good measure, he used the mountebank technique of the medicine men. Partly, he believed in the medieval myth of the *magus*. But his claim to healing power had a new ring. The "virtue" he claimed was the newly recognized power of the individual, the *Renaissance man's presumption that genius is creative*. The artist compared himself with God the Creator; the doctor presumed to be in on the secret of running the universe. His "virtue" elevated him above the law of the land and

—with a side thrust at Nuremberg, Leipzig, and Basle—made him independent of appointment and rules. *"The doctor is not subject to human law, but only to God through the medium of nature."* [5]

Just as Luther delivered the individual's conscience from ecclesiastic tutelage, so Paracelsus asserted that the magus derives his powers directly from God. Genius need not bow to the law; genius makes the law.

> "From the middle of this age the Monarchy of all the Arts has been at length derived and conferred on me, Theophrastus Paracelsus, Prince of Philosophy and of Medicine. For this purpose I have been chosen by God to extinguish and blot out all the fantasies of elaborate and false works, of delusive and presumptuous words, be they the words of Aristotle, Galen, Avicenna, Mesva, or the dogmas of any among their followers." [6]

THE GENIUS

These opinions throw some light on Paracelsus' strange social behavior. At least they tell his part of the story, and give evidence of the role in which he saw himself. His highly developed sensitiveness, so valuable in his art, also accounted for those irritable and "touchy" character traits which proved such a social handicap. It was not till the eighteenth century that society gave recognition to the artist who could not make a worldly success. In the sixteenth century the genius was comparatively a phenomenon. Heretics had been burned at the stake, but their opposition to the established order was seldom based on any conviction of a personal message. It was grounded in some tradition; their idea was peculiar to a minority. In Paracelsus, for the first time, there appears a feeling of a personal call. His message springs from the wells of his own experience and from the Light of Nature which the Holy Spirit gave him. Not as a member of any minority, but as a newcomer and an outsider he challenges society. As an inspired individual he disregards convention and breaks through the tightly knit order of medieval feudalism. His right to be heard is the right of the genius through whom God chooses to speak. "Nature praises me. Of her I am born, her I follow. She knows me, I know her. The light which is in her I have beheld in her." [7]

He completely identifies his message with his personality. Every outrage he suffers personally is a crime against his cause, and every abuse against which he rebels is an injustice done to his person.

Paracelsus was unable to separate his ideas from his person; justice from his indignation at the wrong done him; medicine from the virtue of which he was possessed. Those who failed to see things his way were so much the worse off. They sinned against the Holy Ghost. In one passage he frankly asserts, "They would not punish me, they would punish Christ." [8]

Paracelsus was possessed by his genius and behaved as though he knew it. He demanded submission to the fact— incontrovertible for him—that Right and Truth were with him and that his mission was to save the world from wickedness. If it failed to follow his call, there still was a way to save it against its will. Like Christ, the genius could sacrifice himself for the world. There was a self-destructive martyr urge in Paracelsus. It helps to explain his repetitive pattern of misfortunes, most of which were of his own making.

MAD OR LONELY?

How varied is the timber out of which the great innovators, explorers, discoverers, prophets, and teachers of mankind are hewn! Christopher Columbus was an adventurer and speculator. Martin Luther became a rebel out of piety and contrition. Nicolaus Copernicus staged a revolution in thinking because the accepted view of the universe failed to satisfy his sense of order. Paracelsus explored the eternal nature of man as though that could negate his daily difficulties in living with real people.

The pattern of success and flight, which first emerged in Baden, was repeated in Basle and in Nuremberg and was to be repeated over and over. Paracelsus arrives in glory, quickly makes friends, provokes the mighty and alienates those whose support he needs most. He makes verbal challenges which he is unable to sustain, then waits to succumb to a low intrigue. He never seems to fight to win. He rather acts as though he were testing the loyalty of his friends and the decency of the world at large. Instead of maneuvering himself into an advantageous position, instead of waiting for propitious occasions, he chooses the most untimely moment to make his demands and fire his insults. As though to avoid any appearance of compromise, he makes his boldest claims and his most extravagant charges when his enemies are strongest. Right always must go before expediency; and if persecution is the consequence, well, it just goes to show that innocence is being persecuted. With a certain relief, Paracelsus takes up the burden of the martyr. He was not made to lead a settled life anyway; he seems to enjoy the part of the victim which he plays so well. He sounds somewhat cavalier when he admits: "I was strange and no one could cope with me." [9]

It surely was not all the fault of society, nor of Theophrastus' inability to make his intentions clear. His acts invited hostility. Was he so madly possessed by his call that he had to disregard every other consideration? Was he really so lonely that he could tolerate the strain of his isolation only if it was offset by aggression? Was he simply duplicating the frustrations of his early youth or was he seeking punishment for some neglected duty?

Against what iniquities or what remorse were the persecutions supposed to shield him? Was he afraid of losing himself if he made a success of life or did he need the martyr crown as a confirmation of his call?

Whatever the reason—how analyze a person centuries after his death?—the fact is that Paracelsus was forever torn between his desire to lead and his compulsion toward martyrdom. He never would be an equal among equals. He kept no friends among persons of his standing and education. Two barbers were to share his estate, and most of his disciples left him—that is, those who did not end on the gallows. He was king or beggar, never a gentleman. His association with "teamsters," his drinking, his conceit and his violent language in polemical writings, his litigiousness where he might peaceably have won people over—all suggest that he found it difficult to communicate with learned men. He conversed with them via the printing press. Only when setting his ideas on paper did he communicate. Then probably he was happiest—though even then he was talking over their heads.

He never sustained any dialogue. He entertained and the audience listened; he taught and the disciples learned; he played host and the guests accepted; he scolded, denounced, and conquered, and the Galenic doctors crumbled. It was always a one-way communication.

Yet, he loved people and wanted to be loved. Some of his outcries movingly give evidence of the suffering which his isolation inflicted upon him.[10]

"We have warred for a long time. They drove me out of Lithuania and Prussia, and from Poland, and still it was not enough for them. The Dutch did not like me either, nor the schools, neither Jews nor monks—but thank God, the patients liked me." [11]

CHAPTER 18

Doctors and Money

ANOTHER BOOK ON
MEDICAL ETHICS

> *Happy is he who walks in the
> ways of the Apostles, takes nei-
> ther office nor wife and has no
> possessions.*
>
> PARACELSUS

Paracelsus' quarrels with society were not all due to his isolation as a genius. Even in mundane matters people were unable to "cope with him." Landlords had to sue him for rent, and he was ever evading contracts. He answered with counter-suits and childish, self-righteous letters to the authorities, charging his creditor's action with damaging him. How right or wrong he was in any particular case it is now hard to say; but his attitude was invariably juvenile. He always seems to say: How could they do this to me? As in the Basle incident, he consistently assumed that the magistrates were at his back.

His attitude to patients was unbusinesslike. He either treated them gratis or charged an excessive fee. Canon Liechtenfels was right in calling one hundred guilders exorbitant. Many a court physician got no more in cash during the whole year. Middle class patients usually paid a guilder a visit.

No record is extant of the income Paracelsus received from his patients. The liberal King of Denmark probably paid Paracelsus five hundred guilders a year; few of his generals received more than one hundred. That, however, was an exception. High-placed patients often "forgot" to pay, and physicians had to drive hard bargains in order to subsist. Paracelsus was often cheated both by patients and by other doctors. The court physicians of Margrave Philip of Baden nearly "sucked [sic] all my inventions out of me."

In 1535, he was called to a patient in Amberg, near Regensburg:

"Bastian Kastner, who had been suffering from a sick leg for a long time, had consulted many doctors, but the more remedies he tried the worse he became. He had no rest, and below his knees nothing was left but stench and suppuration. You know how such canceric ulcers develop. This man asked me to see him, promising a good fee as sick people always do while they need us. However, the closer to the cure, the less they think of their promises. So it was here, too. Now it would have been decent to reimburse me for the eight-mile ride on horseback [apparently for the first visit]. But he wouldn't hear of it, as is customary with the rich. So I decided to have nothing to do with such a man. For what should I expect if in the beginning the patient was so filthy? However, Bernhard, who had first persuaded me to go there, undertook to pay a sizable sum in case the man should be healed. So I took the patient on, and put up at his house. Then the following happened, in view of which I advise all physicians to beware of patients who offer room and board. I healed first his arm. . . . However, the art is not in closing the wound. The doctor has to prevent it from opening again. Now Dr. Burzli, a brother of the patient, did not know this, but was trying to hasten the cure. He thought he had learned enough from me, broke into my room like a burglar, stole my medicine, and also used other deceptions." [1]

No brief for the other side exists. Paracelsus' account has prejudiced the case for posterity in his favor. But his own charge turns evidence against him. In an earlier account of the quarrel he failed to mention the theft, but gave evidence of his distrustful and vindictive nature:

"This doctor saw the *Arcana Simplicium* and, judging by its color, thought it was precipitate. So he thought he knew the art, since I had nearly finished the job. He provoked a quarrel and finished the job himself. But they were both cheated, the one because the medicine is not precipitate, the other because he thinks his skin is whole, but inside he is all rotten." [2]

Chuckling maliciously, as in the case of the Margrave of Baden, he rejoiced in his patient's misfortune. His petulant remark would be consistent with quite a different story. What if Paracelsus had quarreled with Dr. Burzli over the length of the treatment, and had left the patient's house in a flurry of rage? The patient may have been a miser; but the doctor seemed to be interested in his money as much as in his health.

TRADE SECRETS

The preceding episode has shown that scientific knowledge was then considered personal property. No doctor would, for the sake of humanity, surrender his trade secrets any more than a gold-maker. Chemists were as jealous of their recipes as any clothmaker of the composition of his dyes. Reading a pharmacological book required the ability of a sleuth and considerable general knowledge, because important information usually was withheld.

Like other doctors Paracelsus feared thefts by competitors. In his writings he constantly reminded the reader that he was only giving hints. In a letter to the town of Sterzing, where he hoped to settle, he named the price for which he would give away all his secrets—an appointment for life.

> "Should you ever be so needful as I am now, you also would disclose the arcana. I should keep my mouth shut if I were provided with a sinecure. This not being the case, I have undertaken to save myself from misery through my knowledge. Blessed is an office which does not require a man to conceal his arcana." [3]

Such exhibits of the low professional ethics of his time alternated curiously with enunciations of the loftiest ideals.

Reform of the relations between doctors and patients, and, in a larger frame of reference, reform of the entire professional code and the status of the medical profession was one of Paracelsus' principal aims. For his personal use, he wrote a supplement to the Hippocratic oath of the doctors:

> "This I swear: To accomplish my system of medicine, not to waver in its defense as long as God grants me the office and to oppose all erroneous medicines and doctrines;
> —to love the sick like my own body;
> —not to trust my eyes, and not to prescribe medicine without understanding;
> —not to accept a fee unless it has been earned;

—not to trust a pharmacist;

—not to guess but to know;

—not to treat any prince or gentleman, except I have my fee in my purse;

—nor any monk nor nun, in particular not in Franconia and Bohemia;

—nor any doctor;

—nor a person who is unfaithful to wife or husband;

—not to undertake any treatment in cases where Nature fails;

—to consider beneath my dignity a person who cheats me out of my fee;

—to treat men of all sects, but no renegade;

—to help women in childbed myself." [4]

The last point is interesting for three reasons. Despite his admiration of "folk medicine," Paracelsus did not trust midwives. He himself performed deliveries though doctors degraded themselves when they did such work. Finally, he had a higher opinion of women than Luther and other contemporaries who accorded little value to a woman's life.

Paracelsus neglected to set down that he would treat the poor without fee, since that was a matter of course for him. He held the human aspect of the medical reform constantly before the public eye. He chastised doctors who did not have the call, even more those who refused to learn from experience, and most of all those who practiced for money only. That was not all, however. He wished to open the medical guild to all who did have the call, and he assailed the caste privileges of doctors as a handicap to the practice of medicine.

OF THE PEOPLE, FOR THE PEOPLE,
BY THE PEOPLE

With somnambulistic lucidity Paracelsus linked his ideas on virtue and nature with his struggle for the recognition of the unlearned physician and of folkloristic medicine. Religion, nature, and humanism, he thought, were on the side of the people, and he almost conducted his campaign for his new medicine as a class war.

"God is the teacher of medicine. Therefore, the doctor shall have his faith from the people. Then he will be in good standing with God, too. From you to God, from the people to you, God wants everybody to live in truth." [5]

Convinced that science must learn from the people and work for the people, he wrote in the vernacular. Luther gave the Germans a language which they could use in prayer without the intervention of the priest. Brunswick, Fries,[6] and Paracelsus tried to make learning independent of Latin. By using the vernacular, Paracelsus sided with the people against the élite:

"I here propose to explain philosophy, firstly as an introduction to medicine; and I am doing so in German in order to take away any snobbishness and to bring science to the common people. Philosophy shall be taught so that she reveals man in his entirety." [7]

Erasmus and other humanists had tried to raise the common man to the refinement of Latinism. Paracelsus and Fries went the opposite way. They tried to raise the language of the common man to the dignity of a literary and scientific medium. Doctors and philosophers obviously had to talk in the language of the people if they wished to be understood. In this, unfortunately, they exposed themselves to misunderstandings. Again Paracelsus was in bad company, this time with the nationalistic movement which also started in this age of confusion.

A new national pride and independence had begun to dissolve the unity of medieval Christianity. Nations liberated their policies, their Church, and their thinking from Rome. National sovereigns established well-integrated states wherein a loyal and patriotic middle class might find opportunity and satisfaction. The small circle of humanists, in this respect the last pillar of medieval universalism, proved helpless against the growing tide of nationalism. The burghers and the common people had no use for an internationalism restricted to the "republic of the scholars." The national state, on the contrary, aligned them with the government against the privileged minority. In Germany, moreover, capitalism was identified with the "foreign" (Roman) law. German simplicity was advocated as against foreign luxuries. German students envied Italian preeminence in culture, and German doctors received lower fees than foreigners. A nationalistic reaction against the monopoly of Galen and Avicenna was in order.

Paracelsus, too, was conscious of his German birth. He recommended home-grown plants as remedies (of course, the signatures indicated them); and occasionally he burst forth in resentment against foreign doctors and foreign doctrines. As a German, Paracelsus desired equality of opportunity with the favored foreigners.

PATRIOTISM

Love of his country fused with Paracelsus' theory of the microcosm when he taught that a German patient needs a German doctor and home-grown remedies. In one of his dedications, he explained that each climate brings forth distinct qualities which promote communication between the doctor, the disease, and the sick. "What good is Avicenna to a Greek, what can Savonarola do for a German?" he asked. Each nation makes its people, and each people has its own character of which it can be proud.

Fries was convinced that "our language is an aboriginal language which does not have to go begging from the Greek and Romans, like French." Both he and Paracelsus regarded themselves as competitors and challengers of the "Welsh" doctors, *i.e.*, the Italian and the French "arch enemies." Fries boasted of a successful cataract operation through which he had outclassed an Italian. Paracelsus complained that the Welsh had usurped the whole "Monarchy" with their erroneous doctrines; and once he complained that they laughed at his medicine "because I am a German."

German biographers have made the most of such patriotic outbursts. But his contemporaries knew better, and his enemies understood that, in using the vernacular, he was identifying himself with the people, not as a nation but as a class. They scorned his "teaching in a language spoken by the teamsters on the road, the merchants on the market place, and the maids at the well." They were right in suspecting that Paracelsus was teaching the common man self-respect. "Shall I be despised because I write for the common man? I should be praised for my endeavors. But while you try to throw me down, you are throwing down the patient." [8]

In recent years, Nazi authors repeatedly tried to assimilate Paracelsus into their philosophy. Nothing could have been more ridiculous.[9] To balance an occasional anti-Semitic remark of his, there are passages in which he defends the Jews. He denied the allegation that they had brought syphilis to Europe. Of course, he wrote as violently against the Jewish doctors as against Galen and Avicenna; but "the baptized Jews are worse *Bescheisser* than the circumcised," he said in his dedication to Klauser. Moreover, he adopted the Jewish Cabbala as a major source of inspiration.

Curiously, scholars always lend their own color-blindness to the great men whom they admire. Paracelsus has not escaped this fate. The Austrian Strunz, otherwise an eminent student of medieval science, has claimed him for "Austriandom," and the Swiss school has indulged all the follies of nationalism—perhaps a more pardonable sin in a small country which has given the world a few very great men. Paracelsus himself certainly was not interested in any sectarianism, least of all nationalism. His references to his nation never exceed three lines —he who wrote lengthy chapters on anything that stirred his interest.

Nor can the indirect claims on his "German soul" be recognized as valid. It is true that for the last hundred years Teutonic, romantic-nationalistic, and reactionary movements have made him their pet hero, and his mysticism and obscure language easily lend themselves to such misinterpretations, particularly by writers who have little knowledge of medieval literature. We hope to have shown that these seemingly romantic and mystic passages have their legitimate place in the Renaissance movement. Far from being uniquely Paracelsian, the most-quoted Paracelsianisms are, rather, typical of his time.

CHAPTER 19

The Matter of Life

THE FIRST STEPS
OF PHYSIOLOGY

> *God has made everything out
> of nothing. But Man He made
> out of everything.*
>
> PARACELSUS

The unfavorable decision of the Nuremberg Council had produced the *Paragranum*. What next? Paracelsus was as isolated, destitute and helpless as ever. He turned to St. Gall where his old friend and teacher, Vadianus (page 31), was acting mayor during the fatal illness of Christian Studer. Vadianus was an eminent scholar and a personal friend of the Swiss reformer, Ulrich Zwingli. As a humanist, he condemned all sectarianism, gave asylum to refugees from persecution, and shielded the local Anabaptists. He referred the ailing mayor,

his patient, to Paracelsus and thus provided him both employment and a refuge.

In Studer's house Paracelsus met his patient's brother-in-law,
Bartholomew Schobinger, who was interested in chemistry. The
two set up a chemical kitchen in the library of a monastery
secularized by the Evangelical party. There, Paracelsus "worked
day and night, writing the first of my Paramiric essays and
teaching medicine to students." [1] It was another of his inter-
ludes of hectic work and blissful sense of power. An observer
who noted all the familiar traits did not mention drinking: "He
is very industrious and rarely sleeps; he never undresses, throws
himself on his bed with boots and spurs, rests for three hours,
then gets up and continues to write." [2]

MAGUS VS. SCIENTIST AND HUMANIST

Once more Paracelsus thought the world was open to him. In
closing the *Opus Paramirum* he defied the "Aristotelian crowd"
and boasted that his medicine was "strange, new, amazing,
unheard of." From the dedication to Vadianus—dated St.
Gall, 1530—we quote:

> "That I may behold such a decision in thee and may not
> spend my time in St. Gall in vain, I feel bound to arouse
> thy interest in the knowledge of nature, that we may both be
> remembered amongst the many who practice medicine. For
> thou art a supporter of medicine and by no means the least,
> and thou wilt discover, in accepting the truth, many things
> which concern the eternal."

Between the lines, one hears echoes of discussions between the
humanist and the naturalist. Obviously, in reply to Vadianus'
praise of the humanities and of the Gospel, Paracelsus asserts
that science says "many things about the eternal." He was still

sure that science would liberate humanity and lead her to the sources of eternal life—for, in medieval fashion, he agreed with his noble interlocutor on one point: possession of the Truth is tantamount to possession of Eternity.

His sober associate Schobinger took alarm at Paracelsus' soaring ideas. In a letter to a third person he voiced his criticism:

"I am glad you are not taken in by alchemy. That is very right, for this art has turned the heads of many rich and great people until this day, and has brought evil to many. But [I am glad that] you indicate your interest in the useful and merry art of distillation which with heat and fire can separate and extract from any matter the *Quinta Essentia,* the subtlest substance and strongest power. This and other works which help men preserve their health and cure sick ones with certain medicines, that is the true art which God has given his beloved.

"When Theophrastus whom you know well lived in the house of my brother-in-law for twenty-seven weeks, he had a great number of such books with him, part of which he surely did not understand himself. The teacher from whom he had learned the art deceived him in many ways. Partly he withheld the truth from him and the other part, which he taught him, he did not make clear enough. So I often found, while he was working with me, that certain things he wrote he did not understand. And that is the reason why the books and recipes he left cannot be of much use to most students. Also, many books have been printed under his name which Theophrastus never saw or made. I know his style well. . . ." [3]

These three personalities, Vadianus, Schobinger, and Paracelsus, epitomize three paths on which sixteenth-century man reached out beyond his allotted place in the medieval universe. The humanist and reformer staked out a field in which the human mind was free, and found a direct way from the individual to the Eternal. The research chemist conquered the world around him by learning more about it and using the knowledge. The scientist-philosopher (who still thought of himself as *magus*) sought possession of the principles which govern the universe.

Schobinger probably was right. The confusion which prevails in Paracelsus' chemical speculations compares unfavorably with the sober formulas of such writers on distillation as Brunswick and Agricola. But, on the other hand, Schobinger had no grasp of the gigantic project Paracelsus was pursuing. In the *Paramiric Essays* he strove at nothing less than a bio-chemical theory of physiology. The haziness of his details came from his visionary obsession with general principles. He strove to bring the mass of undigested data into an orderly, scientific system. "This will purge, that will constipate," he scoffed at the empirical and eclectical knowledge of his contemporaries. There must be, he was sure, one underlying principle which governed all actions of nature. His error, so to say, was due to far-sightedness. Leaping from the world-conquering enthusiasm of the adepts directly into the single-purpose ideas of modern system-builders, he strove for a functional theory of the universe, and in it, a medical anthropology based on the chemical knowledge of his age.

THE THREE SUBSTANCES

The *Volumen Paramirum* (page 133) had formulated the broad principles on which Paracelsus intended to establish his new medicine. Numerous lectures, essays and books implemented the outline with details. Four of these treatises, although composed four years later at Beratzhausen and St. Gall, are so clearly an expansion of the *Volumen Paramirum* that the author referred to them as the *Paramiric Essays* and bound them together in a

book which has received the title *Opus Paramirum*. The preface
provides a clue to the strange title which has baffled commenta-
tors: "Since nothing can be known without knowledge of the
origin and of that which has been ordained, it is proper and
fitting to describe the work *Paramirum*."

The prefix Para-, which Paracelsus also used in his name,
means beyond, besides, or above; mirum apparently is the
Latin word for wonder. The *Opus* (or Work) *Paramirum*,
therefore, may be described as probing beneath the surface,
explaining the wonders, going back to the sources, as was the
program of humanism. An alternative interpretation may be
"the ground of medicine," since Paracelsus repeatedly used this
expression in the *Paragranum*.

To lay down the foundations of medicine, indeed, was the
program of the *Essays*. *Volumen Paramirum* had left open the
question: What causes a tree to decay? The first treatise of *Opus
Paramirum* gave the answer: The growth and decay of matter.
Not the stars, not the humors, but the material which pervades
the whole creation.

Paracelsus did not know our elements. Alchemists before him
had distinguished two basic substances: sulfur (spirits) and mercury (liquids). He added a third: salt (the ashes). All bodies,
he taught, are composed of three substances—sulfur, mercury,
and salt, where

Sulfur represents the gaseous and combustible elements, also
  the forces of the soul, or the principle of energy;
Mercury represents the fluid elements, also the forces of the
  intellect;
Salt stands for the solid elements, also for the principle of
  matter. (See Appendix D.)

Through these three "substances" man partakes in the great
metabolism of nature. Their properties determine his health

and his diseases. If the mercury in him "volatilizes," he may lose his mind, but the mercury can be "fixated" with potable gold. If the salt "sublimates" in the body, it corrodes the organism and causes pain; but strong solvents can flush the salt away. Boldly, Paracelsus asserted that "all diseases can be traced to a coagulation of undigested matter in the bowels." [4] Through the processes of putrefaction and construction, the three substances build up and break down the body. The two functions are inseparable. Just as putrefaction generates vermin (as was then thought) and plant life, so, vice versa, "that which prevents putrefaction also will prevent health." [5] This is the law of organic matter, and to Paracelsus everything was organic. The doctor only has to follow Nature in order to help her cure the disease. "The doctors conceal their ignorance by saying: Such a disease is incurable. They only expose their own folly. God has permitted no disease whose cure He has not provided, too." [6]

The *Paramirum* preached the gospel of medical optimism. In three instances it showed ways to heal diseases which had been held incurable: the "tartaric" diseases, the "invisible" diseases, and women's diseases.

GOUT

To demonstrate the superiority of his views, Paracelsus had to explain his cures in a field where the Galenic doctors acknowledged failure. As a test case, he selected a widespread plague of the Middle Ages, which he considered as a typical case of faulty metabolism: the "tartaric" diseases, *i.e.*, arthritis and similar ailments, which the heavy diet of the Middle Ages brought to an early climax.

Medieval poets describing a hero in his old age usually picture him as a victim of gout. That and related diseases were considered part of the aging process and hence incurable.

Paracelsus took the opposite view. On his epitaph he put the claim that "among other incurable diseases, he was able to cure such dire plagues as dropsy, leprosy, and podagra [gout] with marvelous art and skill." Even today, Paracelsian doctors maintain that arthritis and similar diseases can be cured unless they are in too advanced a state. Dr. Bernard Aschner, of the arthritis ward at the Stuyvesant Policlinic in New York, asserts that his cures are based on Paracelsus' description of "tartar" in the third *Paramiric Treatise*.[7]

Everyone knows what tartar is. The dentist removes it from the teeth. A similar substance is found in old wine casks. It is also found in the gravel and sand which patients eliminate painfully with their urine, and in gall and bladder stones. Paracelsus correctly maintained that this substance is an acid deposit, and that similar crystals, deposited in the joints, cause the pain known as podagra or gout. This substance "burns like hell, and Tartarus is hell"; therefore, he called it tartar, and treated under the name "tartaric diseases" all joint and hip diseases, such as rheumatism, arthritis, gout, stone, and neuralgic ailments such as lumbago and sciatica. "Doctors boast of their anatomy, . . . but they fail to see the tartar sticking to their own teeth." [8]

These deposits, according to Paracelsus, are food residues which the *Archeus* has failed to eliminate. Hence, treatment should be easy. All the doctor has to do is help the body get rid of these substances. They can be dissolved chemically by Rochelle salt (Paracelsus used potassium tartrate, "signed" by its name); they can be "mollified" with laurel oil and resin compounds "until they become soft as honey and the hardened joints can be stretched again and regain their former aspect." They can be attacked physically by strong elimination or by tonics and a healthy diet which makes the *Archeus* work harder. They might even be induced to leave the body by sympathetic magic; for instance, food that contained gravel might invite the stone to join it in elimination—a method which Paracelsus discarded after fruitless experimentation. Finally, Paracelsus suggested that the body be opened near the place of the pain, by creating a rash or a blister, because the pain indicates that "Nature wants an outlet at this spot, and if there is none, make one." French doctors still use a similar method, the *pointes de feu*. One thing, however, he tried to avoid: the dreaded "cutting for the stone." No torture instruments for his patients: Nature, with the help of her own arcana, was supposed to cure everything.

PIONEER OF GYNECOLOGY

Further probing into the vast possibilities which he saw opening up through this method, Paracelsus added to the *Opus Paramirum* two treatises on subjects never before treated in medical books—one on "invisible diseases" (to be discussed in the context of his pioneering work in the field of psychology), the other on gynecology.

"I am not embarrassed to be the first one who dares to write on the diseases of women," he announced defiantly.[9]

Doctors held it beneath their dignity to do the work of midwives. Paracelsus, who helped many a woman in childbed, braved the prejudices of his age to follow his professional conscience. One often wonders what is more to be admired: his scientific zeal or his humanity. It is not without point to mention here what Luther thought of the same subject: "If women die in childbed, that does no harm. It is what they were made for."

In the treatise on women's diseases Paracelsus took the view that women are created differently than men and that their diseases do not concern the "matrix" solely but produce syndromes unique in all respects. Again he decried the futility of trying to cure an isolated member, and he studied the body as a whole, with all its vital forces and according to its particular constitution, in action against the disease. Again the new viewpoint was gained by considering a living organism as a closed system, a cell, or a microcosmos. Again, the art of healing was described as subservience to nature, in contrast to the (allegedly Galenic) interference with nature. Repeatedly, in these Paramiric treatises, Paracelsus reiterated his charge that failure to follow nature was the cause of mistakes in treatment, and led to the prevailing cynicism in the medical guild.

"MUMIA," THE THING NATURAL

In the entire work of Paracelsus, no sentence is repeated as often as the old adage that "Nature heals, the doctor nurses." The *Paramiric Essays* also bear this message: that "Man is his own doctor," *i.e.*, the body takes care of itself and mobilizes the powers which fight the disease. A first application of this principle has been discussed in connection with Paracelsus' surgical practice (page 49). Here we find the same principle in a larger biological and physiological context.

The magic of weapon ointment had a rational foundation. The theory had been formulated by Hippocrates himself: "The forces of nature are the healers of disease." All the writings of Paracelsus are but a paraphrase of this insight and he never tired of repeating it: "Mumia cures all wounds; protect them from external enemies and they will be healed." [10]

Avoiding the knife, the iron, the suffocating smoke, the fasting cures and the weakening venesections, Paracelsus tried to make the *Archeus* work and to mobilize the "mumia": good food, exercise, and fresh air—then an almost revolutionary advice.[11]

The "mumia" of which Paracelsus speaks here is something very different from mummy powder. It is the inner balsam or life power inherent in the flesh. The same man who wrote hundreds of recipes starting with the words "take mumia," simultaneously thunders against all treatments which block this inner balsam.

> "The surgeon should not interfere with mumia's working; he must protect it. Flesh possesses an inner balsam which heals, and every limb has its own cure in it. . . . Wounds need nothing. The flesh grows outward from within, not inward from without." [12]

What is this mumia? Whenever Paracelsus introduces one of his fantastic terms, we have to look for a dyamic concept which he tried to substitute for the static model of medieval science, or for a "wholistic" conception which was to replace a "fragmentary" view. Which force of nature is mumia, we must ask; and which abstraction is it supposed to replace? "Mumia is the doctor. When it fails he is powerless and should not try to heal." [13]

Paracelsus believed that neither in disease nor in healing is the flesh acted upon from without. The disease is of the flesh and the remedy must come from the flesh, too. *The flesh is not a dead husk, animated by some spirit; it is life itself!*

Nor is flesh an exception in the universe. It lives as the macrocosmos lives, because it derives from the macrocosmos. All matter is creative and has an impulse toward perfection. The old biblical image of the Creator, molding the dead clay and then blowing life into some of it, does not fit the matter which Paracelsus imagined at the beginning of time. In his conception, original matter is endowed with an *entelechy*, a force driving it toward perfection. To emphasize this dynamism, he gave it one of those symbolic names which he was fond of inventing, *Iliaster*, a blend of *hyle* (Greek for matter) and *astrum* (Latin for star, constellation, or, in an expanded meaning, destiny). Iliaster is the constructive principle in matter, seeking creation. The destructive force he called *Cagaster* (*caco-astrum*)—evidence of the positive role he assigned to matter. Paracelsus has often been called a "spiritualist." In the light of the life-giving powers which he attributed to matter, he might just as well be called a naturalist. His materialism, however, was not mechanical but biological: "In all matter we find one [type of] man only. He was extracted from the limbo by the Iliaster and is the Protoplastus." [14]

This new principle of the *Protoplastus* rules man biologically. This one of his powerful word inventions has endured. Protoplasm remains the name for the cell material which is the basis of all life and the carrier of heredity.

FORCES OF NATURE

The mumia, the Iliaster, the Arcanum, the Protoplastus, and the other agents in the great drama of nature are neither entirely matter nor spirit. They might best be described as principles or as forces of nature. "Arcanum is not a virtue but *vis* (force), *potentia* (power) rather than virtue." [15]

Scientists had not yet formulated any law of nature. Galileo and Kepler introduced the concept of such laws after Paracelsus' death. For centuries afterward, more phenomena of nature were explained by "forces" than expressed in "laws," in the modern sense. Paracelsus beheld these forces everywhere. They were the *archei* of biology and cosmology which created all the marvels of nature; they were the five "*entia*" which produce diseases; they were the principles of alchemy which perfected the imperfect. Such concepts liberated science from superstitious belief in demons on the one hand, and from magic-astrological preconceptions of a world harmony on the other hand.

Henceforth, *the forces of nature were to rule sovereign in the universe, visible as well as invisible.* No exception is admissible, and anything that is true of the corporeal world must be true of the "sidereal" world, too. "If the visible body can make itself a harness, why may not the invisible body do likewise?"[16] Natural processes, therefore, can be formulated either in terms of "substances" or in terms of "principles"; just as, today, light can be interpreted either in terms of the wave theory or the corpuscle theory. Paracelsus, therefore, was not afraid of using the astrological and spiritualistic terms. To him, they meant "forces of nature" as much as substances did.

This postulate of Paracelsus' method has been understood neither by his occultistic admirers nor by his pseudo-materialistic critics. The message of the *Paramiric Treatises* is precisely that *nothing is "occult" to the scientist,* because through studies "everything occult shall become apparent."[17] Despite fantastic flights into the realm of spiritualism, despite the astrological language and the superstitious references to the "invisible body," the book clearly was written to put Nature on her own feet and to show the omnipresence of material principles.

It does not matter whether the so-called spiritual phenomena are likened to the so-called material ones or vice versa. In Paracelsus' naturalistic method the point to grasp is that both aspects are basically identical.

"With us, it is not spirit but nature. If the herb cures a man, then the herb was not a spirit but a body. This is its virtue. If a doctor cures a patient by his words [through hypnosis?— H.P.], then he is of nature and so is his word. Not the man healed him, but *God by the force of Nature,* . . . Nature has within her visible and invisible forces, visible bodies and invisible, and *all are bodies and are natural.*"[18]

Today the biological concept which assumes a special life power, distinct from physical and chemical laws, is called *vitalism*. This philosophy, with its slightly spiritualistic leanings, was taken up early in the present century, in reaction to the mechanical materialism of the nineteenth century. The vitalism of Paracelsus, on the contrary, had a materialistic base and was in reaction to the mechanical spiritualism of the Middle Ages.

Polemizing against a famed textbook writer, whom he accused of forgetting the "virtues," he emphasized his dynamic view:

> "Macer omits Process, which is as important as Properties. Can he know virtue unless he understands Process?" [19]

With his concept of "forces of Nature," Paracelsus achieved three aims:

> *He made Nature the all-pervading and omnipresent foundation of all science.*
>
> *He liquefied the mechanical model of organic processes, to account for the dynamics of the living cell.*
>
> *He brought human biology into the fold of general biology.*

This included even the psychological factors, which another *Paramiric Treatise* also tried to make comprehensible through the three substances:

"Here I conclude the fourth book of the invisible diseases. You have seen how natural bodies, *through their own natural forces*, cause many things [called] miraculous among the vulgar. Many have interpreted these effects as the works of Saints; others have ascribed them to the Devil; one has called them sorcery, others witchcraft, and all have entertained superstitious beliefs and paganism. I have shown what to think of all that." [20].

CHAPTER 20

The Copernican Turn

INDIVIDUAL AND COSMOS

> *Life is short, art is long; occasion is volatile; experiment is fallacious; judgment is difficult. It is not enough for us to do what we can do; the patient and his environment, and external conditions have to contribute to achieve the cure.*
>
> HIPPOCRATES

> *Dicit Hippocrates vita brevis, Theophratus vita longa. Dico natura naturam curat; Hippocrates, virtus curat morbum.*
>
> PARACELSUS

The age of science is usually dated from the beginning of critical research, just as we date the new age in arts from the appearance of realistic detail in painting and sculpture. In fact, the mass of new data and the increase of factual knowledge were the most impressive achievement of the modern development. However, this was not the cause of the new approach but its consequence. Science is not defined by the data which are its result but by the method through which these results are obtained. In commenting on the first aphorism of Hippocrates, which is the motto of this chapter, Paracelsus said:

> "In the time of Hippocrates, experimental medicine was not yet developed; medicine was used haphazardly. It helped one but injured the other. Therefore, the experiment has been called fallacious. The reason is that knowledge was not in agreement with nature. Doctors did like the smallpox doctor: try any unguent. They did not have any theory yet, but only experience: this will purge, that will constipate. But what it is that purges, and how it purges, remained occult. Therefore they injured one patient for each they cured. *But now we have a theory, and therefore science is progressing and experiment no longer is deceptive.*" [1]

Now we have a theory! Paracelsus' Basle lectures had outlined a broad program of anthropological and biological assumptions. In his treatises on syphilis and on tartarus, he had exemplified some applications of his system. The missing link was physiology. The first of the Paramiric essays was to provide it. Its title, *On the Causes of Disease from the Three Substances, Sulfur, Mercury, and Salt*, indicated its purpose and tendency: it presented the biochemical approach to physiology and etiology. It explained life, health, and disease in terms of material forces of nature. A preliminary review of this and other Paramiric essays has been given. Now the *Opus Paramirum* will be discussed under a different aspect, its contribution to the philosophical struggle of the age.

In the naturalistic theory of Paracelsus, [2] the Macrocosmos became the "*matrix*," the "great *mysterium*," or the "*limbo*"— activated primal matter. [3] Always a great one for dotting his i's, Paracelsus explained that "for the maggots the cheese is the great mysterium." [4] The "three substances" were all-pervading forces of nature which governed the human body as well as all animal bodies and inanimate matter. *All nature was one, comprehensible through a single theory.*

This insight was new and truly amazing, as Paracelsus claimed in the preface to his *Paramirum.* In fact, it was as new as the Copernican hypothesis of the celestial revolutions, and on closer inspection a certain parallelism between the two theories may be found. Incidentally, just as Paracelsus was stimulated by his speculations on microcosmos and macrocosmos, so Copernicus was led to his great innovation by his craving for a more harmonious order of the universe. Though his mathematical method was infinitely more scientific than Paracelsus' chemical experiments, their respective theories were similar not only in boldness but in their impact on philosophy.

BIOLOGY VS. ASTROLOGY

Great as it was, the Copernican theory, published one year after Paracelsus' death, could not at once overthrow a cosmology as deeply rooted in the habits of thought and in religion as the Ptolemaic system. His startling idea met with as much opposition then as, some three centuries later, the Darwinian hypothesis met with—and for the same reason. People felt that such a theory did not concern professional philosophers and scientists alone. Man's place in the Universe was at stake. The privileged position of the earth implied the privileged position of men, God's children created in His image, possessing the powers of intellect and the gift of the soul through which they communicate with the Eternal. If Man no longer occupied the center of the Universe, he was neither the central Microcosmos nor the crown of creation. Such a radically new conception of man and cosmos obviously would not be accepted had not naïve conceptions of the unique place of Man already been shaken. Other scientific, philosophical, and theological developments must have weakened the astrological world view. Man must have been prepared to find himself at the periphery, instead of the center of the universe. In the field of biology, the naturalistic method of Paracelsus had achieved this revolution by putting man on an even footing with animals.

Medieval medicine had set man apart from the rest of the creation. Cows might fall sick, but they had no humors; nor, for that matter, were they related to the stars through the mysterious bonds of astrology, as human beings were. On the other hand, while the human race as a whole was considered lord of creation, the individual human being was strangely short of being "constituted." Each of his members was governed by a different sign of the zodiac. Each of his character traits was directed by an ascendent and planet which he shared with many other individuals. Like the Sleeping Beauty, the epic hero of the Middle Ages seemed to have received each of his likable or uncouth qualities from a different fairy. Moreover, a demon might seize his soul and change his whole personality. Character traits were not understood as the outflow of an integrated personality, but the personality as an assemblage of disconnected adventures and character traits. In most narratives the hero simply "represented" one general virtue or quality. Paradoxically, the higher men valued themselves as a species, the less were they conscious of themselves as moral and biological individuals.

Paracelsus reversed the whole picture. As a bio-chemist, he asserted that man is made out of the same material as the rest of the creation, feeds on the substances which make up the universe, and is subject to the laws which govern their growth and decay. At the same time, each living being is unique, individually constituted, and follows his own destiny.

Like the faces of a coin, the two phases of this shift are inseparable. Not until the species had been removed from the status of God's pet could the individual elevate himself above Nature. The biological revolution which the Paramiric treatises achieved, therefore, was part of the great Renaissance movement which gave to Nature that which belongs to Nature, and thereby freed the individual for new adventures in different realms. Like the revolution of Copernicus, it reversed the relation between macrocosmos and microcosmos. An alliance of Humanism, Science, and mystic religion helped to create the modern concept of personality.

The naturalistic approach to biology was particularly fertile when it led to material assumptions about cause and effect. Astrology could explain the influences of the stars only through analogies. Paracelsus could think of realistic causes—radiation, poisonous exhalations, and "attraction." Speaking of lunatics, he conceded that the Moon is responsible for their disease, "but not by entering into a person; it rather operates through attraction, as the Sun draws humidity from the earth." [5] That was a rational, though mistaken, theory. It assumed the operation of a law of nature and did not presuppose the privileged position of man in the center of the universe.

Biology, on the other hand, entertained the notion that the forces of nature were independent of a divine world plan. The biological approach implied the idea, which Paracelsus formally stated, that each separate body must be studied as a constituted unit, "built of the three substances;" not an assemblage of properties from the firmament, but "mightily constituted in itself."

MYSTICISM DE-MYSTIFIED

The contribution to biological thinking, in Paracelsus' work, should now be clear. He conceived Nature as a self-consistent, self-constituted whole, governed by all-pervading laws which apply to the human body as they apply to inanimate nature. The same substances have built up the universe and man in it. No creature occupies a hierarchic place in the universe. The relations between the parts of the universe are those of cause and effect, things acting and things acted upon.

But this left a problem. All creatures are built out of the same substances; yet each is an individual. The riddle of microcosmos and macrocosmos recurred. Nearly a hundred years earlier, Nicholas de Cusa had tried to formulate similar ideas. He was counted among the mystics because he was unable to solve the riddle of the "coincidence of the opposites." He went as far as to say that "the above" is not distinguished from "the below," and thus made a first step in the direction of Copernicus. Eventually he acknowledged that the problem seemed insoluble and confessed himself in a state of "learned ignorance."

The generation of Paracelsus was bolder. It attacked the same problem from the angle of experimental science. It discovered the individual; it found the same life force in all organisms; it approached the concept of laws of nature. Still the problem remained baffling. Paracelsus, too, sounds difficult, mystical, and "deep" when he tries to disentangle the individual from the cosmos. He never managed to express his problem clearly. For want of a more adequate scientific language, Paracelsus had to state it in the astrological terms of microcosmos and macrocosmos: alike in the constituent elements, similar in their structure, differentiated and opposed in their reciprocal interaction. Or from another angle: in acting upon each other, they are subject to identical laws of nature.

All these shortcomings, however, cannot minimize the boldness of the task Paracelsus had undertaken. To appreciate the audacity of the new thought, one need only look back to St. Thomas Aquinas. He still thought God might change the world any day, or interfere with its course at His pleasure, with only one restriction: God, too, had to comply with the rules of Aristotelian logic. He might make an ass with three tails, but He could not make a triangle with four angles.

The geographical and anatomical discoveries of the Renaissance hardly required any further constitutional curbs on God's wisdom. Copernican astronomy and Paracelsian biology, however, implied a new scientific attitude which called for a new set of laws, which even God had chosen to obey. He had given Nature a Constitution, the laws of nature, with which nobody can interfere. If He wanted to make a donkey with two tails, He first had to instruct the Protoplastus accordingly. The magus, consequently, can predict God from the laws of nature. "I under Him as far as His realm goes, but He under me in my realm." [6]

CHAPTER 21

Power, Freaks, and Frailties of Mind

A COMPASSIONATE SCIENCE

The miracles of the soul are greater than those of heaven.

KEPLER

During his sojourn at St. Gall and on his subsequent wanderings through the German cantons of Switzerland, through Bohemia and Moravia, and in southern Germany, Paracelsus maintained contact with the sorry remnants of the avant-garde of the Reformation. Political failure isolated the Anabaptist fraternities, and the splinter sects sought any means to escape the dire consequences of defeat. Their political leaders were dead, their spiritual directors disheartened or in hiding. The ignorant and ecstatic rank and file fell an easy prey to adventurers, criminals, impostors, neurotics, religious fanatics. Strange practices and mental aberrations took the place of religious services. Mass hysteria, sexual exhibitionism, prophecies, St. Vitus' dance seized upon the simple-minded standard-bearers of the millennium. It was a collective nervous breakdown.

[Some healthier fraternities found asylum among the Hussites in Moravia. There they settled in communist villages and devoted themselves to the Apostolic life which they had been unable to impose on the world at large. In the eighteenth century they became the nucleus of pietism. Some emigrated to America and founded Bethlehem, in Pennsylvania, now the center of the Moravian Church.]

As a companion of theirs, Paracelsus knew the frustrations and sufferings of these simple people who had met with bloody persecution instead of the expected millennial bliss. He knew that their aberrations came from emotional crises and excessive piety, not from devils who possessed their souls. In contrast to his contemporaries, he did not despise or berate them, but lent an understanding doctor's ear to their delusions.

He explained that they were unstable personalities, sometimes at the grip of their instincts, at other times seized by the spirit of God. Because they were emotionally unstable, he argued, others had no right to judge them. Psychic disease is a malady calling for treatment not condemnation—a truth psychiatrists today have still to teach the lay public.

"Though the prophets often are ridiculed because of their simplicity, they are closer to God nevertheless. . . . Our mockery of the fools will be turned against us on the Day of Judgment, and we should not call our brothers fools, because we do not know what is in ourselves. . . . Who shall be lame after death? None. Therefore, none should be called a fool, because nature alone failed." [1]

Rarely before had such words been spoken about the mentally handicapped. (Again the exception is Agrippa of Nettesheim.) Paracelsus did not exclude the mentally ill from his love of humanity. He applied his great power of sympathy and love to an understanding of mental derangement.

THE DESCRIPTIVE METHOD

A great scientific achievement was the reward of this new attitude toward mental patients. It enabled Paracelsus to give clinical account of mental diseases in complete objectivity, detached from moral and religious prejudices. *The descriptive method, which began with him, liberated psychology from the tutelage of theology.*

In Huser's edition of Paracelsus' works and in the edition of Strunz, the treatise on *Invisible Diseases*, written in St. Gall, follows the *Opus Paramirum* as though it were a part of it. Indeed, it continues and rounds out the series of essays which expound the naturalistic method and refute the spiritualistic doctrines of the age. It is Paracelsus' most pagan and materialistic book, and polemizes forcefully against a number of superstitions shared by the multitude, such as wound spells, love potions, curses, and various nostrums against pain. However, he also refuted superstitions which the Church encouraged, particularly the belief in demons, in sacraments of all denominations and sects, relics, ceremonies and saints. He declared that St. Veltlin, St. Kuris, and St. Anthony had no power over the diseases which were associated with them. He even averred that such beliefs were "older than the Christian faith." He traced curses and faith healing back to the ancient Egyptians, and gave Aesculapius and Machaon, the ancient alchemist, credit for the return of medicine to "Nature." Invisible diseases are natural, too.

Similar views were held by other reformers. Paracelsus' origi-
nality lay in his presentation. He analyzes the believers rather
than their beliefs. He is concerned not that erroneous opinions
have gained currency, but that people are so sick as to hold
such opinions; or worse, that they think superstitious practices
have restored their health whereas in truth their illness continues. He warns them repeatedly not to trust their imagination. Pointing to the Anabaptists and explaining the consequences
of succumbing to the incubi, he emphasizes the dangerous
power that resides in "Faith." (The German word *Glaube* here
comes in handy; it means both faith and imagination.) "Faith
may work both ways," he says in the Preface; "with the good it
produces good works, but it leads the evil to evil works." Superstition may make people either sick or healthy.

THE POWERS OF MIND

A disciple of Trithemius and Agrippa, and explorer of the
Orient, Theophrastus always respected the powers of mind.
Now in close contact with fellow-sufferers, he studied spiritual
energy in action. Here is his first-hand description of trance:

"The soul, in an ecstatic state, is self-centered. The person
is blind and deaf. His nose does not smell anything, his hands
feel nothing. Though he can see, he does not know what he
sees. He may hear people talk but does not understand the
words. He may grasp for something but is unconscious of
what he holds in his hands. Such a person seems to be deprived of his senses and the world thinks he is an accomplished fool. In reality he is the wisest man before God,
who lets him know His secrets better than all the wise men
in the world." [2]

He observed that in their madness these patients were capable of supernormal bodily exertion. He saw them dance for days and nights without rest. He saw them laugh for hours and writhe in convulsions. He saw them drop with exhaustion and become deathly rigid, then rise, restored to their full faculties. These astonishing experiences intrigued him, as a scientist and as a human being. And as doctor he saw the practical possibilities which such powers offer to medicine:

"If we are firm in the art of meditation, we shall be like Apostles. We shall not fear death, prison, martyrdom, pain, poverty, toil, hunger. We shall be able to drive out the Devil, heal the sick, revive the dead, move mountains. The practice of the art is based on speculation and meditation." [3]

Paracelsus was awed by the power of *Glaube*. If people could "die in their own way as they proposed to die of their own accord," [4] then, could they not will their cure, too? Again and again he returned to the fascinating idea, investigating it from all sides. "Faith carves images of saints and idols of the mind for us and makes spiritual powers out of them." [5]

His research in this field went back to the days of the "Five Entia." But at that time he was mostly interested in the phenomena of witchcraft. Even then, he tried to explain that a sorcerer cannot cast a spell on a limb unless he gains possession over the mind of his victim.[6] That ruled out two popular theories, (a) that sorcerers operate directly on matter through their will, through the cast of their eye, the pronouncement of a word or some ceremony, (b) that demons can be invoked to do so.

Some might scoff that Paracelsus' approach was still a futile attempt to explain the nonexistent. What matters, however, is the discovery of a most important principle, which became fertile when he applied it to a real problem. Indeed, in St. Gall he found that "nobody can be cured by faith unless the disease was imaginary in the first place." For "imaginary," of course, we would say psychogenic today. Paracelsus was no faith healer, and even in his most absurd magical practices he never forgot that: "It is not the curse or the blessing that works, but the idea. The imagination produces the effect." [7]

He used waxen images to concentrate the patient's mind on the disease, or to persuade a schizophrenic that the sick part of his personality could be destroyed by fire. Everything was done to strengthen the patient's will to recover and his confidence in the doctor's ability to help him. He went so far as to assert that "without faith in our ability to walk, we could not walk." Such insights helped him in his therapeutic practice. With the paralyzed girl in Ingolstadt whose dramatic recovery we have reported earlier, Paracelsus may have used suggestion, possibly even hypnosis.

He also made an experiment "on several persons, and found them willing to concede that I was right." He asked them what they wished to dream, and by artful suggestions evoked the desired hallucinations.

"If this person believes in what I say, he will be sure that it will come true, and see it before his imagination. If he goes to bed with this idea strongly entrenched in his mind, he will experience exactly what I told him." [8]

EXEUNT THE DEMONS

It remained for modern psychoanalysis to make proverbs, slips of the tongue, myths, and dreams subjects of psychological research. Paracelsus, four hundred years earlier, observed that "as we desire things in our hearts, so they appear to us in dreams." [9] Many other instances can be cited where Paracelsus, be it in a flash of inspiration or as the culmination of systematic thought, anticipated modern ideas. We already have mentioned his almost Freudian explanation of nightmares (Chapter 6). His conjectures on the origin of incubi and succubae may have been meaningless; but the psychological insight which they contain has few parallels in the sixteenth century. He was not content with the current explanation of the little monsters as products of the imagination; he traced them to specific sexual, somatically conditioned fantasies.

One qualification, however, is necessary. Today, anyone who admits that hobgoblins have their origin in our imagination will draw the obvious conclusion that they do not exist. It was not so obvious in the sixteenth century. Paracelsus could not question their existence. They plagued his patients. Trustworthy people reported that they had seen them with their own eyes. There was no point in denying that they were a psychological reality, just as saints were a religious reality. But he parted company with his predecessors on a subtle point which is of the greatest importance in the history of psychology. The infamous *Witches' Hammer*, written by the inquisitor of Salzburg, Jacob Sprenger S.J. (c. 1485), sets out to refute writers

> "who deny that there is such a thing as witchcraft and assert that it is purely imaginary. They do not believe that devils exist except in the imagination of the ignorant and vulgar. . . . But this is contrary to our faith." [10]

Even more than philosophy, indeed, psychology was then the handmaiden of theology. Mental disease was treated as sin, since both were held to be caused by demons. The logical prescription was a spell to exorcize the devils. No writer before the beginning of the sixteenth century suggested any other approach.

Paracelsus declared that the explanation, "The Devil does it," is meaningless.[11] Just as he denied that devils have any influence on the diseases of the body, so he rejected "the doctrine of the black-coats," that mental diseases are due to "ghostly beings and threefold spirits." For

> "Nature proves that such statements by earthly gods are quite incorrect and, as we shall explain in this volume, that nature is the sole origin of all diseases." [12]

Demons and witchcraft exist but neither is the cause of mental diseases, except when a sorcerer uses a force of nature to produce the disease. Treatment, therefore, must be applied to the mind. "*Psychologica psychologice*" is the first maxim of any psychiatric clinic. "You should not use a medical treatment as for ordinary diseases; but you have to treat the spirit." [13]

Formulating theories which defied the Church, liberating psychology from the tutelage of theology, denying that saints or demons were responsible for either health or disease, Paracelsus took a place beside Hippocrates in the Hall of Science. *As the father of medicine had proved that epilepsy was not a "sacred disease," so his disciple demonstrated that "St. Vitus' dance" was as natural a disease as any other.*

PIONEER OF PSYCHIATRY

The name which Paracelsus proposed for the disease known as St. Vitus' dance was "*chorea lasciva*," implying a sexual origin. He described this and epilepsy, mania, hysteria, and other mental diseases so clearly, indeed, that today we can follow his clinical experience and form an opinion of the changes which the symptoms have undergone in time. As a surgeon, Paracelsus was particularly interested in the manifestations now called conversion symptoms. He was not misled by them. Although he

prescribed balms, blisters, sedatives, anesthetics, and other med-
ication, he insisted that the "center of the disease" must be
found. If the origin of the disease is psychological, the body
will not be cured before the mind gets well.

We can distinguish three periods in the development of
his psychological insight. The chapter on the *"Ens Spirituale,"*
in the *Volumen Paramirum*, though sparkling with shrewd remarks, is the crudest statement of the theory. He assumed a
parallelism between the body and the "spirit," so that a wound
inflicted on the spirit produces suffering in the body; but, significantly enough, he already made this qualification: "Somatic
diseases are created by the spirit in such a manner that they
have physical effects in agreement with their nature." [14]

The book on *Diseases Which Deprive Man of His Reason*,
written in 1528, is dominated by the chemical ideas which pre-
occupied Paracelsus at that time. Epilepsy (the falling sickness) is explained by the rising of overheated *spiritus vitae* into
the head, leaving a cavity in the body which causes the "caving
in," much in the way one may explain an earthquake. As a
"spiritual" remedy, Paracelsus recommended vitriol and cam-
phor, mixed with opiates, mandrake, quintessence of gold, and
other substances; in conformity with the alchemical concepts,
expounded in Chapters 10 and 11, "the medicine should become spiritual and fine; it should be coagulation *post spiritum.*" [15]
Paracelsus' ideas on mania, St. Vitus' dance, *suffocatio intellectus*
and other mental ailments developed along similar lines. He gave
as their causes undigested excrements, deflections of the *spiritus
vitae* into the laughing nerves, vapors produced by worms, by
food, by cramped posture during sleep, or drying of the brain by
the moon's attraction on the cerebral humors.

Which shows that Paracelsus, while distinguishing the "spiritual" sharply from the "physical" diseases, had a decidedly materialistic notion of "spirit." In fact, his *spiritus vitae* had noth-

ing in common with the "soul" and still less with reason, as will
be shown in the next chapter. He treated all these diseases as
somatic or psychosomatic rather than psychological disorders,
considering the failure of reason a secondary effect.[16]

However, the *spiritus vitae* is will, too. Everything said
about its chemical behavior may be translated into terms of
emotional disturbances. Thus, his description of *chorea* jumps
from glandular to psychological factors, and back. Here he does
full justice to the unconscious factors in the affliction:

> "Their sight and hearing are so strong that unconsciously
> they have fantasies about what they have seen or heard. In
> such fantasies their reason is perverted into the shape im-
> agined." [17]

After another flight into chemical compulsions to dance, he returns to the emotional causes, and approaches the modern concept of the mechanism of "repression":

> "As [the image of a pleasurable feeling] impresses itself
> upon me, all other qualities, blood, and dispositions are
> driven from me, so that they are suppressed and have no
> power. This is followed by deprivation of the senses, but not
> of reason. If my power of reason is taken away and, due to
> my imagination, I act [insensibly]. . . . my lack of will is
> the cause of my disease." [18]

PERSONALITY STRUCTURE

In the third period, beginning at St. Gall, Paracelsus returned
to the interesting phenomenon of will power and "imagination." He followed old ideas of magic and folklore, explaining
dreams and interpreting the power of spells and curses. New
avenues opened up as he followed these leads. For instance, ex-

amining superstitious practices, Paracelsus found examples
where a curse had worked. But how? He was looking for a functional answer, and incidental remarks on the subject showed
how deep his thinking had reached. He suggested that "curses
work against those who utter them, not against the person at
whom they are aimed." [19] He thus unmasked compulsion as a
self-punishment: "A person who loathes himself may inflict the
curse on himself." The inference, that aggression derives from
self-destructive impulses, sounds quite modern.

There is a perceptible turn from mechanistic to functional
theories or explanations, and from interest in "substances" to a
close analysis of personality structure. Paracelsus always sounds
modern when he leaves his psychosomatic recipes and describes
emotional disorders as disturbances of the personality.

Not content with attributing a manic-depressive cycle to ebb
and flood in the "melancholic humor," he described the in-
cidence of mania upon a melancholic, upon a choleric person,
etc. Each, according to his or her predisposition, may produce
a different syndrome; the physician's task is to find the center
of the disease. Not possession by a demon or deficiency of some
humor, but disturbance of the whole personality produces the
morbid state of the patient.[20] The doctors must, therefore,
build up the personality.

Here Paracelsus encountered difficulties. The scientific and
logical tools were lacking to define the task clearly. Psychology
did not exist. The very word was unknown until Gockel introduced it, fifty years after Paracelsus' death. Theology and magic
practices had monopolized the field. The pioneers of descriptive
and clinical psychology had to do all the spade work themselves,
with no scientific terminology to borrow from other sciences for
guidance. They could not distinguish, for instance, between the
curse and the fear it inspires. Primitive folklore proved their
best source for coinage of the required new terms. But they

turned mostly to the ethical literature of their time. Four of the five chapters in the *Invisible Diseases*, therefore, deal with seemingly religious subjects. The categories which Paracelsus used were "faith," "imagination," "spirit," "soul," "reason," "complexion," "temper," and the like. He was well aware of this limitation, and it is to his credit that he pushed his research far enough to come in view of that frontier which only the most recent advances of psychology have crossed.[21] The problem which inflicted the sense of failure on Paracelsus will be discussed in the next chapter.

figure 8

*Johannes Herbst (Oporinus), professor at Basle and publisher
of Vesalius' Fabrica, and one-time amanuensis
of Paracelsus. From a woodcut; Amerbach Collection.*

figure 9

OMNEM IN HOMINE VENVSTATEM
MORS ABOLET.

1541
ISB

"Death and the Maiden." Woodcut by Hans Beham.

CHAPTER 22

Immortality and the Seven Souls

MAGIC, NEITHER WHITE NOR BLACK

With death, all arts and sciences perish. But the works of men go back with the works of ideas to the master to whom they belong.

PARACELSUS

The new psychology and psychiatry cleared some occult techniques of medieval psychiatry of their obscurity. Hypnotism, telepathy, suggestibility, and other psychic forces were known. Trithemius and Agrippa wrote about them. Popular superstitions wove fables around the phenomena. The Church, strangely enough, found some truth in sorcery, necromancy, conjuring, and witchcraft. It recommended the "white magic" of the Saints. "White magic" was invoked by the priests as a recourse against the illicit practices of "black magic."

Paracelsus agreed with the Church that the secrets of occult
powers should not be divulged and their illicit use should be
punished, since "sorcerers" might exploit them for evil purposes. At this point, however, he departed radically from the
doctrine of the Church.

In his definition of sorcery, evil intent alone makes a magic
practice illicit. Both white and black magic work with the same
forces and with the same techniques. No practice is evil in itself or dependent upon evil powers. Both black and white magic
are "natural."

> When we make the diagnosis of a mental disease, we can-
> not speak in a theological style. Not everything that is sacred
> is theology. To know a disease is not a gift of the Christian
> faith; it is a pagan and Jewish art. . . . The magus is neither
> from God nor from the Devil. He is of Nature." [1]

He approached the problem of legitimate and illicit practices
in the same spirit of objective disinterestedness which Machiavelli applied to statecraft. No technique is either good or evil;
any technique may serve good or evil purposes. This motto he
placed underneath his portrait: "All gifts [of nature] are good
[when they come] from God; evil [when they come] from the
Devil."

He went one step further. *Nature is indifferent to purpose.*
It is neither good nor evil. A strong occult power may serve
evil, while a weaker charm may be invoked in a good cause.
"White magic," therefore, is not by its own nature stronger
than "black magic." In fact, there is neither black nor white
magic. The efficacy of a magic practice depends on the efficacy
of the spell or of the magus alone. A saint's relics may have been
Satan's, and is it not true that "our greatest enemy came from
Heaven"? All arts, however, are from God, and whether good
or bad spirits use them, they still remain God's; if a knave uses

them, that does not detract from them. Vice versa, a Christian may "turn the tables on the Devil" and "make him his servant." [2]

Now, what is the strongest spell? We have seen that faith can accomplish more than any formula, spell, gesture, sacred instrument, ritual, or invocation. The power of the magus resides in his faith alone.

"A genuine holy water cannot be found as long as no man is found holy enough to invest water with occult power. . . . If we love the source of good with all our heart, we shall not fall into the power of evil." [3]

The power of his faith saves the believer from the claws of the Devil, not the prayer of his priest nor the sacrament. Superstition here led directly to a modern psychology of religion! It is not the content of the belief that matters, but its intensity alone.

"Whether the subject of our faith be real or false, the effects are alike. I may believe in St. Peter's image as much as I ought to believe in St. Peter himself. The effect will be the same. Of course, that is superstitious; but faith achieves the miracle whether it be the right or the wrong faith." [4]

It needed only one step more in order to liberate psychiatry from the fetters of medieval superstition. All churches and faith-healers point to their cures, saying, "Is not this miracle a proof that our belief must be the right faith? Can science explain this miracle?" Paracelsus had the answer:

"Jesus did not say we would move mountains into the sea if we believe in His power to perform miracles. He did say that our own faith, that the divine power of God in man can achieve the miraculous cure." [5]

This removed psychology from the domain of theology. In effect, exorcists, self-styled sorcerers, and theological wonder-healers were lumped together as impostors. Imagination and faith are the psychic powers which cure psychic diseases and which may "move mountains."

The patient's or the magus' faith may be right or wrong; yet, if they believe strongly enough, they will succeed. The act of praying, not the prayer, helps.

THE INDIVIDUAL BECOMING CONSCIOUS OF HIMSELF

Superstitious beliefs, magic practices, flashes of scientific analysis, and intuitive understanding of the human soul are strangely mixed in Paracelsus' system of psychology. It could not be otherwise, for there was no such science before him. For a long time after him, the standard books on psychology had titles such as *On Demons, On the Power of Heaven Over Human Action, On Immortality*. Treatment of psychological questions was incidental to ethical and theological problems such as Free Will: Is the Will guided by intelligence or predestined fate? Has God allowed the Will to aim at anything but the good?

The first task of any scientific psychology, therefore, was to establish the autonomous individual as the subject of its research. The great painters of the Renaissance, who have preserved the features of their contemporaries, were the first to portray the individual personality. The philosophers of Renaissance humanism—disciples of Aristotle and Plato alike—turned from their old subjects of logic and ontology to a discussion of problems concerning personality, such as Free Will; the relation of senses, soul, and reason; immortality.

Paracelsus moved with the most advanced trends of his time in recognizing the virtue of the individual. But in his endeavor to visualize personality, he came in conflict with the most developed thinking of the Middle Age. According to its keenest minds, the soul cannot be immortal because, being pure intellect, it returns to the world soul, or God, and vanishes in Him. Neither the pious Christian nor the Pagan Renaissance individualist was satisfied with that doctrine. Neither wished to part with his individual soul after death. Some sought the solution by distinguishing two or even more souls, separating that which is universal and immortal from that which belongs to the individual alone and is mortal.

But how could these operate together in a single being? Paracelsus' solution was not original, but his treatment reflects the new concern with personality problems. As a scientist and as a Christian he rejected the immortality of the so-called soul, *i.e.*, the thoughts, instincts, and emotions of the individual, and ridiculed the "resurrection of the dirt." Nor did he wish to reappear to his friends as a "ghost." To take care of ghosts, he invented the *evestrum*—another of his fantastic name creations, this one designed to separate from the soul a something that might enjoy an inoffensive temporary existence apart, advise relatives of approaching danger, even rattle or cause clocks to fall. But ghosts did not answer the question whether he, Theophrastus, might be selected to survive his body to enjoy the bliss of eternal union with God. As a humanist and as a God-seeker, he hoped to be saved as a spiritual individual.

How could he resolve the difficulty? He resorted to a device of Indian and Cabbalistic philosophy. He assumed several spheres of the soul. The lowest animals and plants have only one, and a minor, soul, which just suffices to regulate their organic functions. It is the wisdom of the body, which we have met before under the names of Archeus, Mumia, Iliaster, Protoplastus.

Higher animals have a second soul, through which they participate in the virtues and vices of the planetary spheres. This

second soul is still rather beastly. It governs the instincts. In its
material aspect, it is called "sidereal" or "astral body," "flesh
of Adam." Men who follow their instincts are governed by the
stars and are no better than animals. Indeed, he calls them
wolves, pigs, dogs, sheep, cows, and other totem names, and
means it. Princes who slaughter peasants *are* wolves: rapacious,
power-mad, bloodthirsty. Such souls are clearly not immortal,
not even good enough for Hell.

FREE WILL

In its spiritual and magic aspect, however, the "flesh of Adam"
is called "astral soul." It communicates with material creation
and knows hidden things. It is the site of reason which masters
the forces of nature and creates the arts, and develops that
knowledge which understands magic and the so-called miracles.

It is also there that magic works its way and a low imagination gives birth to the incubi and succubae. Note how consistent
the theory would be were it true. It is laid in the realm of the
predestined and the unfree. Man is subject not only to Nature,
but also to the products of his own creation. The sidereal body
is man's consciousness, but it is conscious only of its dependence.
This is Paracelsus' doctrine of fate and predestination.

Now he enters the realm where freedom begins and which
is properly human. Man also has reason, or a rational soul (intelligence), and he has that noble range of emotions which
is called his soul proper. These higher functions enable man to
be free and to aspire to divinity.

He who lives by his powers of reason is virtually free. He is
not subject to the stars, since he orders his own destiny. He is
free from the power of demons because he refuses to believe
in them. Paracelsus' prescription against obsessions is: Get rid
of superstitions; elect not to live in that sphere where they

hold sway. With this ingenious theory, medieval psychology was able, though admitting the existence of uncanny powers, to deny them that higher reality which belongs to the supernatural.

Now it becomes clear why Paracelsus placed so much emphasis on the doctor's "virtues." The higher the doctor is elevated above the "animal soul," the greater his power over it. The magus is the free man who commands the unfree. The virtues of a pious man break the magic circle of predestination. A different and overpowering magic resides in the highest sphere and is immortal. Hence, Christ and the Apostles transcend even the most virtuous and enlightened magi.

Piety thus is shown as the end, as it was the beginning, of psychology. This seems to agree with the conclusions of theosophical and other sects, notably of the so-called Swiss school. However, at least one important difference separates Paracelsian from theosophic doctrines. Whereas theosophy strives to resolve all psychology into the Brahminic "Atman" (or universal soul), Paracelsus strove to establish the freedom of the individual soul. This made him a Christian.[6]

IMMORTALITY

In contrast to the religions which demand the extinction of the individual, the Christian faith throughout the ages had provided for his personal psychological needs. The medieval Church was a stronghold of urban civilization. The Catholic faith was a refuge of the disturbed conscience; it dealt with the spiritual problems of the individual. When it regressed into barbarism, a movement of regeneration, Catholic mysticism, arose within its fold. Once more it claimed recognition of the soul in the name of the Christian faith. The humanists, we have seen, were animated by the "modern devotion," Paracelsus among them. His explorations into the human soul were grounded in the premise of the Christian faith: that the individual stands in need of redemption precisely because he stands alone in front of his Creator. Here is man's choice, the seat of his personality. This is Paracelsus' doctrine of free will, salvation, and immortality, the sole problem of psychology which the Middle Ages thought worth discussing.

DEATH

Paracelsus often reminded his readers of death. In passages where we least expect it, he suddenly exclaims that "Death is always imminent" and, "We should ponder over death." Death contains all the riddles of philosophy and, paradoxically, it alone distinguishes man from angels and gods. Thus, that which precipitated the question, the problem of death, provided a singular approach to an answer: Death is final, there is no return, no new start for the individual. If death were not the end of the life cycle, there would be no individual.

In possession of the Elixir, we would be like God; but we no longer would be ourselves. Were universal Reason to govern the soul, were personal desires to vanish into unimportance, then Faustus' striving for power would be meaningless. This insight sets an end to the ambition of the magus. Will and Reason are mutually exclusive. Reason is the attribute of Humanity, Will rules the individual. Will dies; Reason is eternal. But if Reason transcends Death, Death is the seal of Will.

We might speculate on and on in this kind of vicious circle. The outcome remains that which Ficino and Pomponazzi, the Italian philosophers, formulated a generation before Paracelsus. Personality is not found in a man's reason; [7] human reason is forever incommensurable with God's; free will is incompatible with immortality. Contrary to what magic taught, *omnis-*

cience and omnipotence are mutually exclusive. Death separates man from his eternal aspirations. The search for the Elixir was vain. Science, after all, though it liberated humanity from ignorance and other evils, failed to liberate the individual from the antinomies of free will and eternity. For once, Paracelsus could not answer a question.

No sooner had Paracelsus grasped the terms of the problem than it took hold of him and never lost its grip on his thinking. Was he to despair of his faith in salvation through science? Was there no hope of final redemption? In true medieval fashion, he eventually resolved the problem by the old device. He postulated a final, surmounting soul, which he supposed to be free through Faith. He called it the "Man of the New Olympus."

But before reaching this solution, Paracelsus went through a period of doubt and despair. Faustus, for the first time, realized that he had given his soul for the possession of magic. For the first time he was afraid to die.

CHAPTER 23

In the Pit

THE DAMNATION OF
DR. FAUSTUS

Let Faustus live a hundred years,
A hundred thousand and—at last—be saved!
Oh, no end is limited to damned souls.
Why wert thou not a creature wanting soul
Or why is this immortal that thou hast!
Ah Pythagoras! Metempsychosis—were that true!
This soul should fly from me and I be changed.

MARLOWE, *Faustus*

Somber were Paracelsus' astrological prognostications for 1532. The state of Germany could not have been worse. The cause of freedom could not have been further from victory. Justice was being trampled, faith was lost.

His patient in St. Gall, Christian Studer, died. From Basle he received the news of Oecolampadius' death. Ulrich Zwingli, to whom he had just dedicated his *Explanation of the Comet*, perished in the battle of Kappel. Reaction was victorious.

The Roman Catholic party was resurgent in all the Swiss

cantons. In St. Gall even the mild Vadianus was unable to appease it. The Abbot reappropriated the monastery and its estate. Paracelsus sought to interest him in his views on psychology and theology, but with little success.

Again his position between the warring sects became untenable. When he proposed going away, Vadianus did not detain him. But he had no place to go to. He left his manuscripts in St. Gall, and all he could do to protect them from destruction was to dedicate them to the Abbot. They were found centuries later, untouched, and to this day only a few of them have been read.[1]

Aimlessly, he wandered between Switzerland and the eastern states of Germany. A police record for 1532 reports that he was "driven out" of Prussia. In the following year he was in Silesia, but did not find whatever he sought there. "I do not know where to wander now. I do not care either, as long as I help the sick."[2]

Broken and destitute, he returns to Switzerland. He has no sponsor for his art. Nobody will print his books.

In the cantons of Appenzell and St. Gall he still has friends, chiefly among the common people. Again he lives with peasants and teamsters. "For I have found that in the common man and peasant, Christian life is most perfect."[3]

Disappointed and desperate, pursued by the magistrates, berated by the learned, derided by the vulgar, forsaken by his disciples, disgusted with worldly riches, and distrustful of worldly honors, he turns to solitude, poverty and meditation. His pride is broken, his scorn abates. He is humble and contrite. For the first time in his life he worries about his salvation.

History reports several notable conversions. In their autobiographies, St. Augustine and Pascal record the shocks which deprived them of their trust in science and reconciled them with faith. Ficino embraced faith during a severe illness. The case of Paracelsus is as remarkable as any, but no circumstantial account of his transformation exists, though his writings and sermons reflect it.

"This time of my writing is ripe. I shall not spare anything I spoiled. The work indicates that the labor is over and the time is ripe. . . . The time of geometry has come to an end, the time of art is over, the time of philosophy [science] has come to an end. The snow of my misery has thawed. The time of growing has ended. Summer is here and I do not know whence it came. It is here. Now is the time to write of many things on which I have ruminated for years, namely of blessed life. . . . Blessed is he to whom God gave the grace of poverty. . . . Make yourself poor, then the Pope and the Emperor will not trouble you, thinking you are foolish. But now you have peace of mind and your foolishness is a great wisdom before the Lord. . . . Therefore the blessed life is not for those who love riches. They will not find anything in this sermon. It is for those who gracefully adopt poverty." [4]

Gone was Paracelsus, the barn-storming discoverer and reformer who believed in the omnipotence of science. His philosophy, if not irreligious, had been materialistic or pantheistic. He had given assurance that man can save himself through his own works. His attitude had been arrogant, his manners rude.

Now he thinks of God, of death and salvation, of the Christian life. He no longer believes that science will liberate humanity. He does not even mourn this lost opportunity. Though he still hates dogmatism, he is interested in questions of theology, and is even sympathetic to rituals, such as the baptism of children, and to images, such as Calvary. He now hopes to be saved by faith. He who had formerly tried to heal the body is now concerned about saving souls. He preaches to the humble men whom he has gathered about him.

RE-ENTER BEELZEBUB

What precisely brought about this change we do not know. Was it the collapse of the insurgent movement? Or the disappointments he experienced when his friends and followers lost their nerve? Was it his new insight into the power of mind? Was he frightened by the occult forces which he believed were revealed to him? We do not know.

In that year, many Anabaptists renounced their radical and atheistic views. With others, as we have seen, the breakdown manifested itself in religious frenzies. Most significant, that same year witnessed the public renunciation of the arch-magus, Agrippa. In 1532, after a lifelong struggle for a scientific philosophy, Agrippa von Nettesheim published his *Declamation on the Incertitude and Vanity of all Science and Arts, and the Excellence of the Word of God.*

The coincidence is striking. We need not credit Paracelsus' claim that "ever since I was twenty years old I wished to write about these things" (theology and apostolic life). There is more truth in a subsequent sentence: "Not only my youth hindered me, also professional matters; astronomy, medicine and other works in science had to be described, all that concerned the Light of Nature." At the beginning, indeed, he had given more importance to science. Later he turned to other affairs—and even these, we know, not strictly celestial.

"Even when I had nearly finished, there intervened many affairs, public and private. Much opposition has lain on my shoulders alone, with no one to support or shield me. Strange people have persecuted me and maligned me, so that I have little reputation among men but only contempt. I have not counted much with logicians and dialecticians in medicine, philosophy, and astronomy. Also, I did not like their pomp and display and their fine speeches to princes and the rich; and therefore I have been forsaken." [5]

And then he continues, describing his disappointment and the disillusion which preceded his change of mind:

"The world cannot be gained by astronomy, which has little value except for its own sake, nor by medicine, which lacks power over all diseases, nor by philosophy, which is held in contempt—but by tradesmen's wealth and courtly manners. That has been my burden unto this day." [6]

Science gains neither honor nor power; and its achievements, he now feels, are meager. "Where I had seen flowers in alchemy, there is but grass." [7]

Paracelsus at last admits defeat. Credit for healing is attributed to God no matter what remedies the doctor applies. To some doctors God has given power to heal one disease, to others He has allotted four or five. This from the man who had once claimed the arcanum for all diseases!

"A hundred shoemakers are in town. Who shall distinguish between them, since all know their craft? So, if a council is held and several opinions are advanced—provided they all are in the spirit—what if they are not all agreed on the method! One method is as good as the other." [8]

Agrippa and Paracelsus, who once had proclaimed themselves God's equals, even His betters in their own field, now see His fingers in every corner of creation. And not only God. The devils and demons, too, return. Spirits populate the universe, play

pranks on people, guard the treasures of the earth. The occult
sciences, on the other hand, are deprecated. When astrology is
mentioned again, it is to show that the Devil has his hand in
the game: "Isn't it a fine excuse for the Devil to shield himself
behind astrology and blame the stars for what he has done?" [9]
The question which had guided all his former studies had
been: Is it true? Now he asks: Is it allowed? The all-pervading
Light of Nature wanes. Medicine no longer stands on chemistry,
but on faith; she avows that she knows nothing, that all her
science is empirical. Avicenna's Canon now is criticized, not because it teaches false doctrine, but because all doctrine is futile:

"Which doctor can say: This pain comes from that spot,
that resides in this member? None. Whatever the Canon says,
is but guesswork. One may find a medicine for this hot pain
and another for that cold disease; that one for young people,
that one for old; this one in this country, that one in another.
Whosoever finds a medicine and its virtues, knows just that
this medicine has such a power against such a disease. He
should not think: This disease originates from that cause or
this one. For the physical bodies are of such a nature that
it is hard to reason about them. One may imagine he knows
something that resembles a theory; but he will find contradictions, and he does not know the substance and origin. Therefore we shall know what medicines there are as though God
had given them to us.

God has given power to the stones, but He might have
willed it differently. The doctor should take this for granted
and not ask the reason why.

Does the stone care why it cures the eye? Or the eye what
color the stone is? So why should the doctor ask questions?
Why should he seek behind nature? It is destruction that
makes the disease, so why should we ask for the cause? The

bandage and the ointment do not ask whether the wound was made by a spear or a sword, or what color it was. Do not look for humor and qualities. Water extinguishes fire, but does not ask what is the nature of fire. It is sufficient that the two be brought together. This is the ground of all medicine." [10]

Virtually every sentence here contradicts one cited earlier.

THE PREACHER

The crisis was so profound, it so completely changed his outlook on life, that his personality was transformed. His style of life altered. The proud Paracelsus became modest and tolerant. He let insults pass. Many an opportunity was allowed to slip by, which formerly he would have seized upon, to deride Galen or his colleagues.

He fasted; divested himself of his clothes and of his money; renounced the study of the Cabbala; abstained from his crucible for months. All his time was spent in meditation, in helping the poor, in serving others—and in writing and preaching.

Once more he wrote furiously, compelled by the need to revise his ideas, digest the new problems, shape his intellectual reconciliation with religion. His meditations were jotted down in disparate chapters of a voluminous and unfinished book, each chapter of which is defective, hurried, and often contradictory.

He never tried to publish these essays which he insisted were meant only for selected readers. The few chapters published four hundred years after his death are singularly lacking in clarity and depth. Where the discussion reaches a difficult point, it drops the problem and peters out in moralizing. The essays, indeed, should rather be called sermons. As such, they are most interesting and expressive. Paracelsus' colorful style suits this kind of literature which flourished in the sixteenth century. In the essay affirming that the highest good is to be found in the spiritual life, he writes: "For if we hold the belly and its fullness for the highest good, the worms will eat it. A poor good over which the worms are master!" [11]

His tense style no longer reflects the spirit of a rebel. It betrays a deeply disturbed conscience and a desperate search for salvation.

THE SALVATION OF DR. FAUSTUS

God cannot be found through the Light of Nature. Science does not lead to liberation. It is Paracelsus' outcry which Marlowe puts in the mouth of Dr. Faustus. (See the motto of this chapter.) He has forfeited salvation. All his efforts have been in vain.

Salvation is assured not through the laws of nature, but through the power that can suspend them. The universe can no longer be conceived as One and divine. Knowledge of good and evil is more important than knowledge of nature. The world is not God's emanation but His creation. The distance between God and man is unbridgeable.

Paracelsus became increasingly conscious of the gulf which separates man, the world, and God. Unable to integrate his knowledge in a monistic world view, he frantically asserts that "I write pagan but yet am a Christian." In his last work, which most followers consider his most important, he sums up the fruit of his contemplations: *"Two kinds of wisdom are in the world; one is eternal, the other mortal."*

His new obsession with the "two worlds" led him to revise all his earlier statements about good and evil. He had maintained at length the dialectical view that good and evil, poison and arcanum, are in everything. Now he asserts that "we cannot

know where God found evil." [12] "God," he had declared, "is
in the world not as its Creator but as its Soul." [13] Now the
God-in-nature is forgotten. Emphasis is put on the Creator
whose "children" we are, and on His Son who renewed man's
life. God no longer is in nature, He is above nature. The conflict is admitted. During the coming centuries, Faith and Science will be at war. Instead of one light, there are two.

Knowledge, Paracelsus always knew, came to man through
loss of Paradise.[14] Now he regrets it. He cares less about knowledge, more about Paradise. Above all, he no longer considers
knowledge the way back to Paradise. The magus is of Nature,
not of God.

All the true mystics recognized both lights as one. Unlike
them, however, Paracelsus was unable to enjoy the suspense of
de Cusa's "coincidence of opposites." Faustus later will bemoan
the tension of the "two souls which, alas, live in my bosom."
Paracelsus, in his misery of the year 1534, longed for rest.

"I started out in the Light of Nature. . . . and finished
in the Light of Eternity." [15]

THE CATHOLIC REFORMATION

The date of Paracelsus' conversion is significant. Since 1530,
the German Protestants had been firmly entrenched behind
the Augsburg Confession, and had lived as a body apart from
the rest of the Christian Empire. Lutherans and Papists vied
for the favors of the Sultan who was threatening Christian
lands. In 1532, Henry VIII had made himself head of the
Church of England. Thomas More had been beheaded. His
friend Erasmus was silent. (He died in 1536.) In 1534, Ignatius Loyola founded the Society of Jesus, starting the spiritual

reform of Catholicism. In the same year, Jan van Leyden established the Kingdom of Christ in Münster. Two years later,
Calvin established his own brand of Christianity in Geneva.
The unity of the Christian world broke apart, just as the unity
of Christian philosophy had broken apart. Paracelsus longed
to restore it.

There could be no question in Paracelsus' mind as to which
church embodied the Light of Faith. All his thinking grav-
itated to the idea of unity, universality, and objectivity. Priests
and Church officials may err or be corrupted, but the Church
itself, which for fifteen hundred years had represented Chris-
tendom as a unity, could not be corrupted.

The great majority of the humanists were imbued with this
concept of Christian unity. These men, who dared to formulate any heresy, never denied the Church's right to declare
them heretical. They thought the Church was in the hands of
unworthy men, but they would not break the unity of the
Christian world over that issue. They sympathized with the
Protestant program of reform. In fact, the Protestants had
adopted a good many humanist tenets. Few humanists, however, were prepared to sacrifice Christian unity for a point of
doctrine. Erasmus courageously held out against the schism despite mudslinging charges of "cowardice." Paracelsus now denounced his former sectarian brothers-in-arms:

"Sects are beastly and often become fierce and mad. . . .
Who else can exterminate abomination except the authorities? Woe to the country whose king does not understand
this. It is better to take measures to prevent madness than
to allow it to grow. . . . If one refuses to believe in the
Church it were better that he had a millstone around his
neck and were thrown into the water than that his art should
degenerate into murder and theft." [16]

"The Church," of course, is the Roman Catholic Church; and this was written by one who was still preaching against its institutions and who, only two years previously, had called Zwingli "a pioneer of truth." But Zwingli was dead and Theophrastus no longer strode the barricade.

CHAPTER 24

Professor of Theology

UNKNOWN ASPECTS
OF THE RENAISSANCE AGE

> *Behold, my well-beloved, what madness holds us? Love God we rather may than either know Him or by speech utter Him. In loving Him we more profit ourselves. We labor less and serve Him more. And yet had we rather always by knowledge never find that thing we seek, than by love possess that which also without love were in vain found.*
>
> PICO DELLA MIRANDOLA

Paracelsus was no longer the wonder doctor. His disciples refused to follow him on his hard road. [1] Wandering from refuge to refuge he spent much of his time in solitary meditation, sometimes in teaching and writing.

Leaving Switzerland to seek refuge, he wandered like the saints and apostles, "without shoes and bag, without even a stick, in token that their realm is not of this world. They walk in Christ's shoes and preach the sweet Lord." [2]

He subsisted by begging, and complained about "those who

begrudge the poor the dish of soup they give him and think day and night how they can avoid giving it to him." [3]

Like the Displaced Person today, he found the doors of every nation closed: "They are driven from land to land, and the door is slammed to as soon as they approach." [4]

Wandering in heat and dust, sleeping on the roadside in every weather, and exposed to all inclemencies, he looked even more miserable than he was. His prospects of a haven grew dim. Feeling utterly destitute he apologized: "Don't shrink from my rags, reader. Let me carry my cross. I have sickness in me, my poverty and my piety." [5]

He arrived at Innsbruck in a state of complete exhaustion. Covered with dust he sought asylum. But the burghers had no use for "charlatans and vagabonds." "The burgomaster of Innsbruck recognized doctors only in silk and at courts, not broiling in the sun in tattered clothes." [6]

Generalizing from his experience he complains: "The poor always are left behind. What shall we think of towns which build sumptuous city halls while the houses of the poor are full of sorrow?" [7]

He preached against luxury. He called the law of the land the Canon of Leviathan, and trade, usury. [8] The old fighter reappeared. He wanted to make Catholicism a religion of the poor. In the name of Christ and of the apostles he rebelled against Pope and Emperor, the wealthy and the·mighty. [9] The more he was ignored, the more desperate became his tidings. If they chose to shut their ears to sweet messages, they would have to listen to the word of the Apocalypse. And here it was— the plague, and with it the call which Paracelsus could not resist.

APOCALYPSIS

The plague has come to the little town of Sterzing. Its population is in flight, leaving their sick to rot. Paracelsus hears the news and hurries there. Here is an opportunity to help people, to study the disease, to be useful again—perhaps to regain a place in the human community. He also has two friends there, Kerner and Poschinger.

Paracelsus helps care for the sick. The plague is halted. But if he expects gratitude, he is mistaken. The citizens order him to leave. [10] The faithful Poschinger not only helps him but offers to accompany him on his further travels—one of the few such instances we hear of.

It is in his letter to the Town of Sterzing, protesting against the ingratitude of the burgers, that he adds to his signature: Professor of Theology—a self-awarded title, assumed both in defiance and irony. Thus Paracelsus derided the local clergy who trembled because his Gospel of Apostolic Life apparently was well received in the taverns. The priests, he charged, unable to answer his arguments, had ordered him deported and had referred his views to the learned theologians of the orthodox universities.

"You daily denounce me because I have spoken the truth at times in taverns and inns, against useless churchgoing, luxurious festivals, vain praying and fasting, giving alms, offering tithes, confession, sacraments, and priestly rules and observances. You accuse me of drunkenness because this has taken place in taverns, and you call me an agitator because you say taverns are not appropriate for truth. But you were silent and well pleased when in the taverns I advised people to give you offerings. If that was proper in inns, then admit

that the truth is proper in inns. But now I will say to the
people: Guard yourselves against the false guardians who are
sent by the Devil. . . . You also tell me to go to discuss
with theologians in Vienna, Ingolstadt, Louvain, Cologne,
where I should be confronted not with peasants and tradesmen, but masters of theology. . . . Know then my answer:
To those will come their equals. Christ never went to Rome.
. . . When I am dead, the truth will live on, for it is Christ
who dies not. And if I were at Louvain and Paris, they would
not punish *me*—upon which they count—they would punish
Christ." [11]

A different Paracelsus reveals himself in the writings of this
period, a God-seeker, a disciple of the Apostles. His self-assur-
ance no longer is based on his confidence in the omnipotence
of the magus. It is derived from his devotion. We have to place
this piety in its proper context before we analyze the specific
tenets of Paracelsus' religion.

THE SILENT ONES

Even before his "conversion," Paracelsus was not irreverent. He
shared the universal belief in God the Father. Like other medieval God-seekers, he believed that studies can put man in rap-
port with God. Knowledge brings Salvation. Such ideas agreed
with the philosophy and theology of St. Thomas and of the
Schoolmen, which taught that faith and reason are but two
aspects of one truth. Medieval theology conceived of Deity as
the crowning aspect of nature. All-powerful creator of the universe or benign ruler, Father of mankind or judge—always
this majestic God of Nature remained impersonal. A human
heart in search of loving comfort had to address prayers to the
brotherly Christ or the motherly Virgin. Who can look at

Gruenewald's tortured Christ without feeling that these people craved a more personal God?

When the foundations of medieval society were shaken, people went in quest of the God of Love, not the one of scripture. The mystics proclaimed the faith of the common man: God is not the monopoly of learned society and of the "classes." He is in every man's heart, a God not of reason and justice, but of love and commiseration, not the ruler above nature, but close to each of us. Scholasticism sought God in the wrong place. "In the soul is the child-bed of Deity," said Meister Eckhardt.

Humanists, mystics, the Brethren of the Common Lot, the Anabaptists, and the common people who followed Savonarola in Florence, Saint Bernardino in Siena, Hans Denk in southern Germany, Jan von Leyden in northern Germany, John Knox in England, and Ignatius Loyola in Spain—they all hoped to be reborn in this new spirit of Christianity. Dissatisfied with the majestic image of Christ the Judge, as Michelangelo painted him on the "Last Judgment," they preferred the original Christ of the Gospel, the loving and pitying apostle of the poor who had lived with the sinners and the humble. As the cult of Mary revived during the fifteenth century, the religion of love was avowed by religious thinkers and scientists alike.

During the crisis of the early sixteenth century, the proponents of this new outlook gathered around themselves all the disinherited and frustrated, all the unprivileged, all who felt deprived of their cultural heritage, all the chips and splinters of the disintegrating society of the Middle Ages.

They belong with those nameless rebels who emerge for a moment in the turmoil of a revolution, then disappear. They never shape the fate of their nation, yet time and again its history seems to center around them. They are despised, persecuted, martyred; they disappear, only to re-emerge later on. Whenever we hear of them, they are portrayed as murderers, arsonists, beggars, vagabonds, atheists, fanatics. Yet, when they refer to themselves, they call themselves the quiet ones, the silent people, the poor, the children of God, the brothers, the pure.

They are laymen who profess the priesthood of mankind; they are paupers who claim the riches of the earth or of heaven. Paracelsus is with them. He feels himself called to help them when they are sick and to hearten them when they despair. Poverty, for him, is a Christian's self-elected duty. Love of one's neighbor is religion. Through charity a man enters into God's grace.

"More than blessed is he who loves the poor," [12] for Evangelical poverty is the prerequisite of any reform, said Paracelsus. And when he denies judges the right to sit in court over their fellow-men, he almost sounds like Tolstoy.

These mystics were not satisfied with the results of the Reformation. They felt a new dogma and a new Pope had taken the place of the old. They considered Luther a renegade; they charged that worldly power had corrupted the Reformation. Looking back, it seemed to them that the Protestant turmoil had interrupted their efforts to fill the Catholic Church with a new spirit.

THE MYSTIC

In an amazingly short time Protestantism became petrified in a new dogmatism, while a spiritual rally revived the old Catholic Church. Paracelsus took his place in the battle. His old fighting spirit returned. He still believed in the heavenly kingdom on earth. His ideas on apostolic life, he was sure, were compatible with the doctrine of the Church.

Again he preached in taverns and by the roadside. He taught the gospel of poverty, of non-violence and humility. He found listeners among the poor, among those who felt betrayed by all the sects, and among the mystics and men of good will who sincerely wished a reform of the Church from within.

Paracelsus declined to take part in the current theological controversies. He characterized Luther and the Pope as "two whores discussing chastity." Nor did he think much of Anabaptist theology. His Church was the one that is in the hearts of men; the others he called "stone churches." His religion was that of Christian love. He scorned ceremonies and rituals, abhorred dogma, and despised priests—in particular the Catholic clergy whom he called a gang of impostors.

Though an ardent Bible reader, he rejected anxious adherence to scriptural texts. To him Lutherans and Zwinglians, who "stood by the Word," were only "sects clad in gospel cloaks." [13] All Scripture, he explained, had to be interpreted through Cabbala or mystic inspiration. Thus he did not doubt that God had revealed the history of creation to Moses. But the prophet, not understanding what he had heard, set it down in garbled "cagastric" (*i.e.*, evil astral, pagan, nature-worshipping) language.[14]

Such independent opinions might have led him to the stake had not his mysticism allowed him some equivocal formulations. He supported the Catholics on the question of Christian unity, and he seemed to agree with Catholic dogma, at least in the much-discussed question of "works" vs. "faith." Indeed, he maintained that works are essential for salvation. But by works he did not mean ceremonies but real self-sacrifice and devotion to mankind. However, he went far beyond Catholic doctrine in maintaining that works need not be done in the "true faith" but are meritorious in themselves. On the other hand, he advocated infant baptism and polemized against Zwingli over the blood and flesh in the sacramental wine and bread. A scientist, one would think, would agree with Zwingli that the bread and wine merely *represent* Christ's flesh and blood; Paracelsus would have no such compromise between science and Faith. He transposed the mystic act of the Eucharist into a realm where there is neither science nor superstition. Faith makes the symbolic consumption of Christ's flesh and blood a real one, the communion through which His body is rearisen. It is the seed of rebirth; the act transforms the naturally divine substance into human virtue.

Religion, in this view, no longer is a philosophy of nature; it becomes a conception of man's destiny. Paracelsus was neither a pantheist like Spinoza nor a liberal Protestant like Renan. Valentin Weigel, the seventeenth-century mysticist, was mistaken when he said: "Theophrastus and I say that God, Primal Matter, and Heaven are all eternal and are all one."

Even at the time when Theophrastus was interested mainly in bridging the gulf between God and nature, this was not correct. But meanwhile his problem had changed. Now he had to bridge the gulf between God and man. *"For the Light of Nature is ignorant of God's ways."*

Up to the Appenzell episode, Paracelsus had considered Christ as a model—a saintly, or perhaps a divine person. His religion was that of the Light of Nature which is inspired by the Holy Ghost. Now Christ became the focal point of faith, the guarantee that salvation was possible. Christ reconciled the "two natures" of man.

Paracelsus' mystic predecessors had been intensely aware of the gulf. Their charming and passionate poetry flowered in the tension between man's divinity and his incompatibility with God. Paracelsus contributed his solution in the beautiful myth of twofold creation. Man, according to his interpretation, was created twice: once through Adam, and a second time, after his fall, through the Word of God. That which was born in the Word is capable of partaking in the Lord's supper and becomes His flesh. It may be resurrected and walk on earth as His son. This mystery was not achieved in Christ alone. It can be repeated in every human being. Thus, he triumphantly concludes, we are not only God's children but His sons, too, meaning that we can be like His Son.

The myth is St. Thomas', the conclusions are Paracelsus', at one with the great humanist traditions of his teachers and predecessors. Mysticism, always intent upon professing the individual's direct relationship to divinity, liberates religion from the barbaric concepts of the tyrant God and places Him in the human heart. Nicholas de Cusa, the spiritual father of the Brethren of the Common Lot, composed this dialogue:

"THE SOUL: Nobody sees Thee unless he hath Thee.
Nobody apprehendeth Thee unless Thou
givest Thee to him.
How shall I have Thee?
How shall I pray to Thee?
Is there anything more absurd than the idea
that Thou shouldst give Thee to me,
Thou who art everything?
And how couldst Thou give Thee unto me
Unless Thou givest me Heaven and Earth
And all that is therein?
"GOD: Be thine, and I shall be thine."

ETERNAL LIFE

The central point in Paracelsus' theology, which distinguished his doctrine sharply from the spiritualistic theology of Protestantism, concerns the location of Heaven and of Hell. Both are on earth and nowhere else. "There is no Paradise after the earth—there only is the Kingdom of God." [15]

Conversely, man was never driven out of Paradise, but stayed right where he had been; only the place itself changed from Paradise to Hell. This beautiful and very down-to-earth myth has found its way into Marlowe's Faustus poem:

"FAUST: Where are you damned?
"MEPHISTO: In Hell.
"FAUST: How comes it then that thou art out of Hell?
"MEPHISTO: Why, this is Hell, nor am I out of it.
            Thinkst thou that I who saw the face of God
            And tasted the eternal joys of Heaven
            Am not tormented with ten thousand Hells?" [16]

It is the split in human existence which torments Paracelsus-Faustus, the humanist and mystic. Humanity has been banned from the face of God because it takes part in nature. Humanity has the means with which to rebuild Paradise on earth. For that it has been twice created. The word of God seeks to become flesh in humanity. Humanity redeems itself and thereby liberates the universe, too, from the animal spirit.[17] The continuous act of this conquest, which must be achieved here below, is the unification with God, achieved through love.

This simple premise resolves all the difficult and intricate, often apparently contradictory, tenets of Paracelsian philosophy and theology. It is unimportant whether the body will be resurrected or not. Paracelsus ridiculed the idea of "the resurrection of the dirt (*Kot*)." What matters is the spiritual resurrection of mankind. For the same reason, he rejected metempsychosis and other subterfuges which may ease the burden of life. Death is final. Whatever man can do to assure his glorification, he must do here and now.

figure 10

Practica Teütsch auff das
M.D.XXXV. Jar. durch den
hochgelerten Theophrastum Paracelsum / Der freyen kün
ste der Artzney vnnd Astronomey / Doctor / dem gemainen
menschen zů nutz gepracticiert / vnd außgangen.

Mars.   Venus.

Title page of Paracelsus' Astrological Practica
for the year 1535, with the figures of Mars and Venus.
Reproduced from Sudhoff's edition
of Paracelsus' works.

figure 11

"Young Man with a Broad-brimmed Hat," by Hans Holbein the Younger, the picture to which Rosicrucian icons of Paracelsus can be traced. From the Amerbach Collection.

It is on religious grounds, therefore, that Paracelsus objected against capital punishment. Even a murderer, he said, should have the opportunity to repent, and after repentance he cannot be executed. He must be given another chance at life.

Paracelsus was an ethical optimist. He strongly believed in the basic kinship between God and man. He was confident that God's divine power can act through each of us as it did through Christ. This set him apart from the Protestants whose ethical pessimism he abhorred. After his conversion he remained a humanist who believed in the perfectibility of man, despite his disheartening experiences of defeat and misery, of human failure and meanness.

More than in any other field in which he plowed, the turn from the Middle Ages to modern times is apparent in Theophrastus' theology. He began with the notion that God can be known scientifically, and that such knowledge perfects man's communion with Him; he ended by admitting that faith and science are incompatible. He sought God in Nature; and found Christ in man's relationship to Him. He began as a monist who seeks to establish the coincidence of the opposites; he ended by admitting the split which is characteristic of modern man.

He earnestly tried to maintain the medieval union of religion and science. He tried the way of St. Thomas, that of the Cabbala, and that of the mystics—and failed in each. From then on, theology and science went different ways, though there still are scientists who persist in the foolish effort to prove God scientifically.

A mystic who could no longer realize the mystic universe, a magus who could no longer visualize the omnipotence of magic, Paracelsus stands at the threshold of modern times.

CHAPTER 25

Success at Last

PARACELSUS' SECOND PEAK

> *A theologist is a man who writes about God without works. A doctor cannot do likewise. Like a Saint's, his word must stand up with his work.*
>
> **PARACELSUS**

With his two friends Poschinger and Kerner, Theophrastus left the ungrateful town of Sterzing and went to Merano. There he "found much honor, happiness and fortune." He had patients, disciples, money, and leisure. But it was never his fate to stay long in one city. On he went into the Veltlin county, famous for its healthy climate.

St. Moritz in the Engadine remains one of the fashionable health resorts of the continent, and the nearby spa of Pfeffer-Ragatz is renowned for its waters. A Benedictine Abbot, Johan

Jacob Ruessinger, was Paracelsus' host. At his request Paracelsus wrote a pamphlet extolling the virtues of the springs whose water is "so acid that . . . (one who drinks it) can digest tartar as an ostrich does iron" (!).

Yet again he failed to settle down. He wandered through the Inn valley, visited his old friends at the Füeger's laboratory in Schwatz, and again worked in the mines and smelters. The Inn valley was then a metallurgical center. Primitive techniques made mining and metal working extremely hazardous. Affections of the lungs gave Paracelsus abundant opportunities to help patients and to study disease. The fruit of these months of work was *the first book ever written on an occupational disease*: *Von der Bergsucht* (On Miners' Consumption).[1] Material for these essays he probably had collected during his earlier experiences in mines and smelters, in Sweden and Dalmatia.

Superstitious contemporaries assumed that miners' diseases were inflicted by the mountain spirits who guarded veins of ore and punished transgression of Nature's taboos. Miners paid with their health for digging into the bowels of the earth and robbing her treasures. To this day European miners preserve this folklore, observe special rites, and are steady churchgoers.

Paracelsus' book dismissed the superstitions. He attributed miners' diseases to poisoning by metal vapors, that is, respiratory afflictions, and treated them as such. This is correct as a general approach, but his details are confused and little can be made of them in modern terms.

Among other errors, Paracelsus applied his tartaric theory to pulmonary afflictions among smelter workers. Metal poisoning is very different from a tartar deposit. Paracelsus might have discovered this had he owned a microscope or had he followed up his own correct observations. Instead, like many another scientist, he was so fascinated by his theory that he did not try to interpret his new observations in any other way. He took it for granted that his discoveries in metabolism applied to everything. Instead of heeding his own advice, to follow nature and experience, he allowed his doctrine to obscure his views.

Nevertheless, the book contains numerous correct observations, broke ground in the field of chemical "arcana," and ignored the hobgoblins.

After his conversion, Paracelsus kept the spiritual world more rigidly apart from the material one. Unlike the Paramiric essays, his scientific works of this period do not attempt to prescribe for the universe while analyzing human diseases.

THE REFORM OF SURGERY

This is even truer of Paracelsus' next work. Written in 1535, the *Great Surgery Book* is the only one of his major works printed during his lifetime. It summarized his experience in the field in which he first specialized. In this curious book he described no operations but concentrated on how to avoid them.

Current histories of medicine give Ambroise Paré credit for first recognizing the importance of cleanliness, and the self-healing properties of wounds. However, a generation before him Paracelsus condemned the barbarous and torturous practices of cauterizing and the greasy salves and dirty plasters which infected wounds rather than healed them.

> "The surgeon," he wrote, "should know that not he but Nature is the healer" (a phrase which Paré, too, used). "Surgery consists in protecting Nature from suffering and accident from without that she may proceed unchecked in her operations." [2]

And he never tires of repeating the immortal advice of Hippocrates:

"A physician who thinks that he heals does not understand the art. You may understand for what purpose there is
a physician. He provides the shield for nature and protects
the injured part against its enemies, so that the foe without
may not retard, poison, or injure the forces of nature, but may
preserve its vital power. He who takes good care of wounds
is a good surgeon (*Wundarzt*)."[3]

The preface was written by Wolfgang Thalhauser, a fellow
alumnus of Ferrara, who was municipal doctor in Augsburg.
Thalhauser denounced the Galenic doctors who concocted their
prescriptions out of books, and continued:

"Comes a barber who does not know more of human complexion than a butcher knows about a pig, cuts, burns, and
mends at his pleasure. Therefore I am glad that God ordered
you to stir this broth and to do away with these hangman's
martyrizations."[4]

The book was a great success. It appeared in two parts, published in July and August, 1536; and the following year a
second printing became necessary. This second edition appeared without Thalhauser's introduction. Did Paracelsus quarrel with his friend? It is not unlikely. Again we have a secretary's reports of Paracelsus' quirks.

"He mumbles to himself for hours. When he speaks to
others they can hardly understand him. He spends much time
before his oven brewing powders but he does not suffer anyone to help him. He gets angry when spoken to. Suddenly he
has a fit and yells like a wounded animal. He gets impatient
with the slightest mistake of his amanuensis."[5]

Again, he quarreled with innkeepers and patients, often over
insignificant sums; and again he resorted to litigation. On the

other hand, according to the same report, he "worked day and night, poking in his vials and dictating until the secretary broke down."

MASTER ADEPT

Stopping at Efferdingen, Paracelsus was the guest of an old friend, Dr. Johann van Brant, a mystic and humanist who was interested in alchemy and occult sciences. Paracelsus rated him as "one of the much-experienced adepts of the Philosophia Magica and a devotee of Apollo and Vulcanus." In long discussions Dr. Brant convinced him that the philosophy of nature needed to be reviewed in the light of mystic religion. This became matter for more Paracelsian books.

A number of volumes and tentative beginnings of books—all his works were started twice—have titles such as *Explanation of Universal Astronomy*, *Occult Philosophy*, and the like. The final work, *Great Astronomy or Sagacious Philosophy of the Great and Small World*, is by far his most ambitious and voluminous work, filling 397 pages—almost the whole of the tenth volume in Huser's edition. It is a compendium of the magical beliefs and superstitions of his time; it also deals with man, the universe, salvation, occult sciences, and related matters, explaining all a magus might wish to know about chiromantics, pyromantics, signatures, characters, phrenology, physiognomy, astrology, the healing power of stones, geometry, algorithm, meteorology, cosmography, sorcerers, witches, ghosts, and technology.

Most disarming are its technological utopias, some of which are reminiscent of Sir Francis Bacon's *New Atlantis*, written a hundred years later. Paracelsus provides formulas for weather forecasting, promises that magic, "with the aid of pipes and crystals," one day will "carry the human voice over a distance of a hundred miles," speculates on artfully constructed mirrors that may project pictures across the mountains or even into the future. The Para-sectarians have not missed this opportunity to claim for their master predictions of the steamboat, the telegraph, radar, and the atomic age, for "in summa, what nature can do in one year, magic can do in a month; this also applies to the growth of the earth. This art is called the Cabbala." [6]

Many profound insights are strewn amidst the rubbish of magic practices. Thus, speaking of geomantics—the art of divining from doodles—Paracelsus explains its operation in approximately the terms used to explain the Rorschach test to a superstitious layman today. In another passage, he calmly interprets Aaron's stick as a phallic symbol—an insight confirmed by modern anthropologists.

One invention that failed and that thus far has baffled his followers, deserves mention: his formula for producing the homunculus.

"If the sperm, enclosed in a hermetically sealed glass, is buried in horse manure for about forty days and properly 'magnetized,' it begins to live and to move. After such a time it bears the form and resemblance of a human being, but it will be transparent and without a corpus. If it is now artificially fed with the *arcanum sanguinis hominis* until it is about forty weeks old, and if allowed to remain during that time in the horse manure, in a continually even temperature, it will grow into a human child, with all its members developed like any other child, such as may have been born of a woman, only it will be much smaller. We call such a being a homunculus, and he may be raised and educated like any other child, until he grows older and obtains reason and intellect, and is able to take care of himself. This is one of the greatest secrets, and it ought to remain a secret until the days approach when all secrets will be known." [7]

Horse dung was known to alchemists as a source of constant, intense heat. It figured in a legend still current in the Salzburg county. The dying Paracelsus, according to this account, ordered his body to be quartered and buried in manure. When it was exhumed, the parts had grown together, and he would certainly have revived but for the zeal of a disciple who hurried too fast through the required ceremonial.

CABBALA

However, the *Philosophia Sagax* is more than a curiosity. It has been called the greatest failure to write the greatest book. The homunculus, like many of Theophrastus' Faustian fantasies, must be interpreted cabbalistically. He is the "little man" because he reflects the "great man" of the macrocosmos. These are symbols of cosmic relations, and Paracelsus—as great a story-teller as Plato and as rich in imagination as Dante—not only used ancient myths freely, but invented new symbols at will. Whenever he felt that his concepts were deficient in clarity he resorted to poetic invention. We have mentioned some of his myths, the evestrum, the seven souls, the twofold birth of mankind. These are more than simple allegories. Some are reminiscent of Blake in the poetic power of their naturalistic symbolism. Where is the Garden of Eden? he asks, and answers: It is the microscosmos of the mother's womb; the garden in which Adam was born is still in a woman's lap.[8] It is the matrix in the athanar, "The Mothers" to whom Goethe takes his Faustus.

The Philosophia Sagax must be read in the light of such cabbalistic myths, and the disciple of Trithemius may also have concealed in his work some "steganographic" message. While it is the most confused book in the German language, it also has been pronounced most profound.

The difficulty justifies reference here to two very lucid analyses of the *Philosophia Sagax*: one by Professor Koyré, the other by Sartorius von Waltershausen.[9] The monograph of Sartorius deserves additional praise as a courageous political act. It was published under the Nazi regime, when an officially sponsored Paracelsus cult engendered nauseatingly identical books exalting Paracelsus as a racist, founder of a "German medicine," and representative of that muddled thinking which some insist on calling mysticism. In this situation, Sartorius, stressing the humanist and theosophical aspects of Paracelsus' philosophy, denied the Nazis the right to usurp Paracelsus as their precursor. In his profound and scholarly study, Paracelsus appears as a Protestant mystic who "opened the world," not as a Catholic mystic who sought reunion with God, as Strunz had asserted. Sartorius calls the *Philosophia Sagax* a great exaltation of the individual, showing the structure of the personality as reflected in the various spheres of the creation. But is not such a philosophy of nature a Catholic heresy rather than Protestant?

Koyré, on the other hand, has taken great pains to reconstruct the Paracelsian cosmology in all its neo-Platonic and hermetical ramifications. If his valuable essay suffers from anything, it probably is an excess of orderliness. Koyré has managed to put together a Paracelsian "system." He apparently did what Paracelsus tried to do but was unable to achieve in the *Philosophia Sagax*—to bring all the contradictory fragments of his uncritical reading and eclectic thinking under one general system. Such a *tour de force* seems incredible, for Paracelsus constantly erected and rejected systems, incorporated new ideas and "forces" (substances) into them, and later forgot them or confused their names. Inconsistencies were bridged simply by creating special realms or spheres where unrelated facts could coexist.

Certainly Paracelsus intended the *Philosophia Sagax* to be an all-embracing system of *Naturphilosophie* such as the romantic movement in Germany brought forth three hundred years later. As it is, however, it appears as a gigantic, though crude, classification system where every phenomenon finds its place in one of the various realms, and each is reflected and modified in all. Where the desirable bond of identification is missing, Paracelsus resorts to "the Holy Cabbala."

This interest in Hebraic mystic philosophy is easy to understand. After his conversion, Paracelsus had to re-define magic and to re-define the place of the individual in the universe. The powers of the magus had to be justified, not only in the Light of Nature, but also before the articles of the Christian faith. Therefore, each of the various fields of knowledge, from necromancy to mathematics, is pursued through the four realms of the Christian cosmology:

Natural science (earth).

Astrology (sky).

The New Olympus (heaven).

Infernal sciences (hell).

With appealing fervor, Paracelsus seeks to show how each object of science takes on different aspects in the four realms and yet remains identical, just as in his alchemy, the material and the spiritual sulfur were identical and yet different. It was an attempt to reconcile the irreconcilable. Of necessity it failed, because Paracelsus here returned to positions he had abandoned when he recognized the gulf between science and faith. Fusing them, he only confused both.

It is this confusion which often is dismissed as mysticism. Wrongly so, we think, for mysticism is a poetic philosophy concerned with the unsolved problem of existence—man's participa-

tion in the below and the above, the unity of microcosm and
macrocosm, the overlapping of science and religion. There is
nothing "mystical" in mysticism, once one comprehends the
task the mystics undertook. It is nothing less than man's eternal
attempt to deny the Fall of Man, to overcome that alienation
which, we have shown, greatly disturbed the conscience of the
Renaissance age, and to ascertain man's power to communicate
with Deity.

CHAPTER 2 6

The Last Fight

DECLINE
AND DEATH

> *Jove strikes the Titans down*
> *Not when they set about their mountain-piling,*
> *But when another rock would crown their work.*
>
> ROBERT BROWNING, *Paracelsus*

T he preface to the first book of the *Sagacious Philosophy* is dated June, 1537, Kromau Castle (near Brno) in Moravia. Johan von Leipnik, Arch-Marshal of Bohemia, a high dignitary of the Empire, lay there paralyzed on his death-bed. By the time he called Paracelsus, it was too late. Paracelsus declared him beyond treatment but lived at his castle for a while. To this day, visitors are shown a "Paracelsus vault" where he had his chemical kitchen.

Paracelsus was once more in the favor of the mighty. On his

way through Bratislava, the town tendered him a banquet. Even the house of Fugger was reconciled. His *Prognostication for the Coming Twenty-four Years* was translated into Latin and seen through the press by a certain Tatius, tutor of the Fugger children. King Ferdinand of Bohemia and Hungary, heir-designate to the German throne, graciously accepted the dedication of this little pamphlet and of the *Great Surgery Book*. Full of new hopes, Paracelsus finally made his way to Vienna. At last, he was ready to be a man of the world like other scholars.

For the last time, the pattern of Paracelsus' life repeated itself. Received with honors, he made many friends, cured many patients, was admired, and "spent lots of money in good company." But within a few months he had completely dissipated his credit and had made so many enemies that nobody dared stand in their way.

King Ferdinand twice received the famous doctor in audience and seemed highly interested in his art and doctrines. He promised a grant of a hundred florins to pay the printing costs of a new book on tartaric diseases.

But again one of those Paracelsian imbroglios, so impossible to disentangle, brought about an overnight reversal. Paracelsus charged that the Treasury never paid him the hundred florins. The Treasury counter-charged that Paracelsus had squandered an advance that should have been paid to the printer. Paracelsus replied that the intriguing court doctors had thwarted his efforts to find a printer. The affair ended with the King characterizing Theophrastus as the most impudent swindler he had ever met. Again triumph turned into disaster. The money gone, Paracelsus had to accept low jobs, that of a matrimonial agent among them. Ben Jonson used the episode in his comedy, *The Alchemist*.

This was his last experience of utter misery. Although but forty-four years old, the weary Paracelsus longed for rest.

HOMECOMING

Throughout all these twelve years Theophrastus had not seen. his father and in all his wanderings had avoided Villach. The praise which he lavished on "my first teacher" is in strange contrast with the absence of any known correspondence between the two. In the meanwhile Wilhelm von Hohenheim had died, a highly respected citizen, doctor, and teacher.

In 1537, Paracelsus returned home to take possession of the estate, but the citizens of Villach did not consider him a desirable successor. During a church service which he attended, the doctors of the town staged a demonstration, demanding that he leave town immediately. Paracelsus this time did not resort to litigation or try to force his presence upon the inhospitable population. He went to St. Veith, about twenty miles from Villach and ten miles from Klagenfurth, the capital of Carinthia, where he had friends at the Archbishop's court. His aim was to stay in the country, to give up wandering, to settle down. When Albert Basa, court physician of the Polish King, called him to Cracow, he declined.

This invitation shows how far Paracelsus' fame had reached. Despite his misfortunes, his ability as a healer was no longer contested. His cures were praised by such men as Rheticus (the popularizer of Copernicus). He was consulted by high functionaries of the Hapsburg administration, among them the Baron von Sonnegg, Governor of Styria.

Yet he was unable to secure a position of permanence, to settle down in Carinthia. Despite desperate efforts to placate the Carinthian Diet, the expected favors were stubbornly with-

held. This time Paracelsus was not to be blamed. He insulted nobody and flattered everybody. He had but one aim—peace. But
this was not enough to offset the ill-repute he had acquired. He
was no longer on the offensive. It was he who was denounced
and had to defend himself against the most childish allegations.

DEFENSE AND ATTACK

For the first time he wrote an apologia. The little work is called
Seven Defensiones (now available in Henry Sigerist's English
edition of *Four Treatises of Paracelsus*). In it Paracelsus defended
himself against seven charges:

> That his theory is new. The reply: If Christ said, "Investigate
> the Scriptures," why should I not say, "Investigate the
> nature of things"?
>
> That he described diseases hitherto not dealt with in medi-
> cine and gave them strange names. The reply: The tradi-
> tional doctors lack the talent to accomplish anything for
> which they lack the words. "What they cannot accom-
> plish through the term, they call incurable."
>
> That his prescriptions are poisonous. The reply: A detailed
> exposition of his principle of chemotherapy: "To sepa-
> rate the good [the arcanum] from the bad."
>
> That he is a vagrant. The reply: True art must be pursued
> where it can be learned.
>
> That he has unjustly attacked the profession and his col-
> leagues. The reply: That a distinction must be made
> between physicians who walk according to the law of
> God and those who walk according to the law of man.
>
> That his manners are coarse and that his pupils have left
> him. The reply: a weak denial.
>
> That he, too, cannot cure all diseases. The reply: No honest
> doctor would promise such a thing.

But, still a fighter, he followed the defense with an attack. In a pamphlet called *The Doctors' Labyrinth*, he summarized his doctrines once more and stated his case against the academic doctors. It is the most readable of his writings, and despite some obvious and gross errors of fact and of method, it deserves translation.

Impatient as he was, he bound the two pamphlets, defense and attack, together and—had he learned to be politic?—added a curious *Chronica of the Land of Carinthia*, in which he lavishly praised its natural resources, people, and government. The whole, together with the still unprinted treatise on the tartaric diseases, he dumped into the lap of the Carinthian Diet, petitioning them to print it.

From his letter of introduction,

"To the Most Honorable, High and Well Born, Venerable, Austere, Scholarly, Noble, Firm, Provident, Honest, Wise, Benevolent, Favorable, Masterly and Affectionate, Dear Gentlemen and Friends, Archbishops, Bishops, Prelates, Counts, Barons, Lords, Knights of the Nobility and Diet of the Archdiocese of Carinthia,"

we quote the following passages:

"Though Christ says if one strikes your right cheek offer him your left, this cannot be my cross here. For He speaks [this] of earthly wealth, where we do not search our treasure. My dealing is with the patients, and in their interest I have to answer as they chide. If I should follow the example of Christ, I would rather remember how He answered the Jewish lies. That they might thereafter know the beam in their own eyes, I have written another book on errors of the doctors. And finally, since the proof of the pudding is in the eating, I have written about the commonest of all diseases in these regions, namely the sand and stone, theory and practice. Now, my colleagues prefer to be where I am not and not to be seen where I am; so they have made a conspiracy to prevent my works from being seen [a reference to the Vienna incident]. Therefore, I decided to offer these three books to my gracious masters, the Diet of Carinthia, which is my father's country in which he lived for thirty-four years and received much benevolence. . . ."

The Diet answered immediately "to the Noble, Highly Scholared, and Famous Gentleman Theophrastus, Doctor of Both Medicines, Our Precious Good Friend and Dear Master," that they would see that the manuscript was printed as soon as possible. However, it was not published until Dr. Birckmann, a disciple, discovered it in the archives twenty years after Paracelsus' death.

PEACE

Paracelsus was now at the end of his career. He was ready to admit that his struggle had been futile. In his *Prognostica for 1538* he wrote: "If I were permitted to settle down, I would make peace and sit tight even if I were provoked."

The portrait Hirschvogel made of him in 1538 shows a man still vigorous and defiant. Two years later, [see title] a new engraving by the same master shows the features of an old man, tired and sad. Both pictures carry the motto:

Alterius non sit quit suus esse potest.

(He who can act on his own,

no man's servant shall be.)

On the later portrait, the defiance is somewhat softened by a second motto: All is good if it comes through God, bad if it comes through the Devil.

In 1540 the Prince Bishop of Salzburg offered him asylum, and Paracelsus spent his remaining days in the town which had once expelled him for subversive activities. As he had promised, he really became quiet. He wrote little and meditated on theological matters. Occasionally there are reports of new miraculous cures and about the even greater miracles of his horse, which carried him to far-away patients at the eleventh hour. Legend followed him wherever he set foot. But the predominant note was one of resignation and melancholy. To a friend and patient, he wrote that his "evening has come, the faces of people at the windows grow more melancholy. The snow of my misery has come. Summer is over."

On the 21st of September, 1541, probably his forty-eighth birthday, he made a will, dictating it to the notary Kalbsohr, "although weak in body and sitting upon my couch, yet sound in reason." First he committed his soul to God Almighty, "confident that His everlasting mercy will not allow the bitter suffering of his only begotten son, our Saviour Jesus Christ, to be unfruitful nor lost on him, a miserable creature."

He ordained three psalms to be sung in church and at each singing a coin to be given to every poor man before the door. He disposed of his meager belongings—ten guilders to a relative on his mother's side, twelve guilders to the executors, all surgical instruments and ointments to the barbers of Salzburg. He also listed two boxes of manuscripts in Augsburg and others at Kromau, at Leoben, and other places, scattered all over the Empire. A significant omission reveals the tragedy of his life: no disciple or trustworthy friend is named to take care of these valuable manuscripts. Paracelsus had no literary executor for his legacy to mankind.

Even in his last hour, he did not forget his enemies. The psalm which he ordained to be sung at his burial reads:

"He shall be like a tree planted by a waterside, that will bring forth his fruit in due season. His leaf shall not wither and whatsoever he does, it shall prosper. My help cometh from God. . . . I will magnify Thee, Oh Lord, for Thou hast set me up and dost not suffer that my enemies triumph over me. . . . Heaviness may endure over night, but joy cometh in the morning."

Three days after he made this will, he died. His disciples attributed his premature death to an overdose of that famous elixir of life he was supposed to carry in the pommel of his sword; his enemies to blows received in a tavern brawl.

He died on the 24th day of September, 1541, two years before Copernicus published the book that removed the earth from the center of cosmology, and Vesalius printed the anatomy which undermined Galen and opened a new approach to the science of medicine.

The epitaph he composed for his gravestone reads:

Here lies buried

Philip Theophrastus

the famous doctor of medicine

who cured wounds, leprosy, gout, dropsy

and other incurable diseases of the body

with wonderful knowledge

and who gave his goods to be divided and distributed

among the poor

In the year 1541 on the 24th day of September

he exchanged life for death

To the living peace, to the entombed eternal rest

The Apology of Faustus

> *The children of perdition are oft-times*
> *Made instruments even of the greatest works.*
> *Beside, we should give somewhat to man's nature,*
> *The place he lives in, still, about the fire*
> *And fume of metals that intoxicate*
> *The brain of man and make him prone to passion.*
> *Where have you greater atheists than your cooks?*
> *Or more profane or choleric than your glass-man,*
> *More anti-Christian than your bell-founders?*
> *What makes the Devil so devilish. . . .*
> *. . . . but his being*
> *Perpetually about the fire and broiling*
> *Brimstone and arsenic. We must give, I say,*
> *Unto the motives and the stirrers up*
> *Of humors in the blood. It may be so.*
> *When as the work is done, the Stone is made,*
> *This heat of his may turn into a zeal*
> *And stand up for beauteous discipline.*

> BEN JONSON, *The Alchemist*

"Of all the doctors I have brought forth," Paracelsus complained, "only two remained in Pannonia, three in Poland, three in Saxonia, one in Slavonia, one in Bohemia, one in Holland—but none in Swabia. Yet, there are numbers who have twisted my instructions to suit their own minds." [1] For twenty years after his death, Paracelsus was almost forgotten. His disciple Torinus, later dean of Basle University, based his course on Galen. He also translated into German the book which, for the following decades, occupied the horizon of medicine, Vesalius' *Fabrica*. The printer who published this epochal anatomy was—Oporinus. It appeared in 1543, a scant two years after Paracelsus' death.

In the same year, another Paracelsian, Rheticus, helped to see to press another book which up to this day has overshadowed anything Paracelsus has written—the Copernican theory of the celestial revolutions.

Paracelsus' own disciples thus were instrumental in eclipsing his memory. Not for long, however. When the Renaissance movement ebbed away, doctors felt free to criticize the classics. Galen's usefulness was questioned while chemical knowledge made progress.

THE PARACELSIANS

Chemical books poured forth from the presses in the third quarter of the sixteenth century, along with a spreading use of chemical drugs. In 1569 the Duke of Bavaria found it necessary "to order the monasteries on his lands to adhere to the teachings of Hippocrates and Galen instead of the new medicine."[2] And in 1572 the Duke of Saxony commissioned Thomas Erastus[3] to refute Paracelsus.

These counter measures indicate the growing popularity of chemical doctors. Moreover, in the 'sixties, disciples and friends[4] of Paracelsus began to publish his works, partly in German, partly in Latin translations. Some of these publications were spurious (disciples may have circulated their own works under their master's name, further evidence of his spreading fame).

Meanwhile, the species Faustus-Paracelsus had not died out. In the sixteenth and seventeenth centuries, people still could see living examples before their eyes—roving medicine men, "chemical doctors" who boasted knowledge of secret powers, some bona fide, others impostors. Although Ben Jonson could satirize the dishonest alchemist as a familiar figure, chemical remedies were winning acceptance. By the end of the sixteenth century, Paracelsus again was in the medical news. The "Paracelsians," or metalists, were in arms against the "herbalists." And a new science, iatro-chemistry (biochemistry) had been founded by advocates of the naturalistic approach. Like the later homoeopathists, hypnotists, Mesmerists, and other offspring of adept medicine, the iatro-chemists were outsiders, as their master had been.

None of the disciples, however, was as good a doctor, as sensitive a magus, or as original a writer as Paracelsus. Many imitated his mannerisms, his mystificatious, his doctrinaire attitudes. None achieved his greatness and few lived up to his humanity, to the ardor of his search for truth, to the strength of his determination to grasp the Kingdom of Heaven. Many stood by the master's words rather than by the spirit of his method.

To make matters worse, some self-appointed disciples proved as rough fighters as the master. Instead of testing and improving their remedies through laboratory research, they created turmoil in the medical profession, accused conservative doctors of ill-will and tyranny, and claimed occult powers as an inheritance from the master. Eventually, they won recognition for chemical remedies, but at the expense of their master's reputation.

As doctors these disciples did little credit to Paracelsus. Their strong chemicals, their crude surgery won the Paracelsians the label of "Dr. Eisenbart," famous for his kill-or-cure methods. They neglected the precautions of dosage, which are the essence of Paracelsus' own chemotherapeutical method. It was not till our century that chemo-therapy, through a new approach, justified Paracelsus' intuitions.

BEFORE THE TRIBUNAL OF HISTORY

As a scientist, Paracelsus had no better fate than most of his
fellows. Few of his formulas have stood the test of history. Most
details of his theories have been relegated to the cabinet of
scientific errors, together with the phlogiston theory of early
chemistry and the "world ether" of rather recent physics. But
Paracelsus' attack liberated medicine from the fetters of
orthodoxy. His "three substances" and his "signed" drugs
proved more stimulating to medical progress than the four-
humor doctrine. The extravagant claims of his disciples kept the
academicians on their toes. The partisan emotions of this discussion still throb in the praise which Paracelsus won from Robert
Boyle (1627-1691), father of modern chemistry:

> "Chymists have put some men in hope of greater cures
> than formerly could be thought possible. Before men were
> awakened by the many promises and some cures of Arnaldus
> de Villanova [and] Paracelsus. . . . many physicians used
> to pronounce a disease incurable. They would rather dis-
> credit the art and detract nature than confess that the two
> could do what ordinary physick could not."

The "ordinary physick" which here stands accused of detract-
ing Nature was the four-humor doctrine. In attacking its
foundations, Paracelsus and his followers claimed "Nature" as
their ally. We have seen that this concept was rather complex.
Its significance ranged from the emphasis on empirical methods
to the epistemological theory that the Light of Nature was lit
in man by the Holy Ghost. *Nature*, it says in the spurious
*Philosophia ad Athenienses, is philosophy made visible; phi-
losophy is invisible nature.* Such propositions earned Paracelsus
the admiration of men like Giordano Bruno who acknowl-

edged that his own thoughts had been formed by Nicholas de Cusa, Copernicus and Paracelsus:

"Who after Hippocrates was similar to Paracelsus as a wonder-working doctor? And, seeing how much this inebriate knew, what should I think he might have discovered had he been sober?"

Bruno, that great martyr of free thought, was himself a magus and alchemist. His theories might be termed inebriate by modern standards, and the reasons for which he supported Copernicus would not be acceptable to any modern astronomer. Yet we call these men great, not because of any specific discovery but because they proclaimed a principle of knowledge. Their speculations often ran wild, and men like Brunswick or Agricola probably made more accurate contributions to chemical instruction than either Paracelsus or Bruno. But Brunswick and Agricola never presumed to "grasp the whole universe," and neither inspired the Faustus legend. In our century, with specialization and positivism paramount in science, there is a tendency to undervalue the merits of speculative philosophy. Historically speaking, the men who pondered over man's place in the universe provided the climate where scientific research, in turn, can produce theories.

Paracelsus' speculations may have been mere guesses, "correct more often than anyone else's, but without knowing anything correctly," as Eliphas Levi phrased it.[5] But they helped formulate a new theoretical framework. The principle of metabolism had to be visualized before its details could be tested. The concept of the biological person, "*the body mightily constituted*," set a basis for further physiological research. The *Ens Spirituale* helped to liberate psychiatry from theology on the one hand, demonology on the other hand. Above all, certain Paracelsian concepts have assumed new significance today in an altogether different setting: *All his categories were dynamic rather than static, and functional rather than structural. He studied the human body as a living whole, its physiology rather than its anatomy, its working, growth, and decay rather than its several members.* That is his meaning when he demands a return to "nature."

In all these fields where he pioneered, Paracelsus contributed more intuition than observation, more ideas than knowledge. Even where he seems to anticipate a modern insight, he did not possess it clearly. There is no point, therefore, in tracing contemporary discoveries back to him. Some have credited him with the invention of chemo-therapy, some consider his ideas on magnetism and suggestion anticipations of Mesmer's and Charcot's work. If that were permissible, then homoeopaths, spiritualists, and faith healers also might claim Paracelsian lineage. He is best understood, however, in terms of his own rebellion against the system which provoked it.

RESURRECTION

Paracelsus is not remembered for his achievements, but for his fight against orthodoxy. Whenever science seemed to have become estranged from nature and medicine disappointed the people, his name as a great healer and friend of the common man re-emerged out of the undercurrents of folk memory. The poor pilgrimaged to his grave; the educated recalled the knight-errant who had discarded the learning of his age to gain higher knowledge.

A Paracelsus myth was in the making even before his works were published. Fakers tried to sell their own manuscripts as his revelations and posthumous messages. Prophecies and instructions for finding the Philosopher's Stone were peddled in his name, as were balms and unguents. *It was during these same thirty years after Paracelsus' death that the Faustus saga took shape.* In the imagination of the populace, the lives of Trithemius, Agrippa, Paracelsus, and Faustus somehow merged. When the poets finally seized upon the fascinating subject, the fusion was complete. The first German *Book of Dr. Faustus* was printed in 1587. A play on which it was based gained a foothold in England, and British actors' companies brought it back to the Continent. For a time it was a standby in puppet repertoires, later to be returned to the stage by some of the greatest dramatic poets.

Time and again, however, a poet of the Faustus epic would go back to the Paracelsian sources. This is particularly true of Goethe. Robert Browning, on the other hand, dramatized the life of Paracelsus without mentioning Faustus; nevertheless, his theme is Faustian. Even Ben Jonson, Shakespeare's friend, who exploited an episode of Paracelsus' life for slapstick comedy, well knew the problem of the magus in a Christian world, as the motto of this chapter shows.

Faustus is the symbol of man's desire for access to the infinite. We speak of modern man's "Faustian drive," his insatiable thirst to know, his unconquerable faith in the powers of his mind, his resolve to use the uncanny as well as the admissible forces of nature. For centuries his aim has been salvation through knowledge, to become like the gods through his own efforts.

The recent emergence of that new species, the scientist-manager and specialist-scientist, somehow obscures this older scientist-philosopher type. When Paracelsus prescribed a medicine, he applied *"the whole world with all its virtues"*; when Faustus wants to "know," his object is not knowledge of everything but insight into the whole. Those who are obsessed with this urge will not be deterred by the observation that it is utopian and that it has never been realized. The great dream of winning salvation through science has recurred so often that we may safely assume its continued recurrence.

UTOPIA

Embracing the universe while he was seeking man, Paracelsus was a utopian. Like all great scientists, he overestimated the possibilities of his science. He strove to discover truths for which the science of his age had neither definitions nor methods of verification. He tried to grasp the whole before he knew the details. His genius was able to feel intuitively what he was unable to prove by reasoning or experiment, still less to express in words.

He tried to understand chemistry without having the notion of elements. He studied biology without ever having seen a cell. He sought to heal wounds when nobody knew how to stop a hemorrhage. He offered a theory of nature when there was no way to distinguish between organic and inorganic processes. He was a psychiatrist, when the very word "psychology" was not yet in the vocabulary. He could see no difference between a man's spirit and the spirit that steamed out of his alembic. He had to say "occult" when he was referring to the forces of nature which are known to the scientist but hidden from the layman.[6] He tried to conceptualize laws of Nature, when only astrological terms were available.

He was fully aware of these shortcomings. It is all too true that Paracelsus not only is a difficult author, but often is obscure and enigmatic, not to say confused and inconsistent. His works are crowded with contradictions which he did not trouble to resolve. His concepts are not well-defined, his language is ill-adapted to handle the difficult problems he proposed to solve. He constantly struggled with words, shouting and yelling when he felt that otherwise he might only stammer. He remonstrated against logical deductions and ridiculed "school philosophy" because his ideas failed to fit any known system. Often they did not reach the phase of articulate thought, but came to him in the form of an aphoristic certitude, based on sympathetic understanding and compassionate intuition rather than on analysis and research.

Searching is not research. Theophrastus was unable either to separate or to integrate the two. Perhaps that was the cause of his failure; certainly it was the cause of his greatness. He sought metaphysical certitude in empirical studies, and formulas in his intuition of the Absolute. In all his studies of nature he never lost sight of the ultimate aim of science: to know the nature of Nature. And vice versa, he believed he held the key to all phenomena of nature because he believed he knew the secret of the whole.

The contributions of the great men who have advanced humanity are of various kinds. Some contributed a definite piece of knowledge to the stock of information on the structure of the universe, the body, the soul, or society. Others invented tools and techniques which facilitated mastery over natural forces. These are the great peaks in history which serve as beacons for the study of man's possibilities.

Paracelsus was not among those who created and stood in the light. He belonged to a third kind of great men—those who explored the darkness and held the torch while mankind traversed the valleys; those who struggled with the truth before knowledge had ripened to formulate it; those who tried to lift the veil before they knew the Goddess behind it.

These, too, are great. They want the full truth when it is easier to compromise with half-truths. They would rather err in their search for right than be right without ever having searched. They would rather be damned while seeking salvation by their own endeavor, than be saved without ever having tried to save themselves.

They are redeemed, asserts Goethe, because they strove. Their efforts, though frustrated, save humanity every day.

Notes

For full titles of quoted works see Appendix E, p. 341-343.

CHAPTER I.

1) *Philosophischer Phoenix*, Danzig, 1682, pp. 75–80. Azoth is the chemical name of mercury. For Red Lion see chapter 11, note 8. For *Spiritus Vitae* see Chapter 10.
2) *Chirurgische Buecher*, 1618, Vol. I, p. 132.
3) *Epistolae Medicinales*, Zuerich, Jan. 16, 1561, quoted by Philip Mason Palmer and Robert Pattison Moore, in *Sources of the Faust Tradition*, Oxford University Press, 1936, p. 100.
4) Huser, Vol. X, p. 10, ed. Aschner, Vol. IV, p. 523. Cf. also Matthew 10:26.
5) Ed. Aschner, Vol. IV, p 12. See Strunz (1937), p. 71.
6) From the *Intimatio*, Chapter 14, *infra*.
7) Ed. Huser, Vol. I, pp. 39 and 220; Vol. V, p. 180; ed. Sudhoff, Vol. VIII, p. 124.
8) Ed. Sudhoff, Vol. XI, p. 85.
9) Ed. Sudhoff, Vol. X, pp. 17*ff*.
10) Ed. Waite, Vol. II, p. 169.
11) Ed. Aschner. Vol. IV, p. 523*ff*., cf. Matth. 7:7 and the Revelation of St. John 3:20.
12) Kristeller-Randall, *The Renaissance Philosophy of Man*, Chicago, 1948, p. 247.

13) Ed. Huser, Vol. IX, p. 261.

14) Introduction to the *Philosophia Sagax*, ed. Huser, Vol. X, p. 16.

15) *Paragranum*, ed. Strunz, p. 98.

16) Ed. Sudhoff, Vol. VII, p. 150; cf. also *Der Hoellenzwang* (The Conquest of Hell), a book ascribed to Dr. Faustus, English in: Rose, *The History of Dr. Faustus*, Dutton, no year.

17) Ed. Huser, Vol. X, p. 16.

18) Ed. Leidecker, p. 58; ed. Huser, Vol. I, p. 48.

19) *Paragranum*, *loc. cit.*, p. 98. On the concept of "Light of Nature" see Strunz (1937), and Hiram Haydn, *The Counter-Renaissance*, Scribner's, 1950.

20) *Archiv fuer Reformationsgeschichte*, Vol. 15, p. 129; cf. also: Nichts ist drinnen, nichts ist draussen . . . (Goethe).

21) Agnes Bartscherer, *Paracelsus, Paracelsisten und Faust*, Dortmund, 1911; Josef Noggler, "Goethe und die Alchemie" in: *Das Antiquariat*, Wien, No. 7/8, April, 1949, p. 112.

22) Christopher Marlowe, *The Tragical History of Dr. Faustus*, Modern Library, p. 50. "Lines, circles . . ." are cabbalistic devices of knowledge. "Stretcheth as far . . . ," see p. 84, *infra*, on the notion that "knowledge gives power."

23) Ed. Sudhoff, Vol. 10, p. 183; also in *Philosophia ad Athenienses;* see Strunz (1937), p. 76.

24) Bartscherer, *op. cit.*

25) Palmer-More, *op. cit.*

26) Ed. Sudhoff, Vol. XII, p. 5.

CHAPTER   2

Motto: ed. Sudhoff, Vol. IX, p. 151.

1) Basilio de Telepnef, *Paracelsus*, St. Gall, 1940, p. 14.

2) Sudhoff, *Paracelsus* (1936), p. 12.

3) We follow Karl Sudhoff (1936). Karl Bittel (*Nova Acta Paracelsica*, 1944/5) dismisses the "Ochsner legend." According to Bittel, Paracelsus' mother was Charlotte Gruetzner. The birthday also may have

been September 21 or December 17. St. Philip's day was November 14.

4) On exhumation, the bones showed the same effects. Cf. Karl Aberle, *Grabdenkmal, Schaedel und Abbildungen des Paracelsus*, 1888.

5) However, Parcelsus himself spoke of his beard: "My beard has more experience than your school bag." Cf. *Nova Acta*, 1947. With Strebel (ibid.), I am inclined to discount the whole story; the boar version in particular is suspect as containing mythological material.

6) Ed. Sudhoff, Vol. X, p. 199; also ed. Sigerist, p. 34, and Sudhoff (1899, II), p. 406.

7) Other interpretations of the name are given in Chaps. 1 and 12. All may be correct since Paracelsus was fond of cabbalistic plays on words and letters.

8) Ed. Sudhoff, Vol. X, p. 353.

9) Gentiane, camomile, fennel, poppy, belladonna, foxglove, chicory, mint, thyme, vervain, St. John's wort, witch-herb, lavender, and others.

10) See Chap. 21. Psychoanalysts might find support for the Ochsner version in Paracelsus' psychological and chemical views. He rejected contemporary opinions on witches, for of course a sick mother would elicit protective, not aggressive, attitudes. Allenby (*Paracelse, Médecin Maudit*) emphasizes the "mother complex" which appears in Paracelsus' allegories and speculations on "Mother Nature," his exaltation of the virgin, his alchemical and cosmological concern with the "matrix" and the "macrocosmos." Goethe converted the alchemical allegory into a myth when he sends Faust down to "The Mothers" as a preliminary to his marriage to Helena. In all this, we follow the older version supported by Sudhoff, but rejected by Bittel. See also: Dr. Lienhardt, *Medizingeschichtliches aus Einsiedeln*, 1941.

11) *On the Miners' Diseases* and *A Book on Nymphs, Sylphs, Pygmies, and Salamanders*, ed. Sigerist.

12) Alchemists believed that color was the essential quality in metals. Tinted lead or mercury was accepted as "chemical gold."

13) Ed. Sudhoff, Vol. XIV, p. 624.

14) Ed. Sudhoff, 1899, p. 296. Bittel concludes that Paracelsus was a stammerer. The passus, however, refers to a discussion in which Paracelsus apparently was shouted down by the audience. The "stammering" may be a figure of speech. Both of his amanuenses who have left memoirs assert that he dictated with such great speed that they hardly could keep up with him.

CHAPTER 3

Motto: Ed. Huser, Vol. IX, p. 422. For this chapter see also: Ernst Troeltsch, *Social Doctrines of the Christian Churches*, 1931; Max Weber, *Protestant Ethics and the Spirit of Capitalism*, 1930; B. L. Manning, *The People's Faith at the Time of Wyclef*, 1919; Hiram Haydn, *The Counter-Renaissance*, 1950; R. H. Tawney, *Religion and the Rise of Capitalism*, 1922; Ernest Cassirer, *Individuum und Kosmos im Zeitalter der Renaissance*, 1926; J. Huizinga, *The Waning of the Middle Ages*, 1925.

1) Telepneff has contributed a concordance of Paracelsus' references to universities and a possible chronology of his visits to these various places (*Nova Acta*, Vol. II). The mere fact that Paracelsus made scathing comments on all these universities, however, does not prove anything. In the case of Cologne, *e.g.*, the *Letters of Obscure Men* had made it possible for all to pass facile judgment.

2) *In Praise of Folly*, quoted by Stefan Zweig. Cf. Paracelsus' encounter with Erasmus, Chap. 13.

3) Ed. Huser, Vol. IX, p. 390. On Paracelsus' Scotism see Appendix C.

4) "The books which God Himself wrote don't lie." Ed. Huser, Vol. II, p. 227. Likewise, Campanella in *De Sensu Rerum*.

5) Quoted by Cassirer, *loc. cit.*, p. 57. On de Cusa see Appendix A, 3.

6) Quoted by Gregory Zilboorg, *A History of Medical Psychology*, New York, 1941.

7) Quoted by Spunda, *Paracelsus*, p. 112. Fritz Werle (*Nova Acta*, 1947, p. 18) shows that Paracelsus was more opposed to astrology in his youth than later. He fails to draw parallels with Pico della Miran-

dola and others who developed in the same way. Cf. ed. Sudhoff, Vol. I, p. 177, and IX, p. 377.

8) Ed. Sudhoff, Vol. X, p. 31; also *Paragranum*, ed. Strunz, p. 26.

9) *Lib. de Metricis*, quoted by Betschart, *Paracelsus*, p. 27. Petrus Ramus, likewise, wrote: "Socrates, in his admirable wisdom, taught that liberal arts should be related to life. The universities, however, teach subtleties useless in practice." In many respects, Ramus is the French counterpart of Paracelsus, whom he praised warmly.

10) *Epistolae Virorum Obscurorum* may also mean: "Letters of obscurantists." The jest was directed against the bigoted clergymen of Cologne who had attacked Reuchlin for his defense of the Cabbala. Rufus Mutianus was a friend of the Italian Platonist and Cabbalist, Pico della Mirandola.

11) Quoted by Telepneff, *Paracelsus*, p. 25.

CHAPTER 4

Motto:. Rabelais, a contemporary of Paracelsus, puts this ironical advice on how to study medicine in the mouth of a grotesque character. Rabelais, learned doctor himself, was critical of Galen and favored Platonist views.

1) See note 5, Chap. 3. Herbert Weisinger (*Journal of the History of Ideas*, Vol. VI, No. 4, October 1945, p. 420) quotes Paracelsus in support of his thesis that Renaissance men conceived the idea of progress. See ed. Sudhoff, Vol. IV, pp. 494 and 539; Vol. X, p. 266; Vol. XI, p. 127; Vol. XII, p. 24–25; Vol. XIV, p. 262.

2) Castiglione cites the case of Dr. Geynes who was not allowed to lecture at Oxford until he had recanted his criticism of Galen.

3) Ed. Huser, Vol. I, p. 170.

4) The proverb, "The blind leading the blind," which Paracelsus used in his Basle lectures, also occurred to Dr. Carpi and accords with Rabelais' gibes at the ignorance of doctors.

5) *Grosse Chirurgie* III, p. 259*ff*, quoted by Dr. Iago Galdston.

6) Quotation from Thorndike, *History of Magic and Experimental Sciences*, Columbia University Press, 1941, Vol. V, p. 500ff.

7) Ed. Huser, Vol. I, p. 170.

8) Goethe, *Faust*, Part I. The "golden tree" symbol occurs frequently in Paracelsus' works, partly as a reference to alchemy, partly pointing to biological ideas, perhaps combining the two in a vitalistic view of cosmology. The "tree" appears frequently in the Cabbala, too.

CHAPTER 5

Motto: ed. Hartman, p. 27.

1) Ed. Sudhoff, Vol. X, p. 31.

2) Ed. Sudhoff, Vol. X, p. 20.

3) Ed. Huser, Vol. I, p. 170; also the full quotation in Chap. 1.

4) Ed. Huser, Vol. I, p. 103.

5) Ed. Strunz, p. 29.

6) Ed. Huser, Vol. IX, p. 309.

7) J. H. Baas, *Geschichte des aerztlichen Standes*, p. 185.

8) Translation by Morley, *Agrippa von Nettesheim*.

9) Ed. Huser, Vol. VII, p. 409; III, p. 213. Ed. Sudhoff, Vol. XI, p. 85.

10) *Chirurgische Buecher*, ed. Huser, p. 309.

11) *Ibid.*

12) *Ibid.*

13) Ed. Sudhoff, Vol. VII, p. 374. See also Chap. 8, note 2, and the motto of the present chapter.

14) Ed. Sudhoff, Vol. I, p. 199; Vol. VII, p. 369.

15) The Ferrara register, unfortunately, is missing, and the only evidence of Paracelsus' right to the doctor's title remains his own assertion before a Strasbourg court where he swore "upon a doctor's oath which he has pledged to the Faculty of Ferrara." This document fails to say whether Paracelsus was doctor of surgery as well as physics.

16) Kolbenheyer, intent upon saving his hero's reputation, has advanced

the ingenious hypothesis that Paracelsus acquired the doctor's title *honoris causa* for his brave fulfillment of doctor's duties during an outbreak of the plague in Italy. Sudhoff, p. 37 of the Introduction to Vol. VIII of his edition, cites evidence to the effect that Paracelsus was graduated at Verona. He quietly abandoned this hypothesis in his biography of 1936 remarking that the Ferrara registers are unavailable.

17) A similar attitude with regard to Paracelsus' magic inheritance will be discussed in Chap. 7.
18) Quoted from Holmyard, *History of Chemistry*, p. 37.
19) Some time between 1513 and 1517, Paracelsus was employed in the Füeger mines at Schwatz (Tyrol) see also note 10, Chap. 10.

CHAPTER 6

Motto: *De Lapide Philosophorum*, quoted by Hartman, p. 330.
1) Quoted by Hartman, p. 181.
2) Ed. Sudhoff, Vol. VIII, p. 292.
3) From *Philosophia Sagax*, quoted by Hartman.
4) *Volumen Paramirum*, ed. Leidecker, p. 16.
5) *Ibid.*, p. 14.
6) Ed. Sudhoff, Vol. XI, p. 377*ff*.
7) Ed. Leidecker, p. 14.
8) Ed. Huser, Vol. III, p. 179; Vol. IX, p. 444. See *infra*, p. 244.
9) Quoted by Hartman, p. 26. Ed. Huser, Vol. VI, p. 336; also refer to p. 107.
10) *A Book on Nymphs . . .*, ed. Sigerist, pp. 213*ff*. See also Agricola, *De Animantibus Subterraneis* (1549).
11) Ed. Sigerist, p. 245.
12) Ed. Matthiessen, p. 168.
13) Ed. Sigerist, p. 246.
14) Ed. Hartman, pp. 138–139: *De Morbis Invisibilibus;* ed. Strebel, Vol. V. p. 367.
15) Ed. Huser, Vol. X, p. 88.

16) Quoted by Sartorius von Waltershausen.—In *De Morbis Invisibili-bus*, (ed. Sudhoff, Vol. IX), Paracelsus ridicules the "ceremoniacs" who muddle magic; there he also calls wound spells "superstitious" and character prophecying a "patched-up art."

17) Ed. Sudhoff, Vol. I, p. 106.

18) Ed. Hartman, p. 120.

19) Matthias Mairhofer, *De principiis discernendi philosophiam a magia* (1581), quoted from Thorndike, Vol. VI, p. 414.

CHAPTER 7

Motto: Hartman, *loc. cit.*, p. 163; ed. Sudhoff, Vol. III, p. 179.

1) Ed. Huser, Vol. II, p. 130.

2) Ed. Sudhoff, Vol. XIII, p. 376.

3) Quoted from *Astronomia Magna* by Strunz, *Paracelsus*, p. 76.

4) Preface to *Great Surgery Book*. Ed. Sudhoff, Vol. X, p. 353. The date to which Paracelsus refers is uncertain. Since Trithemius died in 1516, it might be necessary to assume that Paracelsus stopped in Würzburg before he went to Italy.

5) The Counts of Sponheim were buried in Lavanttal, and Sudhoff (1936) wants us to believe that Paracelsus remembered their mausoleum rather than the cloister. However, in the same passage Paracelsus does remember, not Sponheim, but Lavanttal, in connection with Bishop Erhard. There is no reason why Paracelsus should have mentioned the Abbot of Lavanttal under a name which nobody would recognize, while he was trying to impress his readers with the enumeration of celebrities and scholars of alchemy.

6) Ed. Sudhoff, Vol. VIII, p. 72.

7) Quoted by Thorndike, *loc. cit.*, Vol. VI. p. 439. For comparison, we quote the following passage from Paracelsus' *Labyrinthus Medicorum* in Hartman's transcription (*loc. cit.*, p. 258; cf. also *ibid.*, p. 163):

"To understand the laws of nature we must love her. He who does not understand Maria does not love her; he who does not know God does not love him . . . The more knowledge we obtain, the stronger will be our love and the greater our power. He who knows God has faith in Him; he who does not know Him can have no true faith. He who knows nature will love her, and obtain the power to employ her forces."

The seven steps of transmutation in *De Natura Rerum,* ed. Huser, Vol. VI, p. 330*ff.*

8) Ed. Huser, Vol. I, p. 228.

9) Ed. Sudhoff, Vol. XI, p. 189. Sartorius von Waltershausen believes that Paracelsus was sympathetic to the theosophical conclusion that man brings salvation to the universe. But he cannot cite any pertinent text. The reason will appear in Chaps. 23 and 24. When Paracelsus became interested in salvation, he already had given up the alchemistic philosophy.

10) Hartman, *loc. cit.,* p. 258; see note 7 above.

11) Ed. Sudhoff, Vol. XI, p. 138; also, in ed. Huser, Vol. I, p. 305, he says: "The smaller the dosis, the greater the effect." See ed. Sudhoff, Vol. VIII, p. 180, and Vol. X, p. 277. It is interesting to note what contemporaries understood when they first learned of the new doctrine. John Donne, in his *Ignatius,* accuses Paracelsus of "removing [from poisons] the treacherous quality [by which they can be discerned] so they might safely be given without suspicion [*i.e.,* on the part of the victim] and yet perform their office as strongly."

12) Ed. Huser, Vol. I, p. 228.

13) Cf. the Merseburg Wound Spell, where Wotan joins "limb to limb." Cf. Chapter 11, note 17, where Paracelsus defines his understanding of "like" and "contrary."

14) Ed. Sudhoff, Vol. VIII, p. 107.

15) *Paragranum,* ed. Strunz, p. 29; ed. Huser, Vol. I, p. 103.

CHAPTER 8

Motto: *Seven Defensiones,* ed. Sigerist, *loc. cit.,* p. 25.

1) Ed. Sudhoff, Vol. X, p. 19.

2) Ed. Sudhoff, Vol. VII, p. 374. This passage again shows his shaky defense against the charge that he had not graduated.

3) Preface to *Philosophia Sagax.*

4) *E.g.,* Telepneff, in the 2d vol. of *Nova Acta.*

5) Ed. Sudhoff, Vol. VIII, p. 359.

6) Telepneff's hypothesis. His assumption that Paracelsus was a partisan of the Hanse League is contradicted by his later services under kings, knights, and the City of Venice.

7) Ed. Sudhoff, Vol. I, p. 140. In another passage, however, he says: "Never have I seen Africa."

8) The sword can be seen in the original portrait by Hirschvogel. Later copies and developments show larger and larger pommels and the word AZOTH appears on Rosicrucian pictures. Paracelsus' iconography has been discussed in *Nova Acta.*

CHAPTER 9

For this chapter see the following books:
Preserved Smith, *The Age of Reformation.*
R. H. Tawney, *Religion and the Rise of Capitalism.*
Lindsay, *History of the Reformation.*
Hiram Haydn, *The Counter Renaissance.*

1) Ed. Sudhoff (1899), p. 333.

2) Paraphrase by Strunz, *Paracelsus,* pp. 176-177.

3) Ed. Sudhoff (1899), p. 263. Cf. also ed. Matthiessen, p. 163*ff.*: "We are all created equal."

4) *Surgical Books* (ed. Huser), p. 311.

5) Ed. Sudhoff, Vol. XI. Trithemius also complained that "grocers conspire that none shall sell cheaper." He said that speculators are criminals under Canonic law. Paracelsus would never have quoted the law; he did not recognize it; see note 7.

6) Ed. Huser, Vol. IX, p. 444. See the Albertus Magnus quotation on p. 69.

7) *Archiv fuer Reformationsgeschichte,* quoted by Kayser, par. 294.

Later, in his interpretation of the magic plates at Nuremberg, Paracelsus returned to the difficult subject (ed. Aschner IV, p. 963).
Pondering over the course of the Reformation, he says: "How bad
the thief ever be, that does not make tne hangman honest. Let each
look into his own heart and justify his actions before his conscience
—so will destiny give him his own."

8) Ed. Sudhoff (1899), p. 338. See Chapter 21.
9) Ed. Matthiessen, p. 332; Strebel II, p. 271.
10) Ed. Sudhoff (1899), p. 114.
11) Ed. Matthiessen, p. 105.

CHAPTER 10

Motto: *Astronomia Magna*, quoted by Strunz (1937), p. 76.

1) Ed. Huser, Vol. VI, p. 373; Hartman, *loc. cit.*, p. 296.
2) Terms which Paracelsus used are quoted in Appendix D, others in
Chapter 5, note 18. He introduced words like "reduction," "gas";
see *infra*.
3) See *infra*, on the quintessence, and next chapter, note 14, on elements. Relevant passages: ed. Sudhoff, Vol. III, pp. 105, 118.
4) Cf. T. P. Sherlock, *The Chemical Work of Paracelsus*, AMBIX, Vol.
III, May, 1948, pp. 33–63, London. Also: Ernst Darmstaedter, *Arznei
und Alchemie*, Paracelsus-Studien (*Studien zur Geschichte der
Medizin*, Leipzig, 1931).
5) For convenience we deviate from the chronological order in this
chapter. Since no definite date can be set for Parcelsus' apprentice-
ship at the Füeger laboratory, and the date of the *Archidoxa* is still
controversial, it is impossible to trace any possible evolution of
Paracelsus' chemical views. In later works his terminology is firmer
and detail more accurate, but this proves nothing with respect to
his early training in "distillation" and metallurgy.
6) Works by the ancient scientist Aureolus were in the library of
Theophrastus' father. Paracelsus once signed himself "Aureolus."
Both portraits of Paracelsus by Hirschvogel (chapter 26) give his
name as "Aureolus Theophrastus ab Hohenheim".

7) *Philosophischer Phoenix*, 1682, pp. 75–80.

8) Quoted by Stoddart, *loc. cit.*, pp. 252*ff*. On practical jokes, see p. 122 *infra*.

9) *Chirurgische Schriften*, ed. Huser (1618). It should always be remembered that all alchemists distinguished between "our gold" and "vulgar gold."

10) Ed. Sudhoff, Vol. X, p. 353. It is difficult to date Paracelsus' stay at the laboratory. Most likely 1517, the year before his trip around the world. There is a possibility, however, that he did not meet Sigmund Füeger before 1533, when he worked in several mines in the Inn valley. Füeger was not related to the banking house of the Fuggers. The only interest the two families had in common was metal trading.

11) Ed. Sigerist, p. 198.

12) *Ibid.*, p. 199. Of course: $Cu + H_2SO_4 \longleftrightarrow CuSO_4 + 2H$ and $Fe + CuSO_4 + H_2O = Cu + FeSO_4 + O + 2H$.

13) Quoted by Hartman, *loc. cit.*, p. 330. On transmutation see ed. Huser, Vol. VI, *passim* pp. 265–410, particularly pp. 309, 313, and 402.

14) Ed. Huser, Vol. VI, p. 24. We cannot insist often enough on the realistic (not to say materialistic) meaning which must be given to such words. The "spirit" of alchemical substances is as material or as immaterial as our atoms, electrons, or ions. Parcelsus also conceived the "spirit" as the virtue of each substance. There is no reason, hence, to call him a spiritualist just because he used the word spirit. Such a *quid pro quo* ignores the difference between philosophical and scientific terminology.

15) Ed. Huser, Vol. VI, pp. 45, 48.

CHAPTER II

Motto: *Chirurgische Buecher*, ed. Huser, p. 300. If Cassirer's thesis is correct, the word "*experimentum*" would have come to Paracelsus from de Cusa *via* Pico della Mirandola.

1) The rest of the Oporinus letter will be found on p. 155.

2) Ed. Sigerist, loc. cit., p. 198*ff*.

3) *Chirurgische Buecher*, ed. Huser, p. 378.

4) Ed. Huser, Vol. VI, p. 266.

5) Ed. Sudhoff, Vol. XI, pp. 187–189.

6) Ed. Sudhoff, Vol. XI, p. 196; Strunz, p. 135.

7) Ed. Huser, Vol. V, p. 180; ed. Sudhoff, Vol. X, p. 277.

8) Azoth of the Red Lion is mercury, distilled from mercury oxides. Paracelsus often designates the end product by the name of the origin or components. This observation also may resolve the controversy whether Red Lion might not mean alchemical gold or sulfur. Apparently it is both—gold which results when mercury has lost its sulfur. The formula for *mercurius vivus* has been quoted above under (4).

9) Ed. Sigerist, p. 75.

10) Ed. Huser, Vol. VI, pp. 43 and 55; also p. 274.

11) Ed. Huser, Vol. VI, p. 83, and Vol. V, p. 180; also ed. Huser, Vol. VI, pp. 115–211, 373*ff*.

12) Ed. Huser, Vol. I, p. 220; Vol. V, p. 180; ed. Sudhoff, Vol. III, p. 185.

13) Ed. Huser, Vol. I, p. 305; cf. also ed. Huser, Vol. VII, p. 409. Ed. Kayser, aph. 121.

14) Ed. Huser, Vol. VI, p. 25; likewise in the report on the Pfeffers spa. Ed. Sudhoff, Vol. III, pp. 110–111, 118; Vol. VIII, p. 185.

15) Quoted by Allenby, *Paracelse Médecin Maudit*, p. 38, and by Spunda, *Paracelsus*, p. 144.

16) Ed. Huser, Vol. VI, p. 43; ed. Sudhoff, Vol. III, p. 138.

17) Ed. Sudhoff, Vol. VIII, p. 88; ed. Huser, Vol. I, pp. 39 and 103.

18) Sudhoff (1936) maintains that Valentine's celebrated *Triumph of Antimony*, purporting to be a pre-Paracelsian textbook, is a seventeenth-century falsification written to discredit the Parcelsians. Mercury cures were used by all empirics. Like all earlier alchemists, Paracelsus believed that mercury is "the mother of metals." This "chemical mercury" he called "*Mercurius vivus*." Mercury not only contained all metals but also a mysterious life power which—as *mer-*

curius vitae—rejuvenates the human body. Hence his quicksilver cures. Cf. ed. Huser, Vol. VI, pp. 43–55, 264–269, 309.

19) Ed. Sudhoff, Vol. XI, p. 138.
20) *Opus Paramirum*, First Treatise, quoted from Stoddart's translation, *op. cit.*, p. 215.
21) Sudhoff (1936), p. 107.
22) Ed. Sudhoff, Vol. III, p. 241.

CHAPTER 12

Motto: *Archiv fuer Reformationsgeschichte*, Vol. 59–60, pp. 129–130.
1) Ed. Sigerist, p. 38.
2) Quoted from Sudhoff (1936).
3) Ed. Leidecker, p. 23. This theory has cabbalistic origins.
4) Ed. Leidecker, p. 15.
5) *Ibid.*, p. 17.
6) *Paragranum*, ed. Huser, Vol. I, p. 219.
7) *Volumen Paramirum*, Chap. on "Ens Veneni," ed. Huser, Vol. I, pp. 25–31 (translated by Stoddart, *loc. cit.*, p. 92).
8) The complete text of the letter will be found in Chapter 14.
9) Ed. Huser, Vol. I, pp. 35ff (greatly telescoped version). See ed. Leidecker, p. 35.
10) *Ibid.*, p. 39.
11) *Ibid.*, p. 60; ed. Sudhoff, Vol. XI, p. 15.
12) Ed. Leidecker, p. 58.
13) *Ibid.*, p. 61.

CHAPTER 13

Motto: *De Morbis Invisibilibus*, ed. Strunz.
1) See the "Cacophrastus" poem, Chapter 15.
2) Sudhoff (1936), p. 26.
3) See J. J. Herzog, *Oecolampadius*, Basle, 1843.

CHAPTER 14

1) English by Arthur E. Waite (1894), Vol. II, pp. 169–170. Original in Sudhoff (1936), p. 28.
2) Sudhoff (1936), pp. 46*ff.*
3) Aegidius von der Wiese (quoted in *Paracelsus-Forschungen*, Vol. II, p. 79).
4) Neander published this letter in 1586; its authenticity is doubtful.
5) Sudhoff (1936), p. 50.
6) This is Rosicrucian tradition. However, Holbein probably never met Paracelsus either in Basle or in England. Moreover, the drawing represents a man much younger than Paracelsus was at that time, and bears no resemblance to the authentic portraits by Scorel and Hirschvogel. This writer cannot agree with Sudhoff who has accepted the Holbein portrait as a genuine Paracelsus icon. Many posthumous portraits can be traced to the Holbein drawing as model. Strebel seems to think this proves something.
7) Sudhoff (1936), p. 21. This lampoon seems to allude to the *Philosophia ad Athenienses*, which Hans Kayser has recognized as genuine Paracelsian.

CHAPTER 15

Motto: Nova Acta, Vol. I, p. 79.
1) Abbreviated, quoted by Sudhoff (1936) and Stoddart.
2) Stoddart, p. 132. Allusions are to:
"common simples," p. 56.
Ares, Iliadus, Archaeus (Paracelsian terms for the biological functions), pp. 136 and 215.
Wendolin (Dr. V. Hock), beat Paracelsus in the public discussion in Strasbourg, p. 144.
Africa's creations; cf. Pliny's fantastic reports, p. 44.
3) Ed. Sudhoff, Vol. VIII, p. 57.

4) Ed. Strunz, p. 29; also quoted by Sudhoff (1936).

5) Ed. Hartman, p. 24; cf. also ed. Sigerist, p. 34.

6) Ed. Sudhoff, Vol. IV, Preface.

7) *Ibid.;* in the fourth volume of his edition, Sudhoff sets 1527 as the date of *De Gradibus,* although the dedication to Klauser is dated "November, 1526". At that time, Paracelsus had not yet been appointed town doctor and *ordinarius;* but in the dedication he used both titles—another instance of his carefree assumption of degrees.

8) Ed. Sudhoff, Vol. IV, Preface.

9) The theory of a deliberate trap was first advanced by Robert Browning. Sudhoff and other German scholars accepted the incident as genuine.

CHAPTER 16

1) Ed. Aschner, Vol. IV, p. 963. In an often quoted passage, however, Paracelsus admitted that Luther's enemies "wished to throw into the fire both him and me"—"By calling me Luther they do not mean to honor me. . . . Let Luther defend his cause, I will stand for mine."

2) Ed. Huser, Vol. II, p. 19.

3) Quoted by Sudhoff (1936).

4) So elsewhere: "Just let them swallow it; any boor can give this prescription. For that you don't need Avicenna."

Cf. Hartman, p. 245. In view of such clear evidence to the contrary, it is amazing to find it repeated and copied from one medical history to the other that Paracelsus introduced mercury and antimony cures, or that his great triumph was the eventual adoption of metallic drugs. This misconception is due to the devotees of the "metalist" sect, on the one hand, and the "impostors," on the other hand, who praise but do not read their master.

5) In the German language, the connotations of "germ" and "seed" are interchangeable. Cf. ed. Aschner, Vol. I, p. 523, about *"Samen"* (germs) as causes of infection. He also distinguished two kinds of

"germs," iliastric, *i.e.*, originating in the body, and cagastric, attacking it from without, as in epidemic diseases. Syphilis was cagastric—brought on by an evil star, neither organic nor functional.

CHAPTER 17

Motto: *Paragranum.*
1) Ed. Huser, Vol. II, p. 19. This passage seems to be the source for the report, copied by one compiler from the other, that Paracelsus burned Galen's works in sulfur.
2) Likewise in ed. Huser, Vol. I, p. 170.
3) Ed. Strunz, p. 21.
4) Ed. Sudhoff, Vol. VIII, p. 56.
5) *Paragranum*, ed. Strunz, p. 98.
6) Ed. Waite, Vol. I, p. 19.
7) *Ibid.*, p. 39.
8) Sudhoff (1899), p. 333.
9) Ed. Sigerist, p. 35.
10) See Motto of Chap. 15.
11) Ed. Sudhoff, Vol. VI, p. 180.

CHAPTER 18

Motto: quoted by Bittel, *Paracelsus*, p. 11.
1) Ed. Sigerist, p. 31.
2) Sudhoff (1936).
3) Ed. Huser, Vol. III, p. 19.
4) *Chirurgische Buecher*, ed. Huser, p. 649.
5) Ed. Strunz, p. 98.
6) Fries wrote the first comprehensive textbook of medicine in German, the *Mirror of Medicine* (1518), after Schoeffler's famous incunabulum, *The Garden of Health.*
7) Ed. Huser, Vol. II, pp. 108–109.

8) Ed. Aschner, *Labyrinthus.*

9) Erich Fromm (*Escape from Freedom*) has traced the Nazi ideologies to the Lutheran rebellion of particularism against Roman universalism. A monument of hero worship and Nazi falsifications is Kolbenheyer's Paracelsus novel. A courageous anti-Nazi view was presented by Sartorius (see Chapter 25).

CHAPTER 19

Motto: Ed. Huser, Vol. X, p. 456.

1) The first essay, therefore, was written after the third.

2) Ruetiner's *Chronicle of St. Gall*, page 84, quoted by Sudhoff (1936).

3) Quoted by Sudhoff (1936).

4) *Opus Paramirum*, Third Essay, see below, on Podagra.

5) *Opus Paramirum*, First Essay, Vol. II.

6) *Ibid.*, quoted from Stoddart, p. 120.

7) "Tartaric diseases" are treated in ed. Huser, Vol. II, pp. 244–340; III, pp. 207–338 and 339 (the prescription for Erasmus); IV, pp. 9–37, 246–316, and also *passim* in VII, pp. 300ff (on the effect of spas).

Dr. Bernard Aschner is as controversial a figure as his master. See his *Art of the Healer*, Dial Press, 1942, and *Treatment of Arthritis and Rheumatism*, Froben Press, 1946. Since this is not a medical work, the merits of his claims must be left undiscussed.

8) Ed. Huser, Vol. I, p. 158.

9) *Opus Paramirum*, Fourth Essay.

10) *Opus Paramirum*, quoted by Strunz, p. 108.

11) Although known in the fourteenth century, this advice needed to be reiterated in the sixteenth century.

12) *Opus Paramirum*, First Essay, Vol. II. Identical statements in the *Great Surgery Book* and *Hospital Book.*

13) *Paragranum*, ed. Strunz, p. 77.

14) *De Vita Longa.*

15) *Opus Paramirum,* ed. Sudhoff, Vol. IX, p. 240. See also Friedrich Gundolf, *Paracelsus* (1928).
16) *Opus Paramirum,* Third Essay, quoted by Sudhoff (1936), p. 118.
17) See Chapter 1.
18) *Archiv fuer Reformationsgeschichte,* Vol. 15, p. 129. (Italics supplied.)
19) *Paragranum,* ed. Strunz. (Italics supplied.)
20) Ed. Sudhoff, Vol. IX, p. 325. (Italics supplied.)

CHAPTER 20

1) Ed. Sudhoff, Vol. IX, pp. 39 and 120.
2) We might have called it materialistic as well, if the term had not come to be identified with a narrow and static definition of matter.
3) Stoddart, p. 126.
4) *Philosophia ad Athenienses,* Huser, Vol. VIII, p. 4. The sentence is so typically Paracelsian that it might settle the question of authorship.
5) Ed. Huser, Vol. VIII.
6) See Ernst Cassirer, *Individuum und Kosmos.*

CHAPTER 21

1) Ed. Strebel, Vol. II, pp. 159–163.
2) *De Imaginibus,* ed. Strebel, Vol. II, p. 364.
3) *Ibid.,* p. 365. In the German text, Paracelsus uses the Orphic word "theoria" in the sense of "passionate, sympathetic contemplation." Compare Revelation of St. John, 2:11.
4) *De Morbis Invisibilibus,* ed. Strebel, Vol. V, pp. 337ff.
5) *Ibid.*
6) Ed. Leidecker, pp. 51–52.
7) Ed. Strebel, Vol. II, p. 102.
8) *Ibid.,* pp. 340 and 362.
9) *Ibid.,* p. 165.

10) Quoted by Dr. Gregory Zilboorg in *History of Medical Psychology*.
11) Ed. Leidecker, p. 47.
12) Preface to *Diseases Which Deprive Man of His Reason*, ed. Sigerist, p. 142.
13) Ed. Leidecker, p. 54. Ed. Sigerist, p. 167.
14) Ed. Leidecker, p. 51.
15) Ed. Sigerist, p. 168.
16) "Indeed he was a psychosomaticist . . . centuries before the concept was reborn." Dr. Iago Galdston, *The Psychiatry of Paracelsus, Bulletin of the History of Medicine*, Vol. XXIV, May 1950, p. 215.
   Dr. Gregory Zilboorg gives a different interpretation in ed. Sigerist, p. 133, where he says: "Paracelsus is presenting, in a redundant and perhaps confusing way, the definite conception of psychological illness and of conversion symptoms. Even his discussion of *suffocatio intellectus*, in which he attempts to explain that reason might appear profoundly affected but that actually this disturbance might be but a result secondary to emotional or other psychological disturbance, is as keen a clinical observation as it is modern." (Quoted with permission of the Johns Hopkins Press Co.)
17) Ed. Sigerist, p. 158.
18) *Ibid.*, p. 160.
19) *Ibid.*, p. 181; cf. also ed. Leidecker, p. 52.
20) This point has been emphasized particularly by Dr. Iago Galdston, *loc. cit.*
21) A follower and successor of Paracelsus is Dr. Carl G. Jung, whose studies on psychology and alchemy, psychology and astrology, and psychology and myth have greatly contributed to the understanding of Paracelsus.

CHAPTER 22

Motto: *Philosophia Sagax*, ed. Huser, Vol. X, p. 25.
1) Almost identical in *Volumen Paramirum* and *De Morbis Invisibilibus*.

2) This paragraph summarizes several passages from *De Morbis In-visibilibus*.

3) *Philosophia Occulta*, quoted by Hartman, p. 137. Likewise, Benja-min L. Gordon (*The Romance of Medicine*, p. 497) quotes: "Faith is the cure for all. If we cannot cure a disease by faith it is because our faith is weak on account of our want of knowledge . . . . Imagination is the cause of many diseases. The curing power of medicines consists not so much in the spirit that is hidden in them but in the spirit in which they are taken."

4) Ed. Strebel, Vol. II, p. 241.

5) Quoted by Kayser.

6) My interpretation deviates from the theosophical one of Sartorius von Waltershausen whose ingenious construction, however, com-pels the admiration of anyone who has tried to work out a solution in Paracelsus' works.

7) Cf. Kristeller-Randall, *op. cit.*, notably John H. Randall's introduc-tion to *De Immortalitate*.

CHAPTER 23

1) Only one volume of Section II of Sudhoff's edition, *Theological and Theo-philosophical Works*, edited by W. Matthiessen, has been published. Neither the Nazis nor the Swiss have used the Paracelsus revival to publish more of his manuscripts. Not even the pompous commemorations of the fourth centenary of his death have prompted such an act of piety.

2) Quoted by Telepneff, p. 66.

3) Quoted from Kayser, p. 67.

4) Ed. Matthiessen, p. 83.

5) Quoted by Kayser, Introduction.

6) *Ibid.*

7) Ed. Strebel, Vol. I, p. 73.

8) Ed. Matthiessen, p. 146.

9) Quoted by Kayser.

10) Ed. Matthiessen, p. 98.
11) *Ibid.*, p. 111.
12) *Philosophia Sagax*, ed. Huser, Vol. X, p. 373.
13) *Philosophia ad Athenienses*, ed. Huser, Vol. VIII, p. 24.
14) *De Fundamente Sapientiae*, ed. Huser, Vol. IX, p. 426.
15) Ed. Sudhoff, Vol. XII, p. 273.
16) Ed. Strebel, Vol. II, p. 128.

CHAPTER 24

1) Besides, twenty-one of his pupils have been taken into the hangman's custody.
2) Sudhoff (1936).
3) Ed. Matthiessen, p. 168.
4) *Ibid.*
5) Quoted by Strunz, *Paracelsus*, p. 173.
6) Preface to *Hospital Book*.
7) Quoted by Sudhoff (1936), ed. Matthiessen, p. 163.
8) Ed. Matthiessen, p. 76.
9) *Ibid.*, p. 83.
10) Curiously, two other empiricists had similar experiences, Agrippa von Nettesheim and a certain Thibault who visited Antwerp.
11) Ed. Sudhoff (1899), p. 333. Others would date this passage earlier, as belonging to the Salzburg episode.
12) Strunz, p. 40.
13) English excerpts from these sermons are available in Stoddart, pp. 266*ff*. The second volume of Strebel's edition contains a modern German version.
14) *Book of Azoth*, ed. Aschner, Vol. IV, p. 841*f*—On Luther see chapter 16, note 1.
15) *De Vita Eterna*, also in *Liber Meteorum*, ed. Huser, Vol. VIII, p. 295.
16) Note how this doctrine fits in with Paracelsus' alchemical and bio-

chemical views on the ambivalence of poisons. Sartre has used the same idea in his drama *No Exit*.

17) This conclusion, says Sartorius, is not stated explicitly but is implied in the drift of Paracelsus' ideas. It is just the failure to draw this conclusion, however, which separates Paracelsus from theosophy and keeps him within the bounds of Christian religion. On the verge of drawing the fatal conclusion (that the Universe becomes conscious of itself through its reflexion in the knowledge of the magus) Paracelsus became aware that his was a different problem.

CHAPTER 25

Motto: *Chirurgische Buecher,* ed. Huser, p. 77.

1) Now available in Four Treatises . . . , ed. Sigerist, with an excellent introduction which does justice to Paracelsus' historical significance without overvaluing achievements which are dated. See also Note 10, Chapter 10.

2) Similar citations can be multiplied *ad lib.* in the *Great Surgery Book* and in other works. The *Great Surgery Book* is available *in extenso* only in Huser's edition of 1605. Its main body consists of formulas, prescriptions, and advice which no doctor today would heed. Paracelsus had no knowledge of ligature, did not know how to stop bleeding, and could not possibly know what antisepsis meant. All he could do for his patients was to prevent operations. Moreover, many of his formulas are unintelligible today, and too many start out with "Take mumia." Finally, they contain an unusual number of folk remedies and arch-wisdom—a treasury which most doctors think should remain unlifted.

3) Ed. Huser, Vol. IX, pp. 400ff.
   Cf. quotations in chapter on "Mumia."
   It should be noted, however, that both Hippocrates and Galen recommend the use of boiled water in surgery, and that Hieronymus Brunswick instructed barbers to wash the wounds before dressing. The latter also anticipated Paracelsus in sentences such as this: "The

surgeon shall follow nature, not the other way round. For every
physician is a servant of nature."

Likewise, Petrarch said: "Obey nature, not Galen."

4) *Great Surgery Book*, Preface.

5) Quoted from Sudhoff (1936).

6) Quoted from Kayser, para. 258.

7) Translation by Hartman, p. 303.

8) Ed. Aschner, Vol. IV, p. 864.

9) Sartorius von Waltershausen: *Paracelsus am Eingang der deutschen Bildungsgeschichte;*
Koyré: *Paracelse* in *Revue d'Histoire et de Philosophie Religieuses*, Vol. XIII, March-April, May-June, 1933.

EPILOGUE

1) Ed. Sudhoff, Vol. VI, p. 55.

2) Thorndike, Vol. V, p. 619.

3) Thomas Liebler, 1523-1583, a Swiss.

4) The most important editors were:

Adam von Bodenstein, who was instrumental in making Paracelsus acceptable to princes and other notables.

Michael Toxites (Schuetz); his biography and contributions are discussed in *Nova Acta*, 1948.

Gerhard Dorn, a writer on alchemy and mystic philosophy. He translated Paracelsus' works into Latin, hoping that a "Christian medicine" might be substituted for the Arab and humanist influences.

Johannes Huser, whose German edition, based partly on original manuscripts, partly on copies by disciples, still is the principal source of our knowledge on Paracelsus.

5) Eliphas Levi wrote in the nineteenth century; our contemporary authority, Lynn Thorndike, has tried to revise his judgment in his monumental *History of Magic and Experimental Science*, New York, 1941, Vol. V, pp. 619ff. See Appendix B.

6) Cf. Gregory Zilboorg in ed. Sigerist, p. 133, and Appendix F *infra*.

APPENDIX A: *Some Notes on Magic and Related Subjects*

1) "The early scientist was called *magus*," says Paracelsus, distinguishing magus from "magician," "sorcerer," or "witch." The latter are tricksters or victims of superstitious accusations. "Black magic," in medieval language, is the use of forbidden means for evil ends, mostly with the help of demons or other "infra-natural" powers. "White magic" is the legitimate use of occult powers, mostly with the help of "supra-natural" aids (such as saints, angels, familiar spirits) for good purposes, in particular to counteract "black magic."

The true "magus" disdains all extra-natural help and knows no illicit magic. He relies on his intimate knowledge of Nature's hidden forces alone. "Magic," hence, does not work *miracles*, but uses powers which are *natural*, though they may not be sufficiently known. At its best, it is applied science without adequate insight into the forces at work. At its worst, it is "occult" science, pretending to command para-natural forces or phenomena which do not yield to scientific analysis.

2) "Magic," as distinguished from "superstition" or "nigromancy" (black magic), never attempts to *suspend* the laws of nature. It is distinguished from "science" insofar as it assumes *secret powers* of nature which do not satisfy our notions of *cause and effect*. It resembles superstition in that it seeks unusual effects through

unusual influences. It resembles science in that it assumes the *omnipotence of knowledge.*

The obsession with letters and numbers, characteristic of all magi, points in the direction of mathematical science. Pythagoras and Plato were magi in this sense, and modern technology still is based on the idea that he who has the formula can be all-powerful.

In the magic world view, all matter is governed by certain harmonies which may be expressed in letters, cyphers, numbers, designs, signatures, time intervals, names, or stated correspondences. Everything in the Universe is so related to everything else that any change in one part *immediately* (not through a chain of causes and effects) implies changes in all parts. The most important of these correspondences is the one between the *macrocosmos* (heaven, the zodiac, and the planets) and the *microcosmos* (the human body and its parts). Astrology assumes a one-way dependence between the two, but magic does not exclude mutual dependence.

Summarizing, we shall call "magic" the proto-scientific stage of an art, where results can be anticipated experimentally or surmised in a divinatory and ecstatic way, more often than not with the help of wishful thinking, and always under the assumption that what looks probable to the mind can be realized through the will. Magic is not a short-cut to science, but it may be called science in the Utopian stage.

3) Laymen usually confuse mysticism and magic. Mysticism originally is a theological doctrine, opposed to the method of dialectic. The difference is analogous to the difference between romanticism and rationalism. The mystics claimed direct, intuitive access to God whom they conceived as *"absconditus"* from human reason. In the fifteenth century, however, some of the greatest dialecticians nourished mystic ideas, notably Nicholas de Cusa, whose theory of "learned ignorance" and "coincidence of the opposites" became fruitful in the Renaissance age. From then on, "reason" and "intuition" no longer were considered as alternatives. Hence, Paracelsus was able to profess mystic views without prejudice to his scientific

efforts. On the contrary, the new mystic emphasis on the *individual* and his worldly. *experience* helped him overcome the abstract rationalism of medieval science. There is no direct link between magic and mysticism, however. The only trait they have in common is that modern readers find both obscure.

4) Cabbala (*Kabbalah* in Hebrew) is a neo-platonic and hermetic philosophy as preserved in the oral teachings of the rabbis. Paracelsus only had second-hand knowledge of it. His references are undoubtedly to the so-called older cabbala——the fraternity of magi, alchemists, and astrologers who believed that their studies of numbers, letters, names, stars, and stones would result in the conquest of evil and the coming of Messiah. The younger cabbala, which developed toward mystic religion in Paracelsus' own time, was unknown to him.

5) The magicians of today are not astrologers, but forecasters who relate stockmarket fluctuations to mysterious waves and zones on a chart, the rise and decline of a nation to the myth of a "culture cycle" or of a quasi-biological process of aging; or to the allegedly inevitable "progress" of an allegorical personage called History, Race, Dialectics, or whatever, according to the philosophy of the speaker.

It is highly significant that such magical conceptions, which we would not allow in physics or biology, still persist in the social and political sciences. For indeed, our ways of handling our public affairs are highly irrational, and the individual citizen has little insight into the forces which form his destiny. The history which we share in shaping is so ugly that we are ashamed to admit our own responsibility for it. Rather than end wars and hunger of our own volition, we try to believe that blind, uncontrolled, unintelligible, metaphysical forces drive us and govern our destiny.

In the Midde Ages, it was much easier to see who made war and who kept the grain in storage while people went hungry. Then, what moved the universe and what made the individual tick was the "mystery."

6) Originally, every unexplained phenomenon of nature is a marvel, every undiscovered element or force is an "*arcanum*," every unformulated law is "occult." In Paracelsus' days, the term "occult" applied rightly to all unexplored phenomena. Today, it is used only in referring to supernatural forces. Without prejudice to legitimate and scientific research still to be done in the field of parapsychology, it is all too obvious that the majority of our contemporary occultists have no right to claim Paracelsus as their master, as they do. Instead of doing research in their field, they are having "experiences," or relate gypsy talk. Altogether they have not advanced one step beyond the tall tales which Paracelsus found in his sources. Their aim usually is not to explain the occult as a natural phenomenon, but, on the contrary, to get away from the laws of nature and from the whole concept of science.

7) Paracelsus was neither an "occultist" nor a Christian Scientist. The sect which came closest to his opinions and leanings probably was the masonic fraternity of the Rosicrucians. It flourished in the seventeenth and eighteenth centuries and at that time devoted itself to earnest studies of the occult in a scientific way. Benjamin Franklin was a member and Goethe was sympathetic.

No Rosicrucians, but inspired by related attitudes toward theosophy and alchemy, are two men who exercise great influence in our contemporary thinking, each in his field. The Irish poet William Butler Yeats (1865-1939) certainly was the greatest mystic of our un-mystical century, and his poems can hardly be understood by anyone unacquainted with alchemical symbols. The Swiss psychologist Jung draws heavily on the treasures of ancient mythology, folklore, alchemical and astrological symbolism, and Catholic mysticism. He is also a Paracelsus scholar.

8) In compliance with English usage, I use the word "necromancer," although it strictly means a conjurer of ghosts. With reference to Paracelsus, the correct word would be "nigromancer," one who deals in black magic.

APPENDIX B: *The Historical Approach*

1) The present biography is not "Paracelsian," but seeks to rescue Paracelsus from his adulators, the modern mystics, occultists, faith healers, homoeopaths, folk doctors, and other "sects" (as Paracelsus dubbed the addicts of any prejudice). On the other hand, it does not propose to effect the rescue by exalting him as the "precursor" or even inventor of everything modern in medicine, biology, and psychiatry, like another school of his worshipers. Nor do we deny his shortcomings.

Neither to glean valuable formulas nor to expose gross errors do we read Paracelsus today, but to understand how he faced the problems of his own days. Such understanding must be sought in terms of that age, not ours. To do so, the reader's cooperation is required not only in assimilating certain ideas which had common currency in the sixteenth century, but in forgetting conceptions which he, today, takes for granted. To present Paracelsus' ideas in modern terms would mean not to present them at all. The system of medicine and philosophy against which Paracelsus rebelled may appear primitive and superstitious to us; then, it was highly refined and rationalized—so elaborately systematized, indeed, that progress was handicapped rather than furthered by its most lucid concepts. A new start was necessary, and it is essential to understand that a new departure was made possible by a return to even older ideas which, from the standpoint of Paracelsus' contemporaries, appeared less rational than theirs.

2) All revolutions pretend to return to older traditions of mankind, to nature, or to the essence and true spirit of man. All renovators draw the emotional strength of their cause and a good deal of their ideological strength from the undercurrent of irrational thought, or rather from ideas which science, so far, has failed to integrate in its system of rationalized concepts. Hence, they appear to be anti-rationalistic and reactionary, or romantic and mystic, if not confused. Historical research must remove these disguises. In particular, it must dissociate the original revolutionary impulse from the frozen remnants which, in the meantime, have become highly rationalized systems themselves, mostly reactionary.

The individual theories and opinions of Paracelsus, therefore, have been discussed only inasmuch as they throw light on our principal themes—the transformation of magic into scientific conceptions, and the contributions of the anti-rationalistic undercurrent toward formulating new goals for science.

3) The so-called Renaissance was many things to different historians. Some, like Thorndike, have even denied that there ever was such a thing as the Renissance. Others have defined it in most contradictory terms, one school emphasizing its rationalism, another its irrationalism; one its worship of art, another its return to nature. Whimsically, Hiram Haydn chose to call "counter-Renaissance" the movement which others identify with the Renaissance. (I regret that I saw Mr. Haydn's admirable book only after I had turned in the manuscript to the publisher; otherwise, I would have quoted from it more copiously.) One school, finally gave up all attempts to define the Renaissance, contenting itself with a mere enumeration of sources and characteristics as unrelated as they are unrevealing. Still such breaking-down of a historical movement into collector's items, is more tolerable than the attempts at "functional" interpretation by people ignorant of historical functions. They coordinate a certain idea to a certain class or attribute certain attitudes to "modern," others to "medieval" man. They have failed to grasp the first theorem of historical analysis—that the meaning and historical significance of an idea is determined by its context, not by its content; and they cannot grasp the second, that an event must be

determined in several strata of the sociological and ideological structure. In each of these spheres the event may present a different appearance, and one man may be "progressive" or "modern" in one respect, reactionary or medieval in another. In estimating his historical significance, the sterile search for an appropriate classification is generally of little help. The typical case, rather, is that some of the most reactionary traits are preserved in representatives of the modern ideas and, vice versa, some of the most audaciously modern attitudes emerge first in typical representatives of the obsolescent age. Historical interest then is focussed on the question, how this interpenetration of traits affected the development of the whole. In the case of Paracelsus, I have tried to show how an old concept acted as midwife of the new.

APPENDIX C: *A Note on Theophrastus' Scotism*

Since this aspect has never been discussed, attention is herewith directed on the influence of Duns Scotus on Paracelsus' philosophy. Like other thinkers of the Christian Renaissance, Paracelsus denied that Faith justifies, and asserted that Love does. Both tenets separate the Scotists from St. Augustine, and the humanist mystics from the reformers.

With Duns Scotus, humanists also supported the doctrine of Free Will against St. Augustine and the Reformation leaders. Against the Aristotelians and the "moderns" Paracelsus defended the Platonic doctrine that ideas exist before the objects they designate. All this is "realist," and so is his attitude in the debate on Universals:

"Each form is an embodiment of certain principles. If there were no heat, nothing could be hot; if there were no wisdom, no man could be wise; if there were no art, no man could be artful." (*De Fundamente Sapientiae*, ed. Aschner, p. 423, Hartmann, p. 124.)

The basic scientific optimism of Paracelsus can be traced to Duns Scotus' assertion that God does not change any laws he has given. In the theory of knowledge, the Scotist, anti-Aristotelian ideas of the Dutch Platonists are easy to recognize in Paracelsus' concept of the "Light of Nature."

Scotist terminology also appears in Paracelsus' conceptions of the microcosmos and macrocosmos. Thus, "the great man" means that which is common to all men; but he observes that everything that is in the little man (the individual) also is in the great man (the cosmological replica of man in astrology). Like Duns Scotus and Nicholas de Cusa, he found it necessary to introduce a "principle of individuation" which he variously crystallized in the Iliaster and in the "Protoplastus." In his psychology, he used Duns Scotus' doctrine that Will is superior to Reason. Also, he agreed with Duns Scotus (against St. Thomas) that Reason is distinct from Faith and may lead to different conclusions. The personal soul, for instance, is not immortal in the Paracelsian system, and Duns Scotus said that reason cannot comprehend the idea of immortality. Nevertheless, both Paracelsus and Duns Scotus provide for some kind of immortality which latter-day disciples of an allegedly theosophic Paracelsus would identify with the Vedic Karma. The medieval critics of Duns Scotus, who knew nothing of Indian philosophy, charged him with "Averroism"; and it is much easier to understand Paracelsus' idea of immortality if we assume that it was a Scotist heritage in his background. This is particularly obvious if we compare the structure of the soul in Paracelsus' system with the structure of the material universe. In both cases, he used the neo-Platonic pyramid, proceeding from some primal matter (which also may be the end matter) to the created and processed forms. These ideas are distinctly Scotist. Duns asserted that primal matter exists in all created beings, even in angels. Whether Paracelsus acquired his Platonic-alchemistic ideas directly from Plato's *Timaeus* (which he might have read in the edition of Ficino), or through his cabbalistic and alchemical studies, or whether this system was bequeathed to him by his Scotist teachers, is an open question. The similarity of views, however, is striking.

In his allegiance to Duns, Paracelsus often went out of his way to defend a minor detail of Scotist doctrines. The most striking example is his defense of the Immaculate Conception which later became a Catholic dogma.

In his ontological views, Paracelsus also followed the Scotists, as far as can be determined from scattered remarks. There is no systematic statement of philosophy in his works, however.

For reasons which I expect to explain elsewhere, I also believe that Paracelsus' "vitalism" can be conceived only in a Scotist philosophy—the "mumia" being a distinctly real universal.

Forgoing the temptation of outlining further details of the Platonist and Scotist heritage in the system of Paracelsus, we call attention to the one basic agreement which united him with the "ancients" against the "moderns": the unwavering optimism with respect to the eventual success of science in all fields, which so beautifully ties in with the social optimism of all these thinkers and with their emphasis on free will and the efficacy of "works."

APPENDIX D: *Alchemy*

The Magic Relationships
Between Stars, Body, Metals, Stones, Colors, and Gods
(According to Paracelsus)

Stars	Metals	Colors	Members of the Body	Stones
Saturn	Lead	Green, Black	Spleen, Bones	Diamond
Mercury	Mercury	Yellow, Blue	Lungs, Mouth	Smaragd
Venus	Copper	Indigo, Green	Kidneys, Genitals	Lapislazuli
Jupiter	Tin	Blue, White	Liver	Sapphire
Mars	Iron	Red	Muscles, Blood, Gall	Amethyst
Moon	Silver	Violet, Gray	Head, Brain	Pearl, Quartz
Sun	Gold	Orange	Heart	Chrysolite

These identifications, however, are fluid. Paracelsus denied their validity (ed. Huser, Vol. VIII, p. 350), only to use them two pages further down. His criticism probably applied to the details rather than to the basic theory.

The Magic Tableau of Alchemy

Sulfur	Mercury	Salt
Oily	fluid	firm
that which burns	that which vaporizes	that which remains (ashes)
soul	intellect	body

Sulfur	*Mercury*	*Salt*
feeling	thinking	willing
fire (also air)	water	earth
energy	spirit	mass
resin	arcanum	balm
celestial	astral	visible and tangible
theology	mathematics	philosophy (science of nature)

Explaining the "Tableau," we suggest that Paracelsus used it above all to identify his medical "signatures." Proksch, Paracelsus' most earnest medical critic, holds it against him that he "did nothing but change a few of the alchemical-astrological correspondences." Would this not rather illustrate Paracelsus' empiricism? He readily abandoned the astrological prejudices and the instructions of the Cabbala when he saw that his patients profited from the change, which shows how little the astro-alchemical physics really meant to him.

The concepts of salt, mercury, and sulfur may be taken either literally or figuratively, without danger of overstressing the magic sources of the theory. Before Paracelsus, biochemists recognized only mercury and sulfur—the liquid and the fiery principle involved in the making of gold. Paracelsus introduced "salt," *i.e.*, the ashes of that which remains in the process of combustion. This, of course, is the most material or "thingish" element in the body constitution. The liquid or mercurial element (or principle) may be conceived as the factor of "conscience" or intellect; but as *mercurius vitae* it is also the life power, balm, or humor which keeps the extremes of soul and body together. Thus, as the middle term, it may also be identified with the astral body and with mumia. Punning cabbalistically, Paracelsus also plays on the letter "M", Hebrew "*Mem*," in identifying Mumia, Magnalia, and Massa. On the other hand, "M" is the Mysterium or universe in which the Mumia lives and whose forces it reflects: Macrocosmos-Microcosmos.

But Paracelsus was not consistent in his use of Cabbalistic signs. Mercury is sometimes "*Aleph*" (the first letter of the Hebrew alphabet), sometimes *"Mem."* Of course, sometimes it is material-istically interpreted as "the matrix," at other times it is a spiritual force, alchemy, or the Alcaest (which he naïvely translated into his native dialect as "All-Geist," All-Spirit). Sulfur, of course, is fiery, and as such, will power or soul (Hebrew: *"Shin"*).

These classifications are much admired by the latter-day disciples of Paracelsus and Rosenkreutz. Even Professor Jung seems inclined to find them beautiful. I cannot bring myself to discover much myth-building power in these speculations, even if I take them as pure poetry. On the contrary, Paracelsus deprived these imagos of whatever romance they might have retained before. He strove to make them as rational as possible, though certainly his success was uneven. In his hands, the terms mercury, sulfur, and salt are trans-formed into something which we should like to call, in modern lan-guage, "effective principles," or, in the language of the last century, "forces of nature." This point has been emphasized by Gundolf.

Several attempts have been made to compile a glossary of Para-celsus' terminology. None is applicable to all works alike. The most useful, I have found, is the one in Kayser's Paracelsus anthology. Here follows one which Paracelsus himself appended to his pam-phlet on the Pfeffers spa:

"Sulfur is that which burns, mercury is that which embodies the virtue, salt is that which holds the body together. Matter is a piece you can take into your hand; corpus is the body that con-tains the virtues; species is a piece in itself; *Iliaster* is the prime matter before all creation (its sign is the six-pointed Star of David); *magnalia* are the works of God; *arcanum* is that which must be found through experience; constellation is the unity of the Superior with the things here-below; operation is the effect that Nature may achieve; quintessence is the result of operations strengthening Nature beyond her grade; *putrefactio* exists when something turns into its former essence; digestion is found when something is turned into a different essence; *centrum* is the be-ginning of the disease. . . ."

Other chemical terms have been quoted in Chapter 5, note 18.

Paracelsus did not believe that all matter is composed of the four elements: "The elements should not be understood as a corpus or substance of property, for what is visible is only the frame, and the element is a spirit; it lives in the things as the soul lives in the body." Air is the house that holds all elements together and separates the eternal from the mortal: "It has no above or below, for its roundness cannot see height or depth. Air is incomprehensible and spiritual; it cannot create anything corporeal. It bears dreams and *Fata* and the spirits dwelling in the plants and in blood. . . ." "The four elements are in all things, but not *actu*, they are four complexions."

Paracelsus shared the passion of his contemporaries to divide phenomena into three, four or five realms. Much of what many call his "cosmogony" simply is such an attempt to get the Universe in hand with the aid of a proper filing system. In explaining Paracelsus' philosophy, therefore, it is less important to insist on the number of "elements" and the place each occupies; instead, we are interested in the devices Paracelsus used to make his system all-inclusive, and in his obsession to try again and again until, in the *Philosophia Sagax*, he thought he had laid out the World above and below in one great "Tableau."

APPENDIX E: *Bibliography*

1) *Sources:*

Paracelsus, *Opera Omnia*, ed. Huser, 4°, 12 vols., Basel, 1589–1591.
Quoted as: Ed. Huser, vol. —.
Paracelsus, *Chirurgische Bücher und Schriften*, ed. Huser, Basel,
1605 and 1612, second edition 1618. Quoted as: Surgical Books.
Paracelsus, *Sämtliche Werke*. (The critical standard edition, with
abundant annotations.)
Abt. I: Medizinische, naturwissenschaftliche und philosophische
Schriften, ed. Karl Sudhoff, 14 vols., Munich, 1922–1933. Quoted
as: Ed. Sudhoff, vol. —.
Abt. II: Theologische und religionsphilosophische Schriften, ed.
W. Matthiessen, 1 vol. Quoted as: Ed. Matthiessen.

2) *Modern German editions:*

Paracelsus' Sämtliche Werke in zeitgemässer kurzer Auswahl, 5 vols.,
ed. J. Strebel, St. Gall, 1944–1948. (The selection is arbitrary, the
"translation" often a mere pretext for theosophic editing.)
Paracelsus' Sämtliche Werke (translated into modern German by
Dr. Bernhard Aschner), 4 vols., Jena, 1926. A complete rendition
of the Sudhoff edition, Abt. I. (The translation is readable, though
very free.)

3) *English editions and selections:*

Franz Hartmann, *The Life of Paracelsus and the Substance of His Teachings* . . . extracted and translated from his rare and extensive works, London, 1887. (Theosophical and spiritualistic; translation often very free.)

Edward Waite, *The Hermetic and Alchemical Writings of Paracelsus the Great*, 2 vols., London, 1894. (A scholarly presentation in support of the Rosicrucian view. Excellently translated.)

Henry Sigerist (with C. Lilian Temkin, George Rosen, and Gregory Zilboorg): *Four Treatises of Theophrastus von Hohenheim*, Baltimore, 1941. (Recommended). Quoted as: Ed. Sigerist.

Volumen Medicinae Paramirum, translated by Kurt Leidecker, Suppl. No. 11 to the *Bulletin of the History of Medicine*, Baltimore, 1949. (Recommended.) Quoted as Ed. Leidecker.

4) *Biographical and Bibliographical References and Further Sources:*

Karl Sudhoff, *Versuch einer Kritik der Echtheit der unter dem Namen Paracelsus herausgegebenen Schriften*, Berlin, 1894 and 1899. Quoted as: Sudhoff (1894) and Sudhoff (1899).

Sudhoff and Schubert: *Paracelsus-Forschungen*, Frankfurt, 1887–1889. Quoted as: Sudhoff (1887).

Acta Paracelsica, Munich, 1930–1932, ed. E. Darmstaedter, *Supplement* listing more than 1200 titles of Paracelsiana.

Nova Acta Paracelsica, Basel, 1944ff., ed. Linus Birchner. With new biographical and iconographical material by Birchner, Bittel, Strebel and Telepneff.

5) *Biography and Interpretation* (A Selected List):

Anna M. Stoddart, *The Life of Paracelsus*, London, 1911, 309 pp.

Hans Kayser, *Paracelsus*, ausgewählt und eingeleitet, Leipzig, 1921, 558 pp. (With an excellent introduction and glossary.)

Friedrich Gundolf, *Paracelsus*, Berlin, 1928, 135 pp.

Franz Strunz, *Paracelsus, Idee und Problem seiner Weltanschauung*, Leipzig, 1937, 214 pp. (Excellent presentation of the Catholic viewpoint.)

Karl Sudhoff, *Paracelsus, ein deutsches Lebensbild aus der Renaissancezeit*, Leipzig, 1936, 156 pp. (The authoritative biography.)

Bodo Sartorius von Waltershausen, *Paracelsus am Eingang der deutschen Bildungsgeschichte*, Leipzig, 1935, 216 pp. (A profound study from the standpoint of humanism.)

Will-Erich Peuckert, *Die Geheimnisse*, Leipzig, 1941, 474 pp. (A comprehensive selection, with abundant notes.)

Carl G. Jung, *Paracelsica*, two lectures, Zurich, 1942, 188 pp. (Most interesting details on alchemy and philosophy.)

6) *Poetic Treatments of the Paracelsus and Faustus Themes:*

Christopher Marlowe, *The Tragical History of Doctor Faustus.*

J. W. Goethe, *Faustus.*

Robert Browning, *Paracelsus.*

Hector Berlioz, *Faustus.*

Arthur Schnitzler, *Paracelsus.*

Georg Kolbenheyer, *Paracelsus' Kindheit, Das Gestirn des Paracelsus, Das Dritte Reich des Paracelsus.*

APPENDIX F: *A Note on the Quotations*

Paracelsus wrote in the juicy pre-Lutheran Swiss German dialect which he interspersed with medical and philosophical lingo from school Latin, Greek, Arabic, Hebrew, and with imaginative coinages of his own. Moreover, the style is spiced with German slang, obscenities and epithets of a highly personal character. No translation can possibly render the individual flavor of this gasping, searching, and emphatic attempt to create a scientific medium in the vernacular.

The style is involved, egotistic, sometimes hasty, more often tedious and repetitious, always coarse and ungrammatical. The sense often is not clear either. Paracelsus never seems to have read what he had written. Some of the books which have appeared under his name are transcripts of lectures, or were dictated to inept amanuenses who admitted that they had a hard time following his rapid dictation. In many cases, the hand of a zealous editor is all too visible; conflicting versions of important passages are not rare, and their number increases with every new edition. Nor are the scholars agreed on the number of books to be recognized as genuine.

Our translations are free renderings in modern English, sometimes abridged. Where we have used existing translations or have followed modern German versions, the quotation has been so identified. All modern versions tend, more or less, to mitigate the charming ambiguity of the original. We occasionally say "psychological" where Paracelsus said "spiritual," and "physiological" where he said "natural." Such liberty, however, is not permissible where clarity and readability for the modern reader conflict with the possibility of hidden meanings in the original, or with the translator's obligation to preserve the characteristics of style which betray a lack of training, absence of scientific abstractions, inability to come to grips with the problem, or deficiency of logical tools. (See Gundolf, *op. cit.*, pp. 116ff.)

The greatest difficulty in interpreting and translating Paracelsus is his terminology. It changes from book to book, and even in one and the same book he is not consistent. Whenever he feels that an adequate term is not readily at hand, he invents one or uses another which he remembers having read or used elsewhere, without making a note of it and then using it consistently.

While this difficulty can be evaded in a translation, although not in a German edition, another obstacle can be overcome only by doing violence to the text. It is the use of secret, deliberately mystifying terms and of astro-chemical language, which requires reinterpretation in modern language. Any attempt to translate this terminology into modern chemical or psychological terms must necessarily neglect the metaphysical implications which were present in any reader's mind in the sixteenth century. In most cases, therefore, I have made a literal translation, relying on the reader's imagination for more complete understanding of the text.

Thanks are due to the Johns Hopkins Press for permission to quote translations by Messrs. Sigerist, Temkin, Rosen, Zilboorg and Leidecker. I also checked my translations with those made by Hartman, Stoddart and, above all, Waite. The notes indicate the extent to which I was able to avail myself of pioneer work done by assiduous researchers in this and in related fields. Notably, this may be the right place to acknowledge the immense debt owed to Lynn Thorndike by anyone interested in the history of science.

APPENDIX G Chronology

Year	General Events	Paracelsus and His Contemporaries	Scientific and Literary Events
1492	Arabs driven from Spain	Lorenzo di Medici dies Vives born	America discovered
1493	Maximilian I, Emperor	Paracelsus born	
1494	Fugger Bank founded	Pico della Mirandola dies	Brandt, *Fools' Ship*
1495		Rabelais born	
1497		Melanchthon born	
1498	Vasco da Gama sails to India	Savonarola dies	
1499		Ficino dies	
1500		Hans Sebald Beham born	
1502	*Bundschuh*, uprising of German peasantry	Paracelsus in Villach	
1503		Nostradamus born	Nifo, *On Demons*
1504		Carlstadt Professor in Wittenberg	Cocles, *Chiromancy*
1505		John Knox born	
1506		Columbus dies	Leonardo's "Mona Lisa"
1507		Cesare Borgia dies	
1508		Paracelsus at Tübingen U.	Trithemius, *On Witchcraft*
1509	Henry VIII, King of England	Calvin born	Erasmus, *In Praise of Folly* Dürer's "All Saints"
1511		Paracelsus at Vienna U.	

1513	Leo X, Borgia, Pope	Paracelsus in Ferrara	Machiavelli, *Il Principe*
1514		Vesalius born	*Epistolae Obscurorum Virorum*
1515	Battle of Marignano; *Poor Conrad*, uprising of German peasantry	Lucas Cranach born; Pierre Ramus born	
1516		Trithemius dies	New Testament newly edited by Erasmus; Pomponazzi, *On Immortality*
1517	Luther's 95 Theses	Paracelsus at Füeger's (?)	Thomas More, *Utopia*; Fries, *Mirror of Medicine*
1518		Paracelsus starts his trip around the world; Leonardo da Vinci dies	Magellan sails around the earth; Humanist reform in Erfurt; Religious disputations
1519	Suleiman II, Sultan; Charles V, Emperor; Zwingli starts Swiss Reformation		
1520	Christian II of Denmark invades Sweden; Cortez conquers Mexico; Luther burns the Pope's Bull	Raffael Sanzio dies; Paracelsus in Sweden	Luther's theological pamphlets
1521	Zwickau prophets in Wittenberg; Turks conquer Belgrade	Paracelsus in the Orient	
1522	Knights' uprising in Germany; Turks capture Rhodes	Reuchlin dies; Paracelsus in Dalmatian mines	New Testament translated by Luther

Year	General Events	Paracelsus and His Contemporaries	Scientific and Literary Events
1523	Clement VII, Pope	Hutten dies	
1524	Great Peasant War in Germany	Paracelsus in Salzburg *Archidoxa*	
1525	Reform in Zürich	Thomas Muenzer dies *Volumen Paramirum*	Zwingli, *True Religion* Luther vs. Erasmus, *On Free Will*
1526	Battle at Mohacz	Paracelsus in Strasbourg Machiavelli dies	Paracelsus' German lectures
1527	Sack of Rome	Paracelsus in Basle Durer dies	
1528	Suleiman before Vienna Reform in Basle and St. Gall		
1529	Thomas More, Chancellor Treaty of Cambrai ends war between France and Emperor	Paracelsus in Nuremberg Matthias Grünewald dies *French Disease*	Fracostoro, *Syphilis*
1530	*Confessio Augustana* Spinning wheel invented	*Paragranum* Paracelsus in St. Gall *Opus Paramirum*	Aristotle edited by Erasmus
1531	Battle of Kappel	Zwingli dies Oecolampadius dies	Agrippa, *De Vanitate Scientiae*

1532	National Church in England Religious peace of Nuremberg	Paracelsus in Appenzell Valentin Weigel born	
1534	Prophets rule at Münster Loyola founds Society of Jesus	Paracelsus' conversion	Calvin, *Institutio*
1535		Thomas More dies Agrippa dies *Great Surgery* *Philosophia Sagax* Erasmus dies	Carpi, *Commentary on Mondino*
1536	Calvin in Geneva Suppression of the Münster rebels		
1537	Schmalkald articles	Jan von Leyden dies Paracelsus in Vienna Paracelsus in Villach *Defensiones* and *Labyrinthus*	
1538	Truce of Nice ends third war between France and Emperor		
1540		Paracelsus in Salzburg Vives dies	Biringuccio, *Pirotechnica*
1541	Reformation in Geneva	Paracelsus dies Hans Holbein dies	Michelangelo's "Last Judgment" Copernicus, *Revolutiones* Vesalius, *Fabrica* Paré, *Traité des Plaies*
1543			
1546	Council of Trent	Luther dies	Agricola, *De Re Metallica*

Index